TWO AND TWENTY

TWO AND TWENTY

A Collection of Short Stories

Ralph H. Singleton
OBERLIN COLLEGE

St Martin's Press·New York

To Mercedes

PREFACE

The short story is a comparatively brief piece of narrative fiction, unified in action and theme. It relates the actions of men and women at a time when those actions are fraught with particular meaning. Out of the stream of time there is this brief moment in their lives that has unusual significance. In a sense all their past has led up to this moment, and all their future hinges upon it. And what is true of the characters in the story is true, in some measure, of all of us who read it. For we share a common humanity. Had the events in our life fallen into a different pattern, we might have faced a similar situation. And so we can identify ourselves with the fictitious characters and events, live with them in imagination, and learn with them something of the depths of the human spirit.

I am speaking, of course, of serious fiction, not of the formula story, with its sentimentality, melodrama, and push-button emotional crises. Formula fiction fills the pages of innumerable magazines that crowd our newsstands. Its techniques are standardized and obviously within the range of a large number of people who are willing to work at learning them with diligence.

The misconception persists, however, that even the quality story has a fairly rigid pattern that can be learned and imitated. It is not the same pattern as the formula story, of course, but still a pattern. An analysis of the stories in this volume will demonstrate the falseness of this conception. Every story presents its own problems, which must be met by the author in his own way. What is more, the short story is in a constant state of flux. In the last thirty years the tendency has been to veer away from any crystallization of form in the direction of constant experimentation.

This does not mean, however, that the short story is without form, is independent of technique. If this were so, classes in the analysis of fiction and workshops in the writing of fiction would be a waste of time. A short story is made up of certain elements which can be illustrated and discussed. These include story idea or theme, character, plot, action, setting, point of view. Certain principles and techniques must be mastered by all writers of fiction, and these can be studied and learned.

A close analysis of the way a story is constructed is one of the best ways to appreciate its excellence. In fact, it has long been my personal conviction that courses in the writing of fiction are really laboratory courses in literature. By studying the short story from the point of view of the writer, the student comes away with an appreciation and understanding of fiction that he can get in no other fashion.

My aim in this book is to present a group of stories by British and American authors illustrative of good modern prose fiction, stories that exemplify the principles and techniques of the short story discussed in the Introduction. The stories were selected, in part, because they deal with the experiences of childhood, adolescence, and youth, and as such come within the range of the college undergraduate.

The book is intended both for those who want to learn how to write and for those who want merely to read and enjoy. Both writer and reader profit from a close analysis of technique. The stories selected represent some of the best fiction being written today, as well as outstanding writers of the short story over the last thirty years.

Anyone who discusses the techniques of prose fiction owes a considerable debt to those who have preceded him. That debt I freely and gratefully acknowledge. I should like, also, to express my debt to the many students in my classes in the writing of prose fiction with whom I have worked during the last twenty years. This book is, in a real sense, theirs. And finally, I want to extend my particular thanks to my colleagues at Oberlin College, Professors Andrew G. Hoover and Francis X. Roellinger, who read my discussion of the techniques of the short story and gave me valuable suggestions, and to Elliott Coleman, Director of Writing Seminars, The Johns Hopkins University, who read the manuscript with care.

RALPH H. SINGLETON

CONTENTS

TECHNIQUES OF
THE SHORT STORY

The first thing that the teller of stories must learn is to *tell* the story—not tell *about* it. This means to lean heavily upon sense details and be sparing of explanation and interpretation. A story takes place in time, a *particular* time; in place, a *particular* place. It concerns *particular* people, who act and speak in a *particular* way.

CONCRETENESS

The only way the writer can re-create a series of events for the reader so that he has the illusion of actually being present at the time is to reproduce those events by means of image-producing words. That means sense words: concrete, specific details of sight, sound, touch, smell, taste.

Examine the following paragraphs, taken from Thomas Wolfe's "Death the Proud Brother."

As I put my coin into the slot, and passed on through the wooden turnstile, I saw the man who was about to die. The place was a space of floor, a width of cement which was yet one flight above the level of the trains, and the man was sitting on a wooden bench which had been placed there to the left, as one went down the incline to the tunnel.

The man just sat there quietly at one end of the bench, leaned over slightly to his right with his elbow resting on the arm of the bench, his hat pulled down a little, and his face half lowered. At this moment there was a slow, tranquil, hardly perceptible movement of his breath—a flutter, a faint sigh—and the man was dead. In a moment a policeman who had watched him casually from a distance walked over to the bench, bent down, spoke to him, and then shook him by the shoulder. As he did so, the dead man's body slipped a little, his arm slid over the end of the bench and stayed so, one hand hanging over, his shabby hat jammed down, a little to one side, upon his head, his overcoat open, and his short right leg drawn stiffly back. Even as the policeman shook him by the shoulder, the man's face was turning gray. By this time a few people, out of the crowds that swarmed constantly across the floor, had stopped to look, stared curiously and uneasily, started to go on, and then had come back. Now, a few of them were standing there, just looking, saying nothing, casting uneasy and troubled looks at one another from time to time.

This is the re-creation of experience in visual terms, and, as such, it carries the ring of reality. Note the exactness of the details. Time: "As I put my coin into the slot and passed on through the wooden turnstile, I saw the man. . . ." " . . . a policeman who had watched him casually from a distance walked over to the bench, bent down, spoke to him, and then shook him by the shoulder. . . ." "By this time a few people, out of the crowds that swarmed constantly across the floor, had stopped to look." Place: "The place was a space of floor, a width of cement which was yet one flight above the level of the trains, and the man was sitting on a wooden bench which had been placed there to the left, as one went down the incline to the tunnel." Person: "The man just sat there quietly at one end of the bench, leaned over slightly to his right with his elbow resting on the arm of the bench, his hat pulled down a little, and his face half lowered." " . . . the dead man's body slipped a little, his arm slid over the end of the bench and stayed so, one hand hanging over, his shabby hat jammed down, a little to one side, upon his head, his overcoat open, and his short right leg drawn stiffly back."

Note, also, the specific sense details in the following extracts from stories reprinted in this collection:

2

Roberts knocked on Van Ness's half-open door and a voice said, "Come in."

Van Ness was sitting at his typewriter, which was on a small desk beside the large desk. He was in a swivel chair and when he saw Roberts he swung around, putting himself behind the large desk, like a damn judge.

He had his pipe in his mouth and he seemed to look over the steel rims of his spectacles. The light caught his Phi Beta Kappa key, which momentarily gleamed as though it had diamonds in it.

"Hughes said you wanted me to report here," said Roberts.

"I did," said Van Ness. He took his pipe out of his mouth and began slowly to knock the bowl empty as he repeated, "I did." He finished emptying his pipe before he again spoke.

JOHN O'HARA, "Do You Like It Here?"

But it wasn't so nice for us after the spring came.

In our part of the state, it comes pretty late, as a rule. But it was early this year. The little kids were out with scooters when usually they'd still be having snowfights and, all of a sudden, the radiators in the classrooms smelt dry. You'd got used to that smell for months—and then, there was a day when you hated it again and everybody kept asking to open the windows.

STEPHEN VINCENT BENÉT, "Too Early Spring"

She stood with arrested muscles, outside his door, listening. There was a strange, heavy, and yet not loud noise. Her heart stood still. It was a soundless noise, yet rushing and powerful. Something huge, in violent, hushed motion. What was it? . . .

Softly, frozen with anxiety and fear, she turned the door handle.

The room was dark. Yet in the space near the window, she heard and saw something plunging to and fro. She gazed in fear and amazement.

Then suddenly she switched on the light, and saw her son, in his green pajamas, madly surging on the rocking-horse. The blaze of light suddenly lit him up, as he urged the wooden horse, and lit her up, as she stood, blonde, in her dress of pale green and crystal, in the doorway.

D. H. LAWRENCE, "The Rocking-Horse Winner"

3

Meanwhile, he was wet and cold. He went around to the back of the house and tried one of the basement windows, found it open, raised it cautiously, and scrambled down the cellar wall to the floor. There he stood, holding his breath, terrified by the noise he had made; but the floor above him was silent, and there was no creak on the stairs. He found a soapbox, and carried it over to the soft ring of light that streamed from the furnace door, and sat down. . . .

The east-bound train was plowing through a January snowstorm; the dull dawn was beginning to show gray when the engine whistled a mile out of Newark. Paul started up from the seat where he had lain curled in uneasy slumber, rubbed the breath-misted window glass with his hand, and peered out. The snow was whirling in curling eddies above the white bottom lands, and the drifts lay already deep in the fields and along the fences, while here and there the long dead grass and dried weed stalks protruded black above it. Lights shone from the scattered houses, and a gang of laborers who stood beside the track waved their lanterns.

WILLA CATHER, "Paul's Case"

You will observe that the writers have drawn upon senses other than the sense of sight. Stephen Vincent Benét associates the coming of spring with the sudden awareness of the dry smell of the radiators in the classroom. D. H. Lawrence presents the anxious mother listening terrified to the rushing sounds that emanate from her son's room. Willa Cather pictures Paul, wet and shivering, pulling up a soapbox before the heat escaping around the door of the furnace. Details of sight alone are not adequate to re-create reality, for all our senses respond to the world around us and are responsible for the impressions that come to us. Some of our most vivid recollections may be associated with sense impressions that are not visual: the fretful crying of a baby, the baying of hounds in the distance, the cool, moist smell of the hollow by the river, the sweet, stinging flavor of a piece of peppermint candy.

Sense details do not come naturally to the writer. Explanation and interpretation do. We are accustomed to saying, for example, that the weather yesterday was miserable (which

4

is a comment, not a description). This quite serves our purpose, but not that of the story teller. He must write something like this: "Rain fell in a steady downpour, driven at times in hard, slanting volleys, as cold gusts of wind swirled out of the north."

Explanation is exposition, not narration. It is a statement about something, a statement that comes from the writer, not from the action. Interpretation is a comment, guiding the reader's reaction, instead of letting him make up his own mind from the details that reach him through his senses. Life makes no explanations and no comments. It merely presents people in action, and lets the individual draw his own conclusions. Any interposition of the writer is a threat to the illusion of reality. Too much explanation and interpretation can be compared to drawing a curtain between the reader and the scene. The writer keeps the action screened from the reader while he glances at it himself and explains and comments upon it.

Continual practice in writing concretely, coupled with continual comparison with good narrative prose, will eventually enable the beginning writer to distinguish between telling a story and telling about it. Robert Louis Stevenson tells us that he learned how to write by "playing the sedulous ape," trying to recall and imitate a passage he remembered as being particularly well written and then comparing his version with the original. One advantage of this procedure is that it dispenses with the need of an instructor. Note the following examples of short descriptive passages that might serve as such examples:

It was late in the afternoon, and the light was waning. . . . Somewhere in the distance cows were lowing and a little bell was tinkling; now and then a farm-wagon tilted by, and the dust flew; some blue-shirted laborers with shovels over their shoulders plodded past; little swarms of flies were dancing up and down before the people's faces in the soft air.

MARY E. WILKINS FREEMAN, "A New England Nun"

5

In this description of approaching twilight in a New England countryside, Mrs. Freeman uses the combined suggestion of details of sight, sound, and touch.

Noon lay heavier on the gardens; not our live humming warmth, but the stale exhalation of dead summers. The very statues seemed to drowse like watchers by a death-bed. Lizards shot out of the cracked soil like flames, and the bench in the laurustinus-niche was strewn with the blue varnished bodies of dead flies. Before us lay the fish pond, a yellow marble slab above rotting secrets. The villa looked across it, composed as a dead face, with the cypresses flanking it for candles.

EDITH WHARTON, "The Duchess at Prayer"

Edith Wharton, in this description, gets her effects primarily by comparison. Comparisons are not commentaries, for they are specific and concrete. They substitute one sense image for another for the sake of clarifying and individualizing the picture.

One last word about *telling* the story, not telling *about* it. Remember that *all stories take place in the present.* This does not mean that they are written in the present tense, although some writers shift to the present tense for particularly dramatic passages. It does mean, however, that the writer re-creates events *as they happen.* Prose fiction is not history. Turn to the stories in this collection or look back at the extracts quoted in this introduction. Note that in every instance you, the reader, have the illusion of watching something take place in front of your eyes.

POINT OF VIEW

Point of view is the angle of vision from which a story is told. Its importance can scarcely be overestimated, particularly for the beginning writer. For one thing, it is the greatest single limiting factor in the selection of details. For another, a strictly maintained point of view contributes markedly to the illusion of reality. The business of the writer is to take the reader from his own little world into that of another—

the central character of the story which he is creating. The world of this character is fictitious, but it must seem real to the reader, who must, as I have said, have the illusion of looking on while the action takes place.

In real life everyone is limited to what he himself can directly see and hear and smell and touch and taste. He is limited, also, to the working of his own mind. The thoughts of others lie as much outside his range as the happenings in the next room when the door is closed. He may guess at what goes on in another's mind, but this is inference, not knowledge, inference based upon sense impressions: the tightening of the corners of the mouth, a dilation of the nostrils, a thickening of the voice.

Omniscient Point of View. The fiction writer is not limited by the restrictions of real life. In theory he is omniscient. He can be anywhere at any time, enter the mind of any of his characters at will, reveal their thoughts, relate the action from their mental and physical viewpoint. To do so, however, is fraught with difficulty and danger.

For the reader, as I have said, is not omniscient. If he has been participating in the action through the eyes and mind of one of the characters of the story—the mother, for example—and is suddenly shifted to the point of view of her fifteen-year-old son, then removed from the scene to listen to an explanation by the author, returned to the mother's point of view, then back to her son's, his concentration upon the imaginary world has constantly been interrupted. For every time the point of view shifts, he must make a readjustment.

It is true that the omniscient or shifting point of view is well established by precedent. The reader will accept it as one of the conventions of fiction if the author is skillful enough. Some excellent short stories have been written from the omniscient point of view; for instance, "Paul's Case," by Willa Cather, and "The Rocking-Horse Winner," by D. H. Lawrence. But it presents a great temptation to the writer to talk about his characters rather than present them in action, and it greatly increases his difficulties in securing the singleness of effect that the short story demands. The beginner, in consequence, might do well to avoid the omniscient point of view as an unnecessary obstacle placed in his way when the road to achievement is arduous enough without it.

Dramatic Point of View. The writer may go to the opposite extreme and present the action in a purely objective or dramatic fashion—the point of view of someone at the theater watching a play. This is the point of view of the observer, who relates only those details that come to him through his senses, without comment, and without entering the mind of any of his characters. For a writer to remain completely aloof from the action, refusing to avail himself of the emotions and reactions of any of his characters as a guide to his reader, makes a tremendous demand upon the suggestive power of external details.

For certain types of stories and certain purposes, however, the dramatic point of view is excellent. Arthur Morrison chose it for "On the Stairs," a story revealing vanity, ignorance, and superstition in a London tenement district. The story deals with the death of a young man who might have been saved had his mother not appropriated money contributed for medicine to apply on his funeral. The situation is obvious, and Morrison reveals it largely by letting the reader observe the action that takes place on a landing outside the sick room, three flights up.

"Flight," by John Steinbeck, is also told from the dramatic point of view. The central character, Pepé, has killed a man in Monterey, and must flee for his life into the mountains. Steinbeck follows him on his flight until his eventual death, but always from the point of view of the observer, who watches with mounting tension and horror until the youth is shot down by his pursuers like a hunted animal.

The best examples of the dramatic point of view are to be found in the early stories of Ernest Hemingway. Governed by a desire to avoid any explicit expression of values, Hemingway relies entirely upon the implication of the details themselves, and so the dramatic point of view is admirably fitted for his purpose. Since dialogue is the most objective method of telling a story, Hemingway leans heavily upon dialogue. "The Killers," a story of two triggermen from Chicago invading a lunchroom in a small town to kill a Swede, is a masterpiece of the dramatic method. The influence of Hemingway upon writers like Morley Callaghan, John Steinbeck, Irwin Shaw, and John O'Hara, to mention a few, led for a time to the popularizing of the dramatic point of view, but this influence has been on the wane in recent years.

Personal Point of View. Between the extremes is the personal point of view. Not the angle of vision of someone who sees all, knows all, tells all (omniscient), nor of an outside observer, watching the action like a member of a theater audience (dramatic), but of one of the actors in the drama. The writer identifies himself with this one individual and tells the story as it appears to him. He may tell it in the first person or the third person.

Since the personal point of view limits the writer to the actions witnessed by one individual and to his thoughts and emotions, it serves as a unifying factor, a principle of selection. And since it identifies the reader as well as the writer with one person in the story, it helps maintain the illusion of reality in the fictitious world the writer has created.

First Person. The first-person point of view is the most natural, because it is the point of view of anyone recounting his own experiences. It is the point of view of Stephen Vincent Benét's "Too Early Spring," Sherwood Anderson's "I'm a Fool," Victoria Lincoln's "Down in the Reeds by the River," Ernest Hemingway's "My Old Man." Anderson, Benét, and Hemingway imitate the language as well as the mental outlook of the adolescent whose experiences they are relating. Note, for example, the following:

I'm writing this down because I don't ever want to forget the way it was. It doesn't seem as if I could, now, but they all

9

tell you things change. And I guess they're right. Older people must have forgotten or they couldn't be the way they are. And that goes for even the best ones, like Dad and Mr. Grant. They try to understand but they don't seem to know how. And the others make you feel dirty or else they make you feel like a goof. Till, pretty soon, you begin to forget yourself—you begin to think, "Well, maybe they're right and it was that way." And that's the end of everything.

STEPHEN VINCENT BENÉT, "Too Early Spring"

But, after all, I had to work, and there was no other work to be got. A big lumbering fellow of nineteen couldn't just hang around the house and I had got too big to mow people's lawns and sell newspapers. Little chaps who could get next to people's sympathies by their size were always getting jobs away from me. There was one fellow who kept saying to everyone who wanted a lawn mowed or a cistern cleaned, that he was saving money to work his way through college, and I used to lay away nights thinking of ways to injure him without being found out. I kept thinking of wagons running over him and bricks falling on his head as he walked along the street. But never mind him.

SHERWOOD ANDERSON, "I'm a Fool"

Victoria Lincoln, on the other hand, since she is recalling a childhood experience from some distance, re-creates the situation, the mental outlook, of the adolescent, but writes in the language of the adult:

I came along very slowly, watching Mr. deRocca from the corner of my eyes. He wore a plaid flannel shirt, ragged and, of course, unironed, but fairly clean, and the neck was unbuttoned. I noticed how the flesh under his chin was firm and didn't hang down in wattles, and the cords in his neck didn't stick out. He looked harder and nicer than other old men.

How old was he, really? About fifty, I should guess now, looking back; maybe a little less. But if I had known it then, it would not have changed my picture of him at all. Fifty to eighty in those days were all of a piece in my mind. Mr. deRocca was an old man. And he was nice.

"Down in the Reeds by the River"

Sometimes a writer selects a minor, not a principal, character as the narrator. This is Faulkner's method in "That Evening Sun." Like Victoria Lincoln, Faulkner tells the story of an experience of childhood, recollected as an adult, but the story is not Quentin's, the nine-year-old boy who is the "I" in the story. He is merely the observer through whose eyes we see the action unfolding. The focal character is Nancy, Jesus' wife, who is waiting to have her throat slit by Jesus for her infidelity. This point of view has the particular advantage of enabling the author to tell the story by one who does not understand its significance, but who furnishes the authenticity of an eye witness.

Third Person. Telling the story in the third person does not differ markedly from telling it in the first person if the point of view is strictly adhered to. The writer still identifies himself with one of the characters, usually the focal character, and follows the action through his eyes and mind. In other words, he imposes upon himself the same limitations of first person narrative—with one exception. Since he is outside the character, as well as inside, he can describe his appearance and actions as well as his thoughts and emotions.

This is a great help in characterization, for the "I" in a story cannot reveal himself except by indirection. But it is also a step removed from reality. The verisimilitude of an eye-witness account is lost. Since the story comes to the reader as told by a third person, there is inevitably a partial intrusion of the writer between the reader and the action. And if the writer yields to the temptation to explanation and commentary, the intrusion becomes marked.

A good example of a story told from the third person point of view is Marjorie Kinnan Rawlings' "Black Secret."

The shutters were drawn in the parlor against the afternoon sun. June lay heavy on the street outside, but the room was dark and cool. Hummingbirds droned in the honeysuckle over the window. The fragrance filtered through the shutters. Dickie flat-

11

tened his face against the rose-patterned Brussels carpet. It was pleasantly harsh and faintly dusty. He moved his cheek to the smoothness of his picture book. The page was smooth and slippery. He lay comfortably, imagining that the painted lion under him was alive and his friend. He shook his loose, tucked blouse and pretended that the lion was breathing against him. He wished that it was night, when the new gas lights would flare from their brass pipes on the wall, for their yellow flickering made the lion's eyes move and shine. He lifted his head. The double doors of the parlor were sliding open. He heard his mother speak.

"The garden party was lovely, Mrs. Tipton, but aren't you exhausted?"

Dickie thinned himself to a shadow. If he were quiet, they might let him stay while they talked. There was an excitement in his mother's talk in this room with Mrs. Tipton that he heard no other place and with no other person. The women came into the parlor and Mammy Dee closed the folding doors after them. His mother saw him. She had on her flowered organdie with the ruffled flounces. They touched his ankle as she rustled past him.

Mrs. Rawlings starts her story as though she were writing from omniscience. The descriptive and explanatory details of the first four sentences are limited by no one point of view, surely not by Dickie's. (Note the statement about the street outside, although the physical point of view is clearly inside, with the shutters drawn.) Yet with the fifth sentence she identifies herself with Dickie, an identification she maintains strictly for the rest of the story.

Graham Greene, in "The Basement Room," identifies himself with the seven-year-old Philip, through whose eyes the story is told.

Philip Lane went downstairs and pushed at the baize door; he looked into the pantry, but Baines was not there, then he set foot for the first time on the stairs to the basement. Again he had the sense: this is life. All his seven nursery years vibrated with the strange, the new experience. His crowded busy brain was like a city which feels the earth tremble at a distant earth-

12

quake shock. He was apprehensive, but he was happier than he had ever been. Everything was more important than before.

Baines was reading a newspaper in his shirtsleeves. He said: "Come in, Phil, and make yourself at home. Wait a moment and I'll do the honors," and going to a white cleaned cupboard he brought out a bottle of ginger beer and half a Dundee cake. "Half-past eleven in the morning," Baines said. "It's opening time, my boy," and he cut the cake and poured out the ginger beer. He was more genial than Philip had ever known him, more at ease, a man in his own home.

Point of view is violated, occasionally, by mature writers to secure a particular effect. Graham Greene, for example, in "The Basement Room," shifts his point of view upon occasion to enforce his theme. Train yourself to note if and when the author steps out of character, shifts his point of view, makes comments in his own person. Is he justified in doing so? Wallace Stegner says that point of view is more often "botched" in the work of both beginners and professionals than any other technique of fiction, and that a mixed point of view in the short story is "nearly always fatal." The beginner will profit by adhering strictly to the point of view he has selected.

SIMPLIFICATION (SELECTION)

A third consideration must guide the writer at the outset, the principle of simplification. It governs the selection of sense details and point of view, the creation of character, choice of incident—in fact, all the elements of the short story. The principle is this: A short story is a simplification of life in every particular. Stories do not occur in life, but are a tremendous simplification of what did or might occur.

This is easy to demonstrate. Take plot. In Faulkner's "That Evening Sun," Quentin's recollection of what took place fifteen years ago in Jefferson is limited strictly to events that concerned Nancy. These events, in turn, are limited to her infidelity, her resultant difficulties with Jesus, her husband,

13

and her fear of reprisal. We never see the children unless their activities are connected with Nancy. Their mother is only a voice whose remarks have reference to Nancy. Their father appears only when he is doing or saying something that has reference to Nancy. It must be obvious that the events Quentin relates constitute only a very small part of the total activities of the characters involved during the period covered by the story. Yet all else is rigorously excluded.

Take character. Just as the plot in Faulkner's story is simplified, so are the characters. They are re-created only as they appear in relation to this particular situation. The mother is only a voice, illustrative of an attitude toward Nancy and the Negro race. The father, who plays a more active role, is also an attitude. The things we do *not* know about him are legion. We know nothing about his business, his normal activities, his religion, his friends—indeed, very little about his home life. Even Nancy, the focal character, is portrayed without complexity. She can be summed up by her own words: "I ain't nothing but a nigger . . . It ain't none of my fault."

In life, no one is so lacking in complexity. In a story people are often simplified to the point at which they can be dropped into an appropriate pigeonhole. Other facets of their character are never revealed. In O'Hara's "Do You Like It Here?" Van Ness, with his steel-rimmed spectacles and Phi Beta Kappa key, is little more than the narrow-minded, opinionated guardian of McAllister Memorial Hall, and Roberts is the boy-who-has-been-falsely-accused. In Mrs. Rawling's "Black Secret," Mrs. Tipton is simply the Gossip, with an overweening sense of self-righteousness.

This simplification makes the characters in a story immediately intelligible and keeps their actions consistent. Curiously enough, it makes them more, not less, real to the reader. This is due, I suspect, to the fact that although we recognize *ourselves* to be infinitely complex, we are willing to catalogue others with a phrase.

14

In the same way, the principle of simplification applies to all description—which is not photographic, but highly selective; to all dialogue—which excludes everything not pertinent to the immediate occasion. In studying the short stories in this collection, observe not only what the author says but also *what he leaves out*. Notice how the principle of simplification operates at all times.

STORY IDEA, OR THEME

The short story differs from the novel in one essential particular: singleness of effect. Underlying the action, and controlling it, is always one idea, or theme, which is the unifying element that gives the story meaning. It is the author's interpretation of life, his insight into the principles that govern human behavior.

Another way of saying this, perhaps, is that action *in itself* lacks significance. This is true even though the action involves dramatic conflict. In Wilbur Daniel Steele's story "How Beautiful with Shoes," a girl is abducted by a dangerous lunatic who has escaped from a nearby asylum, and from whom she is eventually rescued, unharmed, after a night of terror. The significance of the story, however, resides in the theme which underlies the experience. For the girl is betrothed to a neighbor's son, whose love-making has been casual and bucolic. In contrast, the lunatic has awakened in her for the first time a realization of the beauty of love and passion, a realization that comes to her as she sits, half-dazed, in the reaction that follows her experience:

"*How beautiful* . . ."
Color overspread her face in a slow wave.
"*How beautiful are thy feet with shoes* . . ."
"Is it only crazy folks ever say such things?"
"*O prince's daughter!*"
"Or call you that?"

The theme of Victoria Lincoln's "Down in the Reeds by the River" is also that of an awakening to the wonder and

15

beauty of love, through an experience of adolescence which, on the surface, might seem ugly and disreputable. As the narrator puts it:

> It was not like the books or the whispered ugly confidence that you remember from your school days; it was quite, quite different. . . . There was something in me—and in the world, too—that I had never known was there before, something powerful and lovely, something powerful and new.

The characters, setting, situation, action are quite different from Steele's story, yet the themes of the two stories, the author's interpretation of experience, are very close indeed.

In Benét's "Too Early Spring," the story idea or theme is the havoc caused by adult misinterpretation of an innocent, even idyllic, experience of adolescence. In the words of Chuck Peters:

> They try to understand but they don't seem to know how. And the others make you feel dirty or else they make you feel like a goof.

This theme is indicated at the outset, and the story goes on to develop it. Hemingway's "My Old Man" has as its theme the terrible disillusionment of a boy who is forced to accept the fact that the father he had idolized had been a crook.

The theme may be specifically stated or left to be inferred by the reader. But it is there all the time, illuminating and giving significance to the action. If the story is well written, the reader will find himself absorbed by the action, engrossed by the characters. But by the time he lays the story down, he knows that he has had an insight into human nature, an interpretation of life.

This theme, or basic idea, is not a moral but an observation. If it poses a problem, that problem need not be solved. But it is, as I have said, the unifying element of the story that gives it meaning. Without it there is no story in the real sense of the word.

16

CHARACTER

The ability to create characters, bring them to life upon the page, is perhaps the greatest single achievement of the story writer. If he can do this, the reader will be willing to forgive him any number of minor faults. For an interest in people, the forces that move them and motivate their actions, is the primary reason for reading fiction. Conversely, if the would-be writer of short stories is not himself intensely interested in the people around him, absorbed by the problems of their own little worlds, consumed with curiosity about what makes them "tick," he ought to forget his ambitions and turn his energies elsewhere.

A few truisms about character in the short story can be stated to begin with. One has already been discussed, briefly, in connection with the principle of simplification: No matter how complex an individual may be in real life, only a few significant traits of his character are presented as he is recreated in the fictitious world of the short story. To use E. M. Forster's classification, the characters in a short story are "flat," not "round." There is seldom time, in a few thousand words, to delineate many varying facets of an individual's personality. Nor is this necessary. Only those aspects of character demanded by the situation are required.

The writer, of course, knows much more about his character than he puts down on the page. He should, in fact, know *everything* about him. The traits he chooses to portray are a *selection* of the significant traits of the character's personality which reveal his attitude toward life and which operate as a deciding factor in the resolution of the dramatic conflict. These significant traits are not merely explained. They are revealed—not once, but over and over again. And thus is created that illusion of reality whereby the reader feels he knows the character, understands him as well as he does his most intimate friends.

17

This limitation of complexity by a selection of significant traits does not mean that the characters in a short story are not *particularized*. In the final analysis, it is the writer's ability to make his characters highly individual that results in their being both real and memorable. The history of memorable characters in fiction is the history of particular individuals. And their very individuality, the thing that marks them from their neighbors, is, in itself, an important aspect of their reality. Flaubert, in giving advice to Guy de Maupassant, said:

When you pass a grocer seated in his doorway, a concierge smoking his pipe, a row of cabs, show me this grocer and this concierge, their attitude, all their physical appearance; suggest by the skill of your image all their moral nature, so that I shall not confound them with any other grocer or any other concierge; make me see, by a single word, wherein a cab-horse differs from the fifty others that follow or precede him.

"Le Roman," preface to *Pierre et Jean*

A second truism is this: A story, unless completely objective, always takes place in the mind of the character. The beginning writer would do well to copy this statement and tack it on the wall over his typewriter. The heart of a story is not what happens, but *what happens to the focal character.* Action is significant only as it affects character. That is why at the end of a story the focal character is usually different from what he was at the beginning.

Examine the stories in this collection. In Irwin Shaw's "Act of Faith," the story does not take place in the external actions, the attempt of Seeger and his companions to secure money to finance their furlough to Paris, but in Seeger's mind. The dramatic conflict is resolved by his decision, and symbolized by his willingness to part with the Luger. In Sherwood Anderson's "I'm a Fool," the narrator's masquerade as a young sportsman from Marietta to impress his companions of the moment constitutes the external action. The story, however, takes place in his mind, the growing realization that his actions have cut him off from the most important thing that life has ever offered him. The dramatic conflict in Dorothy Canfield's "The Apprentice" lies entirely within the thirteen-year-old Peg Wilson. Nothing much *happens*. Her dog, Rollie, has wandered off, and she finds him after an extended search. But the event serves as a release for her pent-up emotions, and dissolves her rebellion at the fancied "injustices" of her parents.

In every instance the focal character has undergone a change as a result of his experience. We can see the implications for his future life. Notice how this is true in other stories, such as "The Basement Room," in which Graham Greene says of Philip: "Life fell on him with savagery: you couldn't blame him if he never faced it again in sixty years." Chuck Peters, in "Too Early Spring," can never recapture the innocence of his first love, and Chet, the young hero in Stegner's "Chip Off the Old Block," will be forever a man. Experience can intimidate and disillusion or develop and strengthen.

This inner experience of character is related to the theme, because, as Christopher La Farge has put it, "Characterization to be successfully real must border forever on universality." The focal character in a well-written short story is both an individual and a type. It is his universality that makes his experience an illumination of human nature.

METHODS OF CHARACTER DELINEATION

Character is revealed in the short story by the same means that it is observed in life. These can be enumerated as follows.

Action. We judge people by the way they act, particularly in a crucial situation. "Actions," it is said, "speak louder than words." What a person *does* presents convincing evidence of what he *is*. In "The Rocking-Horse Winner," Hester's insistence, upon receiving news of the "legacy," that it be handed over

19

to her in one lump sum, is conclusive evidence of the driving greed for money that dominates her. In "Chip Off the Old Block" by Wallace Stegner, Chet's indomitable courage is revealed as he fights single-handed to protect his father's property.

Environment. A person's surroundings, particularly those which he deliberately chooses, including the recreations he prefers, the company he keeps, often furnish us a clue to his character. Willa Cather, in "Paul's Case," characterizes Paul not so much by his theft of company funds as by his predilection for the artificial glitter of the theatrical, his contempt for his teachers, and his overwhelming distaste for the commonplace quality of his own home.

Speech. A person's speech is indicative of his habit of mind, his reaction to people and events. We lean heavily in our judgment of people on what they say and how they say it. Dialogue, in addition to advancing the action, is an excellent means of characterization.

Olson and Seeger, in Shaw's "Act of Faith," are characterized for us at the outset of the story by the dialogue that initiates the action:

"Present it to him in a pitiful light," Olson was saying as they picked their way through the almost frozen mud toward the orderly-room tent. "Three combat-scarred veterans, who fought their way from Omaha Beach to . . . What was the name of the town we fought our way to?

"Königstein," Seeger said.

"Königstein." Olson lifted his right foot heavily out of a puddle and stared admiringly at the three pounds of mud clinging to his overshoe. "The backbone of the Army. The noncommissioned officer. We deserve better of our country. Mention our decorations, in passing."

"What decorations should I mention?" Seeger asked. "The Marksman's Medal?"

"Never quite made it," Olson said. "I had a cross-eyed scorer at the butts. Mention the Bronze Star, the Silver Star, the Croix de Guerre with palms, the Unit Citation, the Congressional Medal of Honor."

"I'll mention them all." Seeger grinned. "You don't think the C.O.'ll notice that we haven't won most of them, do you?"

"Gad, sir," Olson said with dignity, "do you think that one Southern military gentleman will dare doubt the word of another Southern military gentleman in the hour of victory?"

"I come from Ohio," Seeger said.

Description. Although appearance can be very deceiving, it can also be very revealing. Rightly or wrongly, we lay great stress upon physical appearance, including dress, in judging character. The writer presents those details of appearance that reveal inner traits, such as the opal tie pin and red carnation that Paul affects as he stands in judgment before his teachers in "Paul's Case"; the long white fingers, fine black eyebrows, and loosely waved black hair of Ann's mother in Ramona Stewart's "The Promise."

Reactions of Others. The opinions of others, indicated by their express statements or suggested by their physical reactions, guides us, at times, in our own judgment of people. In "My Old Man," Hemingway gives the reader a clue to Joe's father by the reactions of other people to him, and the final revelation to Joe himself comes in the same fashion. In "The Promise," Ramona Stewart characterizes Ann's father by her distaste for him long before he puts in an appearance.

Exposition. Direct explanation of character by the author is an act of omniscience. Unless the story is related in the first person, a direct statement of this kind is exposition, not narration, telling about, not revealing. Edward J. O'Brien called it a "weak and lazy way of going about the matter." In a sense, however, it is an adaptation of one way we learn about people in life. "What is Mrs. X like?" we ask a friend, and receive in reply the same kind of summary of traits that D. H. Lawrence, for example, presents in his opening remarks about Paul's mother in "The Rocking-Horse Winner." Note, however, that Lawrence's point of view throughout this story is omniscient.

Thought. The presentation of a character's thoughts is also an act of omniscience. If, however, the writer enters the mind of only one person in the story, he approximates the conditions of life, for if we are honest we can come to some self-realization by an analysis of our own thoughts. Looking into the thoughts of a character can be tremendously revealing, for the secrets of the heart lie there concealed. Few stories can afford to dispense with this method of characterization, if only for its aid in indicating motivation. Over and over again in the stories here reprinted, you will find the author dipping into the mind of his focal character—sometimes at length, as in Shaw's "Act of Faith," sometimes only for a fleeting glimpse, a brief lifting of the curtain. The techniques for presenting a character's thoughts are many and varied, ranging from stream of consciousness, to comment by the author.

Any or all of these methods of characterization may be used by the writer of short stories. Nothing, as I said before, is more important than the ability to create character. And nothing will be more rewarding in the analyses of these stories than a minute observation of the ways in which the authors have succeeded in bringing their characters to life.

PLOT

Plot is the framework of the short story, the blueprint for the action—that is, those incidents to be worked out and sketched in later. The basis of every story is a conflict between the central character and some opposing force, which lies either inside or outside him (perhaps both). This conflict arises from circumstances that cause an unstable situation (the origin of suspense), and is resolved when the character either overcomes this opposing force or succumbs to it, and the situation becomes stable again. Whatever happens beyond that point is, as we say, "another story."

22

This definition is extremely abstract. But necessarily so. A blueprint is bewildering to many people. They find themselves unable to visualize the completed structure from the skeletal design. Being so abstract, the concept of plot is often difficult to grasp. Character, setting, action—all these are concrete enough. We can *see* the seven-year-old boy in "Black Secret" stretched out on the parlor floor pretending to read his book as he listens to his mother talking to Mrs. Tipton; we can watch him climb into the barber's chair, beat with his fists upon the barber's chest as the meaning of the gosssip comes home to him. But "conflict," "unstable situation," "opposing forces," "resolution"—these are intangibles. It is, however, essential that the writer understand plot; how it differs from action, how it does not manifest itself necessarily in a complicated series of events, how it is related to character, and how its resolution is dependent upon theme.

Plot is not action. A mere sequence of events or an action that illuminates character is not a story. The story begins at the point where dramatic conflict begins—at the point where the focal character finds himself involved with some force which has disturbed the *status quo*. This conflict may come from himself, from another person, from external circumstances. Eventually, through an incident or a series of incidents (action), the logical outcome of character and circumstances, it is resolved, and the *status quo* is restored. There is often a sequel, for in a struggle so intimately related to the fundamental traits of the actors involved, the focal character will usually emerge with the mark of the experience upon him. And since he is always, in some measure, a universal figure, the solution of the conflict has significance, is tied inevitably to the fundamental idea (theme) which gives the story meaning.

Let us look at O'Hara's "Do You Like It Here?," which has a simple framework or design. Humphrey Roberts, the focal character, is accused of stealing a watch by the master of the pre-

23

paratory school in charge of his dormitory. Unable to convince the master of his innocence, he is, at the end of the story, still resting under the shadow of suspicion. That is the plot.

At the outset, Roberts is engaged in his usual routine, studying in his dormitory room. The *status quo* is disrupted by Van Ness, the master, whose suspicion and enmity bring about the dramatic conflict. The action is simple: one main incident (scene) in which the accusation is made and denied. The conflict is resolved at the point where Van Ness dismisses Roberts, still believing in his guilt. It is tragic, because the focal character (Roberts) succumbs to the opposing force (Van Ness). It is also logical, the natural outgrowth of character and situation; it squares with our experience. Underlying the resolution is the story idea or theme: Injustice can inflict a deep injury, cause a burning resentment. This is pointed up by the sequel, which shows Roberts as a changed person, embittered by the experience and facing the prospect of further persecution that will make his future stay in the dormitory intolerable.

The plot of Dorothy Canfield's "The Apprentice" is less obvious, perhaps, because the conflict lies entirely within the thirteen-year-old girl who is the focal character. Again the story is one of "injustice," an adolescent rebelling at the "unfairness" of her parents' treatment of her. In this story, however, the "injustice" is fancied, and the conflict lies between two forces within herself, one which subconsciously recognizes the truth (she was furious that "she had nothing to cry about") and the other, the emotional insecurity of adolescence which motivates her rebellion. The resolution is "happy," her better impulses triumphing over her rebellion, and the *status quo* is restored.

The action consists principally of the girl's search for her missing dog, Rollie, which constitutes the series of events which eventually resolve the conflict. Motivated by her love for the dog and her fear for his safety, she becomes increasingly alarmed, and the reader, who had identified himself with her, shares her concern (suspense). Her subsequent disciplining of her dog "for his own sake," furnishes her emotional release. Her actions evolve naturally from her own character in this particular situation, and the charting of them constitutes the plot, resolved by means of the significant idea (theme) which underlies the story.

Let us look at one further example of plot in Marjorie Kinnan Rawlings' "Black Secret." The unstable situation is brought about by external circumstances: Dickie's overhearing of the "black secret." His seven-year-old innocence has come into conflict with the existence of evil, which is "resolved" when he discovers its meaning through the idle gossip in the barber-shop, and its association with his adored Uncle Baxter. Since the knowledge of evil has overcome his innocence, the ending is "unhappy." Actually, there is no real solution to the conflict of good and evil, only an overwhelming sense of agony and disillusionment in the realization that such anomalies exist, which is the theme of the story.

From these illustrations you can see that plot does not depend upon a complicated series of events, often super-imposed upon the characters. Dramatic conflict does not mean a whirlwind of activity. Plot is intimately related to character and story idea—is, in fact, the logical working out of the story idea in terms of the revealed traits of the characters.

ACTION

Action, as we have seen, may have one of two functions: to characterize the actors, and to advance the plot. Often it does both at the same time. Action is the characters' *doing* something. By an extension of terms, it includes the characters *saying* or *thinking* something. For dialogue and thought can advance the plot as well as physical movement. In Irwin Shaw's "The Girls in Their Summer Dresses" and Hemingway's "The Killers," the story advances almost entirely by dialogue. In

25

James Thurber's "The Secret Life of Walter Mitty," it advances almost entirely by Mitty's thoughts.

In the modern short story action is portrayed primarily by means of the scene. Consequently the beginning writer must learn to recognize a scene and how to present action in this fashion.

The Scene. A scene is an episode, limited in time and place, with the action slowed down so that the reader can watch it take place in front of him. It is a unit of action, self-contained, furthering the dramatic conflict, with a sequel which leads to further action or which resolves the conflict.

In "Too Early Spring," for example, after a running account of the summer's activities, the action turns suddenly into a scene:

> I was sitting under the four pines, one night, right down by the edge of the water. There was a big moon and they were singing. It's funny how you can be unhappy and nobody knows it but yourself.

Notice how the action at this point is limited in time and place, in marked contrast to the summarizing narrative preceding it. This is the initial scene of the story, which introduces the dramatic conflict in the person of Helen Sharon. It ends abruptly some eight hundred words later. Note the summarized action in the paragraph that follows:

> And yet I didn't see her again till we were back in High. Mr. Sharon's uncle died, back East, and they closed the cottage suddenly. But all the rest of the time at Big Lake, I kept remembering that night and her little face. . . .

There are three scenes in "Too Early Spring," linked by passages of summarizing narrative. The significant action, significant because it marks the progress of Chuck Peters' relations with Helen Sharon and the working out of the theme, is related in these scenes. Chuck Peters' activities with "the gang" and on the basketball floor take place "off stage," and

26

are related in summarizing narrative. The story offers an excellent illustration of these two means of presenting action. "Black Secret" is written in two scenes. The first, set in the Merrill parlor, introduces the dramatic conflict; the second, set in the barbershop nearby, resolves it. In both scenes the action consists primarily of dialogue and the reaction to what is said in the mind of the focal character, seven-year-old Dickie. Dickie's physical movements consist largely in turning over the pages of his storybook, running to the barbershop to get a haircut, climbing into the chair, bursting into tears, beating on the barber's chest, and running out of the barbershop and down the street. Since all of the action takes place in less than an hour, there is no need for summarizing narrative, and the action is presented entirely in these two scenes.

"The Basement Room," in contrast, is packed with action. The boy Philip is involved in a whirlwind of events: quarrels between a man and his wife, secret meetings, murder, an arrest. He is pulled at by both man and wife; he loses himself on the city streets; he is questioned in a police station. There are, in fact, ten scenes in all, plus one brief interlude of summarizing narrative. These scenes might be labeled as follows: (1) With Baines in the Basement Room, (2) Lunch, (3) The Street, (4) The Tea Shop, (5) The Nursery, (6) Supper, (7) The Return of Mrs. Baines, (8) Flight, (9) The Police Station, (10) The Arrest.

In spite of this flurry of activity, the real story takes place in the mind of Philip, and underlying it is always the theme, the basic idea of the story. As he keeps this theme in front of the reader, Graham Greene remarks at one point:

> He would never escape that scene. In a week he had forgotten it, but it conditioned his career, the long austerity of his life. . . .

"Do You Like It Here?" has practically no physical activity whatever. Roberts gets up from his study table in response to the summons from Van Ness, walks down to the master's

27

quarters for an interview, then back to his own room. The action is presented in two scenes and an epilogue, and consists largely of dialogue and the thoughts of the focal character.

The Flashback. The flashback is past action necessary to the understanding of the present situation. Except in the omniscient or objective story, it is presented through the recollections of the character whose point of view the reader shares. In "The Apprentice," for example, there is a brief flashback to her parents' "bossiness" in order to account for the girl's mood. In "I'm a Fool," there is an extended flashback to the focal character's experience as a swipe at the racetrack in order to account for his knowledge of horses and racing stables. The current tendency is to plot the short story in such a fashion that a flashback is unnecessary, but it is still an integral part of the technique of presenting action.

Physical movement, dialogue, thought—presented primarily in a scene, but sometimes in summarizing narrative—these are the ingredients of action in the short story. Because action leads to more action—in other words, has a sequel—a succession of scenes, one growing out of the other, can sometimes give the appearance of plot. But a narrative without plot is inconclusive; it stops, not ends. It is, as we say, "without point." Action has significance only as it contributes to the design of the short story and the underlying theme.

SETTING

Stories don't take place in a void, but in a specific place at a specific time. This time and place constitute the setting, the background for the action. In Faulkner's "That Evening Sun" the story takes place in a southern town named Jefferson "fifteen years ago"; in Stegner's "Chip Off the Old Block" the story takes place in a frontier town in Saskatchewan, Canada, November 4–11, 1918. Time and place contribute to a third aspect of setting which is all important—atmosphere, that real but intangible feel of a locale which is its distinctive character-istic. Chet's home in Saskatchewan is worlds removed from Quentin's in Jefferson. Physical surroundings, living conditions, customs, social milieu—all contribute to make the atmosphere of the two locales as different as night and day.

Setting, then, is the environment that surrounds the char-acters and influences them and their actions. It is the *total* environment, including the physical objects associated with the characters: the lignite-burning stove in the kitchen, the double-barreled shotgun hanging over the mantel, the cows in the barn, the muskrat traps under the riverbank, the school-house made over into a hospital. Setting never exists for its own sake, but for its interrelation with the characters: what they are and what they do. In the words of Chekhov, "If a gun is hanging on the wall in the first paragraph, shoot it before the end of the story."

Selection plays as important a part in creating the setting as it does in delineating character and action. It is important to localize the story for the reader in time and place so that he can see what goes on, but it is also important to limit the details to what is strictly relevant to the author's purpose. In "Chip Off the Old Block," for example, Chet's isolation from his neighbors, the deserted street, the dead rabbit swinging by its feet from his hand, his pa's gun under his arm are all details which not only contribute to the visualization of the scene as he returns from his hunting excursion but are relevant to the action that follows, in which he forces the half-breed Louis and his companion from the house. More important still is the rough, hard-bitten, but forthright atmosphere that pervades the Mason home and which Chet inevitably shares. His father is "tougher than boiled owl," and Chet proves that he can be just as tough, a man among men.

Setting is also related to point of view. The significant details are those that are significant in the eyes of the char-acter through whom the reader sees the story. The loneliness

29

of the unbroken fields of snow, unmarked by sled tracks or fox-and-goose paths, is observed by Chet and has a sobering influence upon him. In "Too Early Spring," Chuck Peters describes the setting by the lake that night he got acquainted with Helen Sharon in the following recollected details: "I was sitting under the four pines—right down by the edge of the water. There was a big moon and they were singing." It was the kind of singing that "sounded mysterious across the water," that "hurt" him to listen to. The place where the two of them, later, had a picnic is merely "an old house, with the windows gone, on top of a hill . . . There weren't any chairs or tables but we pretended there were." And the setting for the final scene is merely "in front of the fire in the living room" of the Sharon home where it was "quiet and lovely and firelight made shadows on the ceiling." In "The Promise," the apartment in which they are living reminds Ann of her mother, "full of gay, unrelated pieces," from the "impressionistic French water color on the wall over the piano" and the "Copenhagen china cat" on the rug beneath it, to the sofa and chairs that "had originally been lemon-yellow modern but like most of Louise's ideas . . . hadn't worked out too well" and were now "covered with red and green chintz slip-covers." The fireplace "didn't heat but they burned colored powder in it at night and it was very pretty."

Setting in a short story is not created by lengthy descriptions, but by a word here, a phrase there. It is not concocted out of the blue, but comes from recollected experience. Few writers possess the power to imagine a setting with which they are not familiar. Faulkner writes of the south because he knows the south, as does Marjorie Kinnan Rawlings. Wallace Stegner sets his story of Chet's emergent manhood in Saskatchewan because he lived there as a youth. The beginning writer should follow their example and limit his settings to the places that he knows; knows well, has a feeling for. The environment of our early years has a special influence upon us, and the beginning writer in setting his stories should turn his eye inward and backward.

STYLE

Style in prose fiction is the author's characteristic manner of expressing himself, his use of language. A writer's style is evidenced by the words he chooses, the images he selects, both literal and figurative, the sound of the word in the phrase, the rhythm and structure of his sentences. Style, in other words, is *how* a writer expresses himself in contrast to *what* he says.

All mature writers of fiction tend to develop a style which is distinctively their own. Thus Faulkner does not write like Hemingway, and Katherine Anne Porter does not write like Katherine Mansfield. Each of these authors is a craftsman in his own right; each has developed a characteristic mode of expression over years of literary apprenticeship. "Style," said Buffon, "is the man." But he did not mean by that remark that words set down casually or carelessly can have "style." For Buffon was speaking of artists who have so perfected their method of writing that it truly reveals them.

Take Hemingway, for example. Some of the characteristic elements of his style are the following: a simple sentence structure with a striking lack of subordinate elements, the piling up of statement after statement, joined, if at all, with the conjunction *and;* the use of concrete sense detail, a vivid re-creation of the sense world, but few comparisons, few figures of speech, and those usually of the simplest sort; a heavy dependence upon dialogue, an excellent transcript of colloquial rhythms. This Hemingway style effectively represents an attitude toward life that one associates with him, the attitude of a spectator, one who looks and depicts, but refuses to comment.

A careful analysis of a writer's style can help in an understanding of the writer as much, some times, as can an analysis,

31

let us say, of his attitude toward his characters or the underlying theme of his story.

Saying precisely what one means is one of the most difficult acts in the world; it takes great effort even on the part of a great writer. Charles Dickens has been called the greatest "natural genius" of all the English novelists. Yet an examination of his manuscripts reveals layer upon layer of revision, even, at times, on the proof sheets that came back from the printer. And many of those distinctive elements that characterize his style can be observed taking shape in his revisions. The writer who achieves success is the one who has the dogged perseverance to write and revise, write and revise. Thomas Wolfe wrote to his former teacher in Asheville, North Carolina: "I have learned that writing is hard work, desperate work, and that (as Ben Jonson said) 'who casts to write a living line must sweat.'"

The writing of fiction can be learned. But, as many of the authors of stories in this anthology have also testified, it is not easy. Stephen Vincent Benét said at one time: "Writing is a job to be done like any job. It's a profession to be learned like any profession. It isn't learned in a month or a year—it takes time."

Robert Louis Stevenson, who was self-taught, insisted that analysis plus constant imitation is the only method of learning how to write. It is clear that Hemingway learned something from Sherwood Anderson, and that Irwin Shaw and John O'Hara, in turn, learned a good deal from Hemingway. There is nothing in this procedure which stifles originality. No artist suffers from studying the masters of his craft.

John Ciardi, in an article in the *Saturday Review of Literature*, December 15, 1956, while insisting that writing "cannot in fact be taught," went on to say that, paradoxically enough, "creativity can not spring from the untaught. Creativity is the imaginatively gifted recombination of known elements into something new."

The student of writing must become aware of the fact that success calls for a capacity for criticism, ultimately self-criticism. The key to success is to learn to read well, to criticize and evaluate responsibly, and then to apply the same criteria to one's own work.

SHERWOOD ANDERSON

Sherwood Anderson was born on September 13, 1876, in Camden, Ohio, a little town in the northeastern part of the state. His boyhood was spent in Clyde, Ohio, the prototype for Winesburg, Ohio, which gave its name to the novel that established his reputation.

Nothing in his early years, however, suggested the possibility of his becoming an outstanding writer of fiction. One of five boys, in a family of five boys and three girls, he was so often absent from school earning money to augment the family income that he acquired the nickname "Jobby." His formal education came to an end at fourteen, with the death of his mother, although years later, after drifting from job to job, and serving briefly in the army during the Spanish American War, he studied for a year at Wittenberg Academy, Springfield, Ohio.

After that abbreviated college experience, he spent six years in Chicago as a writer of advertising copy and five years in Elyria, Ohio, as manager of the Anderson Manufacturing Company, a mail-order firm he had incorporated for selling roofing paint. At thirty-six, he was well on his way to becoming a well-established, prosperous businessman.

In his years as an advertising man in Chicago he had started to write fiction in his spare time, and now, in Elyria, he began to devote more and more time to his writing, at the *expense of his business. This conflict of interests led to a breakdown which resulted in his walking out of the paint factory on November 12, 1912, never to return.*

Going back to Chicago, he once more wrote advertising copy for a living, but spent his major efforts working over the stories that were revolving in his mind. His first published story, an inconsequential sketch called "The Rabbit Pen," came out in Harper's Magazine, *July 1914, when he was thirty-eight. He fell in with the so-called "Chicago group" of writers—Theodore Dreiser, Ben Hecht, Carl Sandburg, and Floyd Dell, among others. Dell, in particular, believed in him and helped him get* Windy McPherson's Son *published in 1916. It was quickly followed by* Marching Men *(1917) and* Mid-American Chants *(1918). Then, in 1919, came* Winesburg, Ohio, *a "Group of Tales of Ohio Small Town Life," a few of which had originally been printed in* The Little Review, The Seven Arts, *and* The Masses. *Its fresh approach and experimental techniques brought Anderson into wide public notice. Sinclair Lewis published* Main Street *the following year, and the two novelists were often linked together in the public mind. Virginia Woolf wrote in the* Saturday Review of Literature *that "of all American novelists the most discussed and read in England at the present moment are probably Mr. Sherwood Anderson and Mr. Sinclair Lewis."*

Anderson never equaled in his later years the fiction he wrote in the twenties, but he made his own contribution to American literature in those days when his experiments were opening up new paths, and part of that contribution was a group of first-rate short stories. Among them "I'm a Fool," published originally in Dial, *was reprinted in* The Best American Short Stories of 1922. *Four more of* *his stories were reprinted in this anthology between 1923 and 1929. Three others received O. Henry Memorial Awards, "Death in the Woods" winning second prize in 1926. In 1921 Anderson received the Dial Award of $2,000 for the best original work by an American writer, an award won the following year by T. S. Eliot.*

Always willing to aid young writers, in the days that he was living in New Orleans, he helped William Faulkner get his first novel published.

He has written three autobiographies: A Story Teller's Story *(1924),* Tar: a Midwest Childhood *(1927), and* Memoirs *(1942), published after his death on March 8, 1941. None of them, however, can be taken at face value, Anderson himself admitting that as a storyteller he could not be expected to tell the truth.*

I'M A FOOL

It was a hard jolt for me, one of the most bitterest I ever had to face. And it all came about through my own foolishness too. Even yet, sometimes, when I think of it, I want to cry or swear or kick myself. Perhaps, even now, after all this time, there will be a kind of satisfaction in making myself look cheap by telling of it.

It began at three o'clock one October afternoon as I sat in the grandstand at the fall trotting and pacing meet at Sandusky, Ohio.

To tell the truth, I felt a little foolish that I should be sitting in the grandstand at all. During the summer before I had left my home town with Harry Whitehead and, with a nigger named Burt, had taken a job as swipe with one of the two horses Harry was campaigning through the fall race meets that year. Mother cried and my sister Mildred, who wanted to get a job as school teacher in our town that fall, stormed and scolded about the house all during the week before I left. They both thought it something disgraceful that one of our family should take a place as a swipe with race horses. I've an idea Mildred thought my taking the place would stand in the way of her getting the job she'd been working so long for.

But after all I had to work and there was no other work to be got. A big lumbering fellow of nineteen couldn't just hang around the house and I had got too big to mow people's lawns and sell newspapers. Little chaps who could get next to people's sympathies by their sizes were always getting jobs away from me. There was one fellow who kept saying to everyone who wanted a lawn mowed or a cistern cleaned that he was saving money to work his way through college, and I used to lay awake nights thinking up ways to injure him without being found out. I kept thinking of wagons running over him and bricks falling on his head as he walked along the street. But never mind him.

I got the place with Harry and I liked Burt fine. We got along splendid together. He was a big nigger with a lazy sprawling body and soft kind eyes, and when it came to a fight he could hit like Jack Johnson. He had Bucephalus, a big black pacing stallion that could do 2.09 or 2.10 if he had to, and I had a little gelding named Doctor Fritz that never lost a race all fall when Harry wanted him to win.

We set out from home late in July in a box car with the two horses, and after that, until late November, we kept moving along to the race meets and the fairs. It was a peachy time for me, I'll say that. Sometimes, now, I think that boys who are raised regular in houses, and never have a fine nigger like Burt for best friend, and go to high schools and college, and never steal anything or get drunk a little, or learn to swear from fellows who know how, or come walking up in front of a grandstand in their shirt sleeves and with dirty horsey pants on when the races are going on and the grandstand is full of people all dressed up— What's the use talking about it? Such fellows don't know nothing at all. They've never had no opportunity.

But I did. Burt taught me how to rub down a horse and put the bandages on after a race and steam a horse out and a lot of valuable things for any man to know. He could wrap a bandage on a horse's leg so smooth that if it had been the same color you would think it was his skin, and I guess he'd have been a big driver, too, and got to the top like Murphy and Walter Cox and the others if he hadn't been black.

Gee whizz, it was fun. You got to a county seat town maybe,

say, on a Saturday or Sunday, and the fair began the next Tuesday and lasted until Friday afternoon. Doctor Fritz would be, say, in the 2.25 trot on Tuesday afternoon and on Thursday afternoon Bucephalus would knock 'em cold in the "free-for-all" pace. It left you a lot of time to hang around and listen to horse talk, and see Burt knock some yap cold that got too gay, and you'd find out about horses and men and pick up a lot of stuff you could use all the rest of your life if you had some sense and salted down what you heard and felt and saw.

And then at the end of the week when the race meet was over, and Harry had run home to tend up to his livery stable business, you and Burt hitched the two horses to carts and drove slow and steady across country to the place for the next meeting so as not to overheat the horses, etc., etc., you know.

Gee whizz, gosh amighty, the nice hickorynut and beechnut and oaks and other kinds of trees along the roads, all brown and red, and the good smells, and Burt singing a song that was called Deep River, and the country girls at the windows of houses and everything. You can stick your colleges up your nose for all me. I guess I know where I got my education.

Why, one of those little burgs of towns you come to on the way, say now, on a Saturday afternoon, and Burt says, "let's lay up here." And you did.

And you took the horses to a livery stable and fed them and you got your good clothes out of a box and put them on.

And the town was full of farmers gaping, because they could see you were race horse people, and the kids maybe never see a nigger before and was afraid and run away when the two of us walked down their main street.

And that was before prohibition and all that foolishness, and so you went into a saloon, the two of you, and all the yaps come and stood around, and there was always someone pretended he was horsey and knew things and spoke up and began asking questions, and all you did was to lie and lie all you could about what horses you had, and I said I owned them, and then some fellow said, "Will you have a drink of whisky?" and Burt knocked his eye out the way he could say, offhand like, "Oh, well, all right, I'm agreeable to a little nip. I'll split a quart with you." Gee whizz.

But that isn't what I want to tell my story about. We got home late in November and I promised mother I'd quit the race horses for good. There's a lot of things you've got to promise a mother because she don't know any better.

And so, there not being any work in our town any more than when I left there to go to the races, I went off to Sandusky and got a pretty good place taking care of the horses for a man who owned a teaming and delivery and storage business there. It was a pretty good place with good eats and a day off each week and sleeping on a cot in the big barn, and mostly just shoveling in hay and oats to a lot of big good-enough skates of horses that couldn't have trotted a race with a toad. I wasn't dissatisfied and I could send money home.

And then, as I started to tell you, the fall races come to Sandusky and I got the day off and I went. I left the job at noon and had on my good clothes and my new brown derby hat I'd just bought the Saturday before, and a stand-up collar.

First of all I went downtown and walked about with the dudes. I've always thought to myself, "put up a good front," and so I did it. I had forty dollars in my pocket and so I went into the West House, a big hotel, and walked up to the cigar stand. "Give me three twenty-five cent cigars," I said. There was a lot of horse men and strangers and dressed-up people from other towns standing around in the lobby and in the bar, and I mingled amongst them. In the bar there was a fellow with a cane and a Windsor tie on, that it made me sick to look at him. I like a man to be a man and dress up, but not to go put on that kind of airs. So I pushed him aside, kind of rough, and had me a drink of whisky. And then he looked at me as though he thought he'd get gay, but he changed his mind and didn't say anything. And then I had another drink of whisky, just

41

to show him something, and went out and had a hack out to the races all to myself, and when I got there I bought myself the best seat I could get up in the grandstand, but didn't go in for any of these boxes. That's putting on too many airs.

And so there I was, sitting up in the grandstand as gay as you please and looking down on the swipes coming out with their horses and with their dirty horsey pants on and the horse blankets swung over their shoulders same as I had been doing all the year before. I liked one thing about the same as the other, sitting up there and feeling grand and being down there and looking up at the yaps and feeling grander and more important too. One thing's about as good as another if you take it just right. I've often said that.

Well, right in front of me, in the grandstand that day, there was a fellow with a couple of girls and they was about my age. The young fellow was a nice guy all right. He was the kind maybe that goes to college and then comes to be a lawyer or maybe a newspaper editor or something like that, but he wasn't stuck on himself. There are some of that kind are all right and he was one of the ones.

He had his sister with him and another girl and the sister looked around over his shoulder, accidental at first, not intending to start anything—she wasn't that kind—and her eyes and mine happened to meet.

You know how it is. Gee, she was a peach. She had on a soft dress, kind of a blue stuff, and it looked carelessly made, but was well sewed and made and everything. I knew that much. I blushed when she looked right at me and so did she. She was the nicest girl I've ever seen in my life. She wasn't stuck on herself and she could talk proper grammar without being like a school teacher or something like that. What I mean is, she was O.K. I think maybe her father was well-to-do, but not rich to make her chesty because she was his daughter, as some are. Maybe he owned a drug store or a dry goods

42

store in their home town, or something like that. She never told me and I never asked.

My own people are all O.K. too, when you come to that. My grandfather was Welsh and over in the old country, in Wales, he was—but never mind that.

The first heat of the first race come off and the young fellow setting there with the two girls left them and went down to make a bet. I knew what he was up to, but he didn't talk big and noisy and let everyone around know he was a sport, as some do. He wasn't that kind. Well, he come back and I heard him tell the two girls what horse he'd bet on, and when the heat was trotted they all half got to their feet and acted in the excited, sweaty way people do when they've got money down on a race, and the horse they bet on is up there pretty close at the end, and they think maybe he'll come on with a rush, but he never does because he hasn't got the old juice in him, come right down to it.

And, then, pretty soon, the horses came out for the 2.18 pace and there was a horse in it I knew. He was a horse Bob French had in his string, but Bob didn't own him. He was a horse owned by a Mr. Mathers down at Marietta, Ohio.

This Mr. Mathers had a lot of money and owned a coal mine or something, and he had a swell place out in the country, and he was stuck on race horses, but was a Presbyterian or something, and I think more than likely his wife was one, too, maybe a stiffer one than himself. So he never raced his horses hisself, and the story round the Ohio race tracks was that when one of his horses got ready to go to the races he turned him over to Bob French and pretended to his wife he was sold.

So Bob had the horses and he did pretty much as he pleased and you can't blame Bob; at least, I never did. Sometimes he was out to win and sometimes he wasn't. I never cared much about that when I was swiping a horse. What I did want to know was that my horse had the speed and could go out in front if you wanted him to.

And, as I'm telling you, there was Bob in this race with one of Mr. Mathers' horses, was named "About Ben Ahem" or something like that, and was fast as a streak. He was a gelding and had a mark of 2.21, but could step in .08 or .09.

Because when Burt and I were out, as I've told you, the year before, there was a nigger Burt knew, worked for Mr. Mathers, and we went out there one day when we didn't have no race on at the Marietta Fair and our boss Harry had gone home.

And so everyone was gone to the fair but just this one nigger, and he took us all through Mr. Mathers' swell house and he and Burt tapped a bottle of wine Mr. Mathers had hid in his bedroom, back in a closet, without his wife knowing, and he showed us this Ahem horse. Burt was always stuck on being a driver, but didn't have much chance to get to the top, being a nigger, and he and the other nigger gulped that whole bottle of wine and Burt got a little lit up.

So the nigger let Burt take this About Ben Ahem and step him a mile in a track Mr. Mathers had all to himself, right there on the farm. And Mr. Mathers had one child, a daughter, kinda sick and not very good-looking, and she came home and we had to hustle and get About Ben Ahem stuck back in the barn.

I'm only telling you to get everything straight. At Sandusky, that afternoon I was at the fair, this young fellow with the two girls was fussed, being with the girls and losing his bet. You know how a fellow is that way. One of them was his girl and the other his sister. I had figured that out.

"Gee whizz," I says to myself, "I'm going to give him the dope."

He was mighty nice when I touched him on the shoulder. He and the girls were nice to me right from the start and clear to the end. I'm not blaming them.

And so he leaned back and I gave him the dope on About Ben Ahem. "Don't bet a cent on this first heat because he'll go like an oxen hitched to a plough, but when the first heat is over go right down and lay on your pile." That's what I told him.

Well, I never saw a fellow treat any one sweller. There was a fat man sitting beside the little girl that had looked at me twice by this time, and I at her, and both blushing, and what did he do but have the nerve to turn and ask the fat man to get up and change places with me so I could set with his crowd.

Gee whizz, amighty. There I was. What a chump I was to go and get gay up there in the West House bar, and just because that dude was standing there with a cane and that kind of a necktie on, to go and get all balled up and drink that whisky, just to show off.

Of course, she would know, me setting right beside her and letting her smell of my breath. I could have kicked myself right down out of that grandstand and all around that race track and made a faster record than most of the skates of horses they had there that year.

Because that girl wasn't any mutt of a girl. What wouldn't I have given right then for a stick of chewing gum to chew, or a lozenger, or some licorice, or most anything. I was glad I had those twenty-five cent cigars in my pocket, and right away I give that fellow one and lit one myself. Then that fat man got up and we changed places and there I was plunked down beside her.

They introduced themselves, and the fellow's best girl he had with him, was named Miss Elinor Woodbury, and her father was a manufacturer of barrels from a place called Tiffin, Ohio. And the fellow himself was named Wilbur Wessen and his sister was Miss Lucy Wessen.

I suppose it was their having such swell names got me off my trolley. A fellow, just because he has been a swipe with a race horse, and works taking care of horses for a man in the teaming, delivery and storage business, isn't any better or worse than anyone else. I've often thought that, and said it, too.

But you know how a fellow is. There's something in that kind of nice clothes, and the kind of nice eyes she had, and the way she looked at me, awhile before, over her brother's shoulder, and me looking back at her, and both of us blushing.

I couldn't show her up for a boob, could I?

I made a fool of myself, that's what I did. I said my name was Walter Mathers from Marietta, Ohio, and then I told all three of them the smashingest lie you ever heard. What I said was that my father owned the horse About Ben Ahem, and that he had let him out to this Bob French for racing purposes, because our family was proud and had never gone into racing that way, in our own name, I mean. Then I had got started, and they were all leaning over and listening, and Miss Lucy Wessen's eyes were shining, and I went the whole hog.

I told about our place down at Marietta, and about the big stables and the grand brick house we had on a hill, up above the Ohio River, but I knew enough not to do it in no bragging way. What I did was to start things and then let them drag the rest out of me. I acted just as reluctant to tell as I could. Our family hasn't got any barrel factory, and, since I've known us, we've always been pretty poor, but not asking anything of anyone at that, and my grandfather, over in Wales—but never mind that.

We set there talking like we had known each other for years and years, and I went and told them that my father had been expecting maybe this Bob French wasn't on the square, and had sent me up to Sandusky on the sly to find out what I could.

And I bluffed it through I had found out all about the 2.18 pace in which About Ben Ahem was to start.

I said he would lose the first heat by pacing like a lame cow and then he would come back and skin 'em alive after that. And to back up what I said I took thirty dollars out of my pocket and handed it to Mr. Wilbur Wessen and asked him would he mind, after the first heat, to go down and place it on About Ben Ahem for whatever odds he could get. What I said was that I didn't want Bob French to see me and none of the swipes.

Sure enough the first heat come off and About Ben Ahem went off his stride, up the back stretch, and looked like a wooden horse or a sick one, and come in to be last. Then this Wilbur Wessen went down to the betting place under the grandstand and there I was with the two girls, and when that Miss Woodbury was looking the other way once, Lucy Wessen kinda, with her shoulder you know, kinda touched me. Not just tucking down, I don't mean. You know how a woman can do. They get close, but not getting gay either. You know what they do. Gee whizz.

And then they give me a jolt. What they had done when I didn't know, was to get together, and they had decided Wilbur Wessen would bet fifty dollars, and the two girls had gone and put in ten dollars each of their own money, too. I was sick then, but I was sicker later.

About the gelding, About Ben Ahem, and their winning their money I wasn't worried a lot about that. It come out O.K. Ahem stepped the next three heats like a bushel of spoiled eggs going to market before they could be found out, and Wilbur Wessen had got nine to two for the money. There was something else eating at me.

Because Wilbur come back after he had bet the money, and after that he spent most of his time talking to that Miss Woodbury, and Lucy Wessen and I was left alone together like on a desert island. Gee, if I'd only been on the square or if there had been any way of getting myself on the square. There ain't any Walter Mathers, like I said to her and them, and there hasn't ever been one, but if there was, I bet I'd go to Marietta, Ohio, and shoot him tomorrow.

There I was, big boob that I am. Pretty soon the race was over, and Wilbur had gone down and collected our money, and we had a hack downtown, and he stood us a swell dinner at the West House, and a bottle of champagne beside.

47

And I was with that girl and she wasn't saying much, and I wasn't saying much either. One thing I know. She wasn't stuck on me because of the lie about my father being rich and all that. There's a way you know. . . . Craps amighty. There's a kind of girl you see just once in your life, and if you don't get busy and make hay then you're gone for good and all and might as well go jump off a bridge. They give you a look from inside of them somewhere, and it ain't no vamping, and what it means is—you want that girl to be your wife, and you want nice things around her like flowers and swell clothes, and you want her to have the kids you're going to have, and you want good music played and no ragtime. Gee whizz.

There's a place over near Sandusky, across a kind of bay, and it's called Cedar Point. And when we had had that dinner we went over to it in a launch, all by ourselves. Wilbur and Miss Lucy and that Miss Woodbury had to catch a ten o'clock train back to Tiffin, Ohio, because when you're out with girls like that you can't get careless and miss any trains and stay out all night like you can with some kinds of Janes.

And Wilbur blowed himself to the launch and it cost him fifteen cold plunks, but I wouldn't ever have knew it if I hadn't listened. He wasn't no tin horn kind of a sport.

Over at the Cedar Point place we didn't stay around where there was a gang of common kind of cattle at all.

There was big dance halls and dining places for yaps, and there was a beach you could walk along and get where it was dark, and we went there.

She didn't talk hardly at all and neither did I, and I was thinking how glad I was my mother was all right, and always made us kids learn to eat with a fork at table and not swill soup and not be noisy and rough like a gang you see around a race track that way.

Then Wilbur and his girl went away up the beach and Lucy and I set down in a dark place where there was some roots of old trees the water had washed up, and after that, the time, till we had to go back in the launch and they had to catch their trains, wasn't nothing at all. It went like winking your eye.

Here's how it was. The place we were setting in was dark, like I said, and there was the roots from that old stump sticking up like arms, and there was a watery smell, and the night was like—as if you could put your hand out and feel it—so warm and soft and dark and sweet like an orange.

I most cried and I most swore and I most jumped up and danced, I was so mad and happy and sad.

When Wilbur come back from being alone with his girl, and she saw him coming, Lucy she says, "We got to go to the train now," and she was most crying, too, but she never knew nothing I knew, and she couldn't be so all busted up. And then, before Wilbur and Miss Woodbury got up to where we was, she put her face up and kissed me quick and put her head up against me and she was all quivering and— Gee whizz.

Sometimes I hope I have cancer and die. I guess you know what I mean. We went in the launch across the bay to the train like that, and it was dark too. She whispered and said it was like she and I could get out of the boat and walk on the water, and it sounded foolish, but I knew what she meant.

And then quick, we were right at the depot, and there was a big gang of yaps, the kind that goes to the fairs, and crowded and milling around like cattle, and how could I tell her? "It won't be long because you'll write and I'll write to you." That's all she said.

I got a chance like a hay barn afire. A swell chance I got.

And maybe she would write me, down at Marietta that way, and the letter would come back, and stamped on the front of it by the U.S.A. "there ain't any such guy," or something like that, whatever they stamp on a letter that way.

And me trying to pass myself off for a bigbug and a swell— to her, as decent a little body as God ever made. Craps amighty. A swell chance I got.

And then the train come and she got on, and Wilbur

Wessen come and shook hands with me, and that Miss Woodbury was nice too, and bowed to me and I at her and the train went and I busted out and cried like a kid.

Gee, I could have run after that train and made Dan Patch look like a freight train after a wreck, but socks amighty, what was the use? Did you ever see such a fool?

I'll bet you what—if I had an arm broke right now or a train had run over my foot—I wouldn't go to no doctor at all. I'd go set down and let her hurt and hurt—that's what I'd do.

I'll bet you what—if I hadn't a drunk that booze I'd a never been such a boob as to go tell such a lie—that couldn't never be made straight to a lady like her.

I wish I had that fellow right here that had on a Windsor tie and carried a cane. I'd smash him for fair. Gosh darn his eyes. He's a big fool—that's what he is.

And if I'm not another you just go find me one and I'll quit working and be a bum and give him my job. I don't care nothing for working and earning money and saving it for no such boob as myself.

WILLA CATHER

Willa Cather was born on December 7, 1873, in Win-chester, Virginia, but the absorbing influence in her life began in 1883 when her father pulled up stakes and moved to the unbroken prairie of south-central Nebraska. Just before the publication of One of Ours, *which received the Pulitzer Prize for prose fiction in 1922, she made the comment that "the years from eight to fifteen are the formative period in a writer's life, when he unconsciously gathers basic material. He may acquire a great many interesting and vivid impressions in his mature years," she added, "but his thematic material he acquires under fifteen years of age."*

Miss Cather was nine when she rode horseback, like a tomboy, across the prairie; she was eleven when the family moved to Red Cloud, the village to which she was to return again and again in her mature years. She was a brilliant child, independent in her thinking and forthright in her expression. When she graduated from the Red Cloud High School at sixteen, she delivered the commencement address, an oration entitled "Superstition versus Investigation."

Before she could enter the University of Nebraska, in Lincoln, she was required to spend a year at The Latin School, a preparatory academy. An essay she wrote on Carlyle was published in the Lincoln paper, the State

Journal, *and the resultant notoriety convinced Miss Cather that she should become a writer. That she was destined to become a great writer seems to have been the opinion of everyone at the university, including Chancellor James Hulme Canfield, father of Dorothy Canfield. Miss Cather did nothing to destroy that impression. She quickly took over the undergraduate literary magazine, the* Hesperian, *to which she contributed short stories, verse, criticism; she edited the yearbook, the* Sombrero; *she published a short story in a Boston magazine. A course in journalism, taught by Will Owen Jones, managing editor of the* State Journal, *led to her writing for the Sunday edition of the paper. She became the paper's dramatic critic, and her caustic comment on anything she believed to be inept or shoddy won her quite a reputation as a young critic. She graduated in 1895, barely skimping through in mathematics, a freshman requirement that she finally passed in her senior year.*

In 1896, at the age of twenty-three, she left Nebraska for Pittsburgh, where she spent the next ten years, the first five in journalism, the last five teaching English in the high school. Her first post was in the editorial office of the Home Monthly; *later she joined the staff of the* Pittsburgh Daily Leader. *She continued to haunt the theater and music halls and to write dramatic criticism. She published an occasional poem in* Critic, Criterion, McClure's, *and elsewhere and several stories in the* Home Monthly *and* Cosmopolitan. *A collection of poems,* April Twilights (1903), *was followed by a volume of short stories,* The Troll Garden (1905), *which included "Paul's Case," published originally in* McClure's. *The publication of this book led to her being offered a position on the staff of*

McClure's *in 1906. Two years later she became its managing editor, a post she held until her resignation in 1912.*

During her years at McClure's she started writing the novels upon which her reputation is largely founded. Alexander's Bridge *appeared in 1912, followed by* O Pioneers! *(1913), part of which was written in the Southwest, an area which was to become a second source of inspiration and to lead, eventually, to* Death Comes for the Archbishop *(1927), one of her best-loved novels. Not until the publication of* One of Ours *(1922) did she become a popular success. She continued to write short stories.* Youth and the Bright Medusa *(1920) reprinted four of the stories in* The Troll Garden, *with four additional.*

In 1937 she reread all of her fiction and made some major revisions in preparing it for publication in The Novels and Stories of Willa Cather, *a deluxe library edition published in 1937 and 1938. Her final novel,* Saphira and the Slave Girl *(1940), was added later. When she died on April 24, 1947, she was already a minor American classic.*

During her life she received three prominent awards for her fiction: the Howells medal from the National Institute of Arts and Letters, in 1930; the gold medal from the same Academy in 1944, when she was seventy; and the first annual Prix Femina Americaine for Shadows on the Rock *in 1933. Her own comments on the art of writing appear in* On Writing, *a group of critical studies published in 1949.*

PAUL'S CASE

It was Paul's afternoon to appear before the faculty of the
Pittsburgh High School to account for his various misdemeanors. He had been suspended a week ago, and his father had
called at the Principal's office and confessed his perplexity
about his son. Paul entered the faculty room suave and smiling.
His clothes were a trifle outgrown, and the tan velvet on the
collar of his open overcoat was frayed and worn; but for
all that there was something of the dandy about him, and he
wore an opal pin in his neatly knotted black four-in-hand, and
a red carnation in his buttonhole. This latter adornment the
faculty somehow felt was not properly significant of the contrite spirit befitting a boy under the ban of suspension.

Paul was tall for his age and very thin, with high, cramped
shoulders and a narrow chest. His eyes were remarkable for
a certain hysterical brilliancy, and he continually used them
in a conscious, theatrical sort of way, peculiarly offensive in a
boy. The pupils were abnormally large, as though he were
addicted to belladonna, but there was a glassy glitter about
them which that drug does not produce.

When questioned by the Principal as to why he was there,
Paul stated, politely enough, that he wanted to come back to
school. This was a lie, but Paul was quite accustomed to lying;
found it, indeed, indispensable for overcoming friction. His

Reprinted from *Youth and the Bright Medusa* by Willa Cather, by
permission of Alfred A. Knopf, Inc. Copyright 1905, 1920 by Willa Cather.

teachers were asked to state their respective charges against him, which they did with such a rancor and aggrievedness as evinced that this was not a usual case. Disorder and impertinence were among the offenses named, yet each of his instructors felt that it was scarcely possible to put into words the real cause of the trouble, which lay in a sort of hysterically defiant manner of the boy's; in the contempt which they all knew he felt for them, and which he seemingly made not the least effort to conceal. Once, when he had been making a synopsis of a paragraph at the blackboard, his English teacher had stepped to his side and attempted to guide his hand. Paul had started back with a shudder and thrust his hands violently behind him. The astonished woman could scarcely have been more hurt and embarrassed had he struck at her. The insult was so involuntary and definitely personal as to be unforgettable. In one way and another, he had made all his teachers, men and women alike, conscious of the same feeling of physical aversion. In one class he habitually sat with his hand shading his eyes; in another he always looked out of the window during the recitation; in another he made a running commentary on the lecture, with humorous intent.

His teachers felt this afternoon that his whole attitude was symbolized by his shrug and his flippantly red carnation flower, and they fell upon him without mercy, his English teacher leading the pack. He stood through it smiling, his pale lips parted over his white teeth. (His lips were continually twitching, and he had a habit of raising his eyebrows that was contemptuous and irritating to the last degree.) Older boys than Paul had broken down and shed tears under that ordeal, but his set smile did not once desert him, and his only sign of discomfort was the nervous trembling of the fingers that toyed with the buttons of his overcoat, and an occasional jerking of the other hand which held his hat. Paul was always smiling, always glancing about him, seeming to feel that people might be watching him and trying to detect something. This conscious expression, since it was as far as possible from boyish mirth-fulness, was usually attributed to insolence or "smartness."

As the inquisition proceeded, one of his instructors repeated an impertinent remark of the boy's, and the Principal asked him whether he thought that a courteous speech to make to a woman. Paul shrugged his shoulders slightly and his eyebrows twitched.

"I don't know," he replied. "I didn't mean to be polite or impolite, either. I guess it's a sort of way I have, of saying things regardless."

The Principal asked him whether he didn't think that a way it would be well to get rid of. Paul grinned and said he guessed so. When he was told that he could go, he bowed gracefully and went out. His bow was like a repetition of the scandalous red carnation.

His teachers were in despair, and his drawing master voiced the feeling of them all when he declared there was something about the boy which none of them understood. He added: "I don't really believe that smile of his comes altogether from insolence; there's something sort of haunted about it. The boy is not strong, for one thing. There is something wrong about the fellow."

The drawing master had come to realize that, in looking at Paul, one saw only his white teeth and the forced animation of his eyes. One warm afternoon the boy had gone to sleep at his drawing board, and his master had noted with amazement what a white, blue-veined face it was; drawn and wrinkled like an old man's about the eyes, the lips twitching even in his sleep.

His teachers left the building dissatisfied and unhappy; humiliated to have felt so vindictive toward a mere boy, to have uttered this feeling in cutting terms, and to have set each other on, as it were, in the gruesome game of intemperate reproach. One of them remembered having seen a miserable street cat set at bay by a ring of tormentors.

As for Paul, he ran down the hill whistling the Soldiers'

Chorus from *Faust,* looking wildly behind him now and then
to see whether some of his teachers were not there to witness
his light-heartedness. As it was now late in the afternoon and
Paul was on duty that evening as usher at Carnegie Hall, he
decided that he would not go home to supper.

When he reached the concert hall the doors were not yet
open. It was chilly outside, and he decided to go up into the
picture gallery—always deserted at this hour—where there
were some of Raffelli's gay studies of Paris streets and an airy
blue Venetian scene or two that always exhilarated him. He
was delighted to find no one in the gallery but the old guard,
who sat in the corner, a newspaper on his knee, a black
patch over one eye and the other closed. Paul possessed himself of the place and walked confidently up and down, whistling under his breath. After a while he sat down before a
blue Rico and lost himself. When he bethought him to look
at his watch, it was after seven o'clock, and he rose with a
start and ran downstairs, making a face at Augustus Caesar,
peering out from the cast-room, and an evil gesture at the
Venus of Milo as he passed her on the stairway.

When Paul reached the ushers' dressing-room half a dozen
boys were there already, and he began excitedly to tumble
into his uniform. It was one of the few that at all approached
fitting, and Paul thought it very becoming—though he knew
the tight, straight coat accentuated his narrow chest, about
which he was exceedingly sensitive. He was always excited
while he dressed, twanging all over to the tuning of the strings
and the preliminary flourishes of the horns in the music-room;
but tonight he seemed quite beside himself, and he teased and
plagued the boys until, telling him that he was crazy, they put
him down on the floor and sat on him.

Somewhat calmed by his suppression, Paul dashed out to
the front of the house to seat the early comers. He was a model
usher. Gracious and smiling he ran up and down the aisles.
Nothing was too much trouble for him; he carried messages

and brought programs as though it were his greatest pleasure in life, and all the people in his section thought him a charming boy, feeling that he remembered and admired them. As the house filled, he grew more and more vivacious and animated, and the color came to his cheeks and lips. It was very much as though this were a great reception and Paul were the host. Just as the musicians came out to take their places, his English teacher arrived with checks for the seats which a prominent manufacturer had taken for the season. She betrayed some embarrassment when she handed Paul the tickets, and a *hauteur* which subsequently made her feel very foolish. Paul was startled for a moment, and had the feeling of wanting to put her out; what business had she here among all these fine people and gay colors? He looked her over and decided that she was not appropriately dressed and must be a fool to sit downstairs in such togs. The tickets had probably been sent her out of kindness, he reflected, as he put down a seat for her, and she had about as much right to sit there as he had.

When the symphony began Paul sank into one of the rear seats with a long sigh of relief, and lost himself as he had done before the Rico. It was not that symphonies, as such, meant anything in particular to Paul, but the first sigh of the instruments seemed to free some hilarious spirit within him; something that struggled there like the Genius in the bottle found by the Arab fisherman. He felt a sudden zest of life; the lights danced before his eyes and the concert hall blazed into unimaginable splendor. When the soprano soloist came on, Paul forgot even the nastiness of his teacher's being there, and gave himself up to the peculiar intoxication such personages always had for him. The soloist chanced to be a German woman, by no means in her first youth, and the mother of many children; but she wore a satin gown and a tiara, and she had that indefinable air of achievement, that world-shine upon her, which always blinded Paul to any possible defects.

After a concert was over, Paul was often irritable and

wretched until he got to sleep,—and tonight he was even more than usually restless. He had the feeling of not being able to let down; of its being impossible to give up this delicious excitement which was the only thing that could be called living at all. During the last number he withdrew and, after hastily changing his clothes in the dressing-room, slipped out to the side door where the singer's carriage stood. Here he began pacing rapidly up and down the walk, waiting to see her come out.

Over yonder the Schenley, in its vacant stretch, loomed big and square through the fine rain, the windows of its twelve stories glowing like those of a lighted cardboard house under a Christmas tree. All the actors and singers of any importance stayed there when they were in the city, and a number of the big manufacturers of the place lived there in the winter. Paul had often hung about the hotel, watching the people go in and out, longing to enter and leave schoolmasters and dull care behind him forever.

At last the singer came out, accompanied by the conductor, who helped her into her carriage and closed the door with a cordial *auf wiedersehen*,—which set Paul to wondering whether she were not an old sweetheart of his. Paul followed the carriage over to the hotel, walking so rapidly as not to be far from the entrance when the singer alighted and disappeared behind the swinging glass doors which were opened by a Negro in a tall hat and a long coat. In the moment that the door was ajar, it seemed to Paul that he, too, entered. He seemed to feel himself go after her up the steps, into the warm, lighted building, into an exotic, a tropical world of shiny, glistening surfaces and basking ease. He reflected upon the mysterious dishes that were brought into the dining-room, the green bottles in buckets of ice, as he had seen them in the supper party pictures of the Sunday supplement. A quick gust of wind brought the rain down with sudden vehemence, and Paul was startled to find that he was still outside in the slush of the gravel driveway; that his boots were letting in the water and his scanty overcoat was clinging wet about him; that the lights in front of the concert hall were out, and that the rain was driving in sheets between him and the orange glow of the windows above him. There it was, what he wanted—tangibly before him, like the fairy world of a Christmas pantomime; as the rain beat in his face, Paul wondered whether he were destined always to shiver in the black night outside, looking up at it.

He turned and walked reluctantly toward the car tracks. The end had to come some time; his father in his night-clothes at the top of the stairs, explanations that did not explain, hastily improvised fictions that were forever tripping him up, his upstairs room and its horrible yellow wall paper, the creaking bureau with the greasy plush collar-box, and over his painted wooden bed the pictures of George Washington and John Calvin, and the framed motto, "Feed my Lambs," which had been worked in red worsted by his mother, whom Paul could not remember.

Half an hour later, Paul alighted from the Negley Avenue car and went slowly down one of the side streets off the main thoroughfare. It was a highly respectable street, where all the houses were exactly alike, and where business men of moderate means begot and reared large families of children, all of whom went to Sabbath-school and learned the shorter catechism, and were interested in arithmetic; all of whom were as exactly alike as their homes, and of a piece with the monotony in which they lived. Paul never went up Cordelia Street without a shudder of loathing. His home was next the house of the Cumberland minister. He approached it tonight with the nerveless sense of defeat, the hopeless feeling of sinking back forever into ugliness and commonness that he had always had when he came home. The moment he turned into Cordelia Street he felt the waters close above his head. After each of these orgies of living, he experienced all the physical depression which follows a debauch; the loathing of respectable beds, of common food, of a house permeated by kitchen odors; a shuddering repulsion for the flavorless, colorless mass of every-day existence; a morbid desire for cool things and soft lights and fresh flowers.

The nearer he approached the house, the more absolutely unequal Paul felt to the sight of it all; his ugly sleeping chamber; the cold bathroom with the grimy zinc tub, the cracked mirror, the dripping spiggots; his father, at the top of the stairs, his hairy legs sticking out from his nightshirt, his feet thrust into carpet slippers. He was so much later than usual that there would certainly be inquiries and reproaches. Paul stopped short before the door. He felt that he could not be accosted by his father tonight; that he could not toss again on that miserable bed. He would not go in. He would tell his father that he had no car fare, and it was raining so hard he had gone home with one of the boys and stayed all night.

Meanwhile, he was wet and cold. He went around to the back of the house and tried one of the basement windows, found it open, raised it cautiously, and scrambled down the cellar wall to the floor. There he stood, holding his breath, terrified by the noise he had made; but the floor above him was silent, and there was no creak on the stairs. He found a soap-box, and carried it over to the soft ring of light that streamed from the furnace door, and sat down. He was hor-ribly afraid of rats, so he did not try to sleep, but sat looking distrustfully at the dark, still terrified lest he might have awakened his father. In such reactions, after one of the experi-ences which made days and nights out of the dreary blanks of the calendar, when his senses were deadened, Paul's head was always singularly clear. Suppose his father had heard him get-ting in at the window and had come down and shot him for a burglar? Then, again, suppose his father had come down, pistol in hand, and he had cried out in time to save himself, and his father had been horrified to think how nearly he had killed him? Then, again, suppose a day should come when his father would remember that night, and wish there had been no warning cry to stay his hand? With this last supposition Paul entertained himself until daybreak.

The following Sunday was fine; the sodden November chill was broken by the last flash of autumnal summer. In the morning Paul had to go to church and Sabbath-school, as always. On seasonable Sunday afternoons the burghers of Cordelia Street usually sat out on their front "stoops," and talked to their neighbors on the next stoop, or called to those across the street in neighborly fashion. The men sat placidly on gay cushions placed upon the steps that led down to the sidewalk, while the women, in their Sunday "waists," sat in rockers on the cramped porches, pretending to be greatly at their ease. The children played in the streets; there were so many of them that the place resembled the recreation grounds of a kindergarten. The men on the steps—all in their shirt sleeves, their vests unbuttoned—sat with their legs well apart, their stomachs comfortably protruding, and talked of the prices of things, or told anecdotes of the sagacity of their various chiefs and overlords. They occasionally looked over the multitude of squabbling children, listened affectionately to their high-pitched, nasal voices, smiling to see their own proclivities reproduced in their offspring, and interspersed their legends of the iron kings with remarks about their sons' progress at school, their grades in arithmetic, and the amounts they had saved in their toy banks. On this last Sunday of November, Paul sat all the afternoon on the lowest step of his stoop, staring into the street, while his sisters, in their rockers, were talking to the minister's daughters next door about how many shirtwaists they had made in the last week, and how many waffles someone had eaten at the last church supper. When the weather was warm, and his father was in a particularly jovial frame of mind, the girls made lemonade, which was always brought out in a red-glass pitcher, ornamented with forget-me-nots in blue enamel.

62

This the girls thought very fine, and the neighbors joked about the suspicious color of the pitcher.

Today Paul's father, on the top step, was talking to a young man who shifted a restless baby from knee to knee. He happened to be the young man who was daily held up to Paul as a model, and after whom it was his father's dearest hope that he would pattern. This young man was of a ruddy complexion, with a compressed, red mouth, and faded, nearsighted eyes, over which he wore thick spectacles, with gold bows that curved about his ears. He was clerk to one of the magnates of a great steel corporation, and was looked upon in Cordelia Street as a young man with a future. There was a story that, some five years ago—he was now barely twenty-six—he had been a trifle "dissipated," but in order to curb his appetites and save the loss of time and strength that a sowing of wild oats might have entailed, he had taken his chief's advice, oft reiterated to his employees, and at twenty-one had married the first woman whom he could persuade to share his fortunes. She happened to be an angular school mistress, much older than he, who also wore thick glasses, and who had now borne him four children, all near-sighted, like herself.

The young man was relating how his chief, now cruising in the Mediterranean, kept in touch with all the details of the business, arranging his office hours on his yacht just as though he were at home, and "knocking off work enough to keep two stenographers busy." His father told, in turn, the plan his corporation was considering, of putting in an electric railway plant at Cairo. Paul snapped his teeth; he had an awful apprehension that they might spoil it all before he got there. Yet he rather liked to hear these legends of the iron kings, that were told and retold on Sundays and holidays; these stories of palaces in Venice, yachts on the Mediterranean, and high play at Monte Carlo appealed to his fancy, and he was interested in the triumphs of cash boys who had become famous, though he had no mind for the cash-boy stage.

63

After supper was over, and he had helped to dry the dishes, Paul nervously asked his father whether he could go to George's to get some help in his geometry, and still more nervously asked for car fare. This latter request he had to repeat, as his father, on principle, did not like to hear requests for money, whether much or little. He asked Paul whether he could not go to some boy who lived nearer, and told him that he ought not to leave his school work until Sunday; but he gave him the dime. He was not a poor man, but he had a worthy ambition to come up in the world. His only reason for allowing Paul to usher was that he thought a boy ought to be earning a little.

Paul bounded upstairs, scrubbed the greasy odor of the dishwater from his hands with the ill-smelling soap he hated, and then shook over his fingers a few drops of violet water from the bottle he kept hidden in his drawer. He left the house with his geometry conspicuously under his arm, and the moment he got out of Cordelia Street and boarded a downtown car, he shook off the lethargy of two deadening days, and began to live again.

The leading juvenile of the permanent stock company which played at one of the downtown theaters was an acquaintance of Paul's, and the boy had been invited to drop in at the Sunday night rehearsals whenever he could. For more than a year Paul had spent every available moment loitering about Charley Edwards's dressing-room. He had won a place among Edwards's following not only because the young actor, who could not afford to employ a dresser, often found him useful, but because he recognized in Paul something akin to what churchmen term "vocation."

It was at the theater and at Carnegie Hall that Paul really lived; the rest was but a sleep and a forgetting. This was Paul's fairy tale, and it had for him all the allurement of a secret love. The moment he inhaled the gassy, painty, dusty odor behind the scenes, he breathed like a prisoner set free, and

64

felt within him the possibility of doing or saying splendid, brilliant things. The moment the cracked orchestra beat out the overture from *Martha,* or jerked at the serenade from *Rigoletto,* all stupid and ugly things slid from him, and his senses were deliciously, yet delicately fired.

Perhaps it was because, in Paul's world, the natural nearly always wore the guise of 'ugliness, that a certain element of artificiality seemed to him necessary in beauty. Perhaps it was because his experience of life elsewhere was so full of Sabbath-school picnics, petty economies, wholesome advice as to how to succeed in life, and the unescapable odors of cooking that he found this existence so alluring, these smartly-clad men and women so attractive, that he was so moved by these starry apple orchards that bloomed perennially under the limelight.

It would be difficult to put it strongly enough how convincingly the stage entrance of that theater was for Paul the actual portal of Romance. Certainly none of the company ever suspected it, least of all Charley Edwards. It was very like the old stories that used to float about London of fabulously rich Jews, who had subterranean halls, with palms, and fountains, and soft lamps and richly apparelled women who never saw the disenchanting light of London day. So, in the midst of that smoke-palled city, enamored of figures and grimy toil, Paul had his secret temple, his wishing-carpet, his bit of blue-and-white Mediterranean shore bathed in perpetual sunshine.

Several of Paul's teachers had a theory that his imagination had been perverted by garish fiction; but the truth was, he scarcely ever read at all. The books at home were not such as would either tempt or corrupt a youthful mind, and as for reading the novels that some of his friends urged upon him—well, he got what he wanted much more quickly from music; any sort of music, from an orchestra to a barrel organ. He needed only the spark, the indescribable thrill that made his imagination master of his senses, and he could make plots and pictures enough of his own. It was equally true that he was not stage-struck—not, at any rate, in the usual acceptation of that expression. He had no desire to become an actor, any more than he had to become a musician. He felt no necessity to do any of these things; what he wanted was to see, to be in the atmosphere, float on the wave of it, to be carried out, blue league after blue league, away from everything.

After a night behind the scenes, Paul found the school-room more than ever repulsive; the bare floors and naked walls; the prosy men who never wore frock coats, or violets in their buttonholes; the women with their dull gowns, shrill voices, and pitiful seriousness about prepositions that govern the dative. He could not bear to have the other pupils think, for a moment, that he took these people seriously; he must convey to them that he considered it all trivial, and was there only by way of a joke, anyway. He had autograph pictures of all the members of the stock company which he showed his classmates, telling them the most incredible stories of his familiarity with these people, of his acquaintance with the soloists who came to Carnegie Hall, his suppers with them and the flowers he sent them. When these stories lost their effect, and his audience grew listless, he would bid all the boys good-by, announcing that he was going to travel for a while; going to Naples, to California, to Egypt. Then, next Monday, he would slip back, conscious and nervously smiling; his sister was ill, and he would have to defer his voyage until spring.

Matters went steadily worse with Paul at school. In the itch to let his instructors know how heartily he despised them, and how thoroughly he was appreciated elsewhere, he mentioned once or twice that he had no time to fool with theorems; adding—with a twitch of the eyebrows and a touch of that nervous bravado which so perplexed them—that he was helping the people down at the stock company; they were old friends of his.

The upshot of the matter was, that the Principal went to Paul's father, and Paul was taken out of school and put to work. The manager at Carnegie Hall was told to get another usher in his stead; the doorkeeper at the theater was warned not to admit him to the house; and Charley Edwards remorsefully promised the boy's father not to see him again.

The members of the stock company were vastly amused when some of Paul's stories reached them—especially the women. They were hard-working women, most of them supporting indolent husbands or brothers, and they laughed rather bitterly at having stirred the boy to such fervid and florid inventions. They agreed with the faculty and with his father, that Paul's was a bad case.

The east-bound train was plowing through a January snowstorm; the dull dawn was beginning to show gray when the engine whistled a mile out of Newark. Paul started up from the seat where he had lain curled in uneasy slumber, rubbed the breath-misted window glass with his hand, and peered out. The snow was whirling in curling eddies above the white bottom lands, and the drifts lay already deep in the fields and along the fences, while here and there the long dead grass and dried weed stalks protruded black above it. Lights shone from the scattered houses, and a gang of laborers who stood beside the track waved their lanterns.

Paul had slept very little, and he felt grimy and uncomfortable. He had made the all-night journey in a day coach because he was afraid if he took a Pullman he might be seen by some Pittsburgh business man who had noticed him in Denny & Carson's office. When the whistle woke him, he clutched quickly at his breast pocket, glancing about him with an uncertain smile. But the little, clay-bespattered Italians were still sleeping, the slatternly women across the aisle were in open-mouthed oblivion, and even the crumby, crying babies were for the nonce stilled. Paul settled back to struggle with his impatience as best he could.

67

When he arrived at the Jersey City station, he hurried through his breakfast, manifestly ill at ease and keeping a sharp eye about him. After he reached the Twenty-third Street station, he consulted a cabman, and had himself driven to a men's furnishing establishment which was just opening for the day. He spent upward to two hours there, buying with endless reconsidering and great care. His new street suit he put on in the fitting-room; the frock coat and dress clothes he had bundled into the cab with his new shirts. Then he drove to a hatter's and a shoe house. His next errand was at Tiffany's, where he selected silver-mounted brushes and a scarf-pin. He would not wait to have his silver marked, he said. Lastly, he stopped at a trunk shop on Broadway, and had his purchases packed into various traveling bags.

It was a little after one o'clock when he drove up to the Waldorf, and, after settling with the cabman, went into the office. He registered from Washington; said his mother and father had been abroad, and that he had come down to await the arrival of their steamer. He told his story plausibly and had no trouble, since he offered to pay for them in advance, in engaging his rooms; a sleeping-room, sitting room and bath.

Not once, but a hundred times Paul had planned this entry into New York. He had gone over every detail of it with Charley Edwards, and in his scrap book at home there were pages of description about New York hotels, cut from the Sunday papers.

When he was shown to his sitting room on the eighth floor, he saw at a glance that everything was as it should be; there was but one detail in his mental picture that the place did not realize, so he rang for the bell boy and sent him down for flowers. He moved about nervously until the boy returned, putting away his new linen and fingering it delightedly as he did so. When the flowers came, he put them hastily into water, and then tumbled into a hot bath. Presently he came out of his white bathroom, resplendent in his new silk underwear, and playing with the tassels of his red robe. The snow was whirling so fiercely outside his windows that he could scarcely see across the street; but within, the air was deliciously soft and fragrant. He put the violets and jonquils on the tabouret beside the couch, and threw himself down with a long sigh, covering himself with a Roman blanket. He was thoroughly tired; he had been in such haste, he had stood up to such a strain, covered so much ground in the last twenty-four hours, that he wanted to think how it had all come about. Lulled by the sound of the wind, the warm air, and the cool fragrance of the flowers, he sank into deep, drowsy retrospection.

It had been wonderfully simple; when they had shut him out of the theater and concert hall, when they had taken away his bone, the whole thing was virtually determined. The rest was a mere matter of opportunity. The only thing that at all surprised him was his own courage—for he realized well enough that he had always been tormented by fear, a sort of apprehensive dread that, of late years, as the meshes of the lies he had told closed about him, had been pulling the muscles of his body tighter and tighter. Until now, he could not remember a time when he had not been dreading something. Even when he was a little boy, it was always there—behind him, or before, or on either side. There had always been the shadowed corner, the dark place into which he dared not look, but from which something seemed always to be watching him—and Paul had done things that were not pretty to watch, he knew.

But now he had a curious sense of relief, as though he had at last thrown down the gauntlet to the thing in the corner.

Yet it was but a day since he had been sulking in the traces; but yesterday afternoon that he had been sent to the bank with Denny & Carson's deposit, as usual—but this time he was instructed to leave the book to be balanced. There was above two thousand dollars in checks, and nearly a thousand in the bank notes which he had taken from the book and quietly transferred to his pocket. At the bank he had made out a new

69

deposit slip. His nerves had been steady enough to permit of his returning to the office, where he had finished his work and asked for a full day's holiday tomorrow, Saturday, giving a perfectly reasonable pretext. The bank book, he knew, would not be returned before Monday or Tuesday, and his father would be out of town for the next week. From the time he slipped the bank notes into his pocket until he boarded the night train for New York, he had not known a moment's hesitation.

How astonishingly easy it had all been; here he was, the thing done; and this time there would be no awakening, no figure at the top of the stairs. He watched the snowflakes whirling by his window until he fell asleep.

When he awoke, it was four o'clock in the afternoon. He bounded up with a start; one of his precious days gone already! He spent nearly an hour in dressing, watching every stage of his toilet carefully in the mirror. Everything was quite perfect; he was exactly the kind of boy he had always wanted to be.

When he went downstairs, Paul took a carriage and drove up Fifth Avenue toward the Park. The snow had somewhat abated; carriages and tradesmen's wagons were hurrying soundlessly to and fro in the winter twilight; boys in woolen mufflers were shoveling off the doorsteps; the avenue stages made fine spots of color against the white street. Here and there on the corners whole flower gardens blooming behind glass windows, against which the snowflakes stuck and melted; violets, roses, carnations, lilies of the valley—somehow vastly more lovely and alluring that they blossomed thus unnaturally in the snow. The Park itself was a wonderful stage winter-piece.

When he returned, the pause of the twilight had ceased, and the tune of the streets had changed. The snow was falling faster, lights streamed from the hotels that reared their many stories fearlessly up into the storm, defying the raging

Atlantic winds. A long, black stream of carriages poured down the avenue, intersected here and there by other streams, tending horizontally. There were a score of cabs about the entrance of his hotel, and his driver had to wait. Boys in livery were running in and out of the awning stretched across the sidewalk, up and down the red velvet carpet laid from the door to the street. Above, about, within it all, was the rumble and roar, the hurry and toss of thousands of human beings as hot for pleasure as himself, and on every side of him towered the glaring affirmation of the omnipotence of wealth.

The boy set his teeth and drew his shoulders together in a spasm of realization; the plot of all dramas, the text of all romances, the nerve-stuff of all sensations was whirling about him like the snowflakes. He burnt like a faggot in a tempest.

When Paul came down to dinner, the music of the orchestra floated up the elevator shaft to greet him. As he stepped into the thronged corridor, he sank back into one of the chairs against the wall to get his breath. The lights, the chatter, the perfumes, the bewildering medley of color—he had, for a moment, the feeling of not being able to stand it. But only for a moment; these were his own people, he told himself. He went slowly about the corridors, through the writing-rooms, smoking-rooms, reception-rooms, as though he were exploring the chambers of an enchanted palace, built and peopled for him alone.

When he reached the dining room he sat down at a table near a window. The flowers, the white linen, the many-colored wine glasses, the gay toilettes of the women, the low popping of corks, the undulating repetitions of the *Blue Danube* from the orchestra, all flooded Paul's dream with bewildering radiance. When the roseate tinge of his champagne was added— that cold, precious, bubbling stuff that creamed and foamed in his glass—Paul wondered that there were honest men in the world at all. This was what all the world was fighting for,

71

he reflected; this was what all the struggle was about. He doubted the reality of his past. Had he ever known a place called Cordelia Street, a place where fagged-looking business men boarded the early car? Mere rivets in a machine they seemed to Paul,—sickening men, with combings of children's hair always hanging to their coats, and the smell of cooking in their clothes. Cordelia Street—Ah, that belonged to another time and country! Had he not always been thus, had he not sat here night after night, from as far back as he could remember, looking pensively over just such shimmering textures, and slowly twirling the stem of a glass like this one between his thumb and middle finger? He rather thought he had.

He was not in the least abashed or lonely. He had no especial desire to meet or to know any of these people; all he demanded was the right to look on and conjecture, to watch the pageant. The mere stage properties were all he contended for. Nor was he lonely later in the evening, in his loge at the Opera. He was entirely rid of his nervous misgivings, of his forced aggressiveness, of the imperative desire to show himself different from his surroundings. He felt now that his surroundings explained him. Nobody questioned the purple; he had only to wear it passively. He had only to glance down at his dress coat to reassure himself that here it would be impossible for anyone to humiliate him.

He found it hard to leave his beautiful sitting room to go to bed that night, and sat long watching the raging storm from his turret window. When he went to sleep, it was with the lights turned on in his bedroom; partly because of his old timidity, and partly so that, if he should wake in the night, there would be no wretched moment of doubt, no horrible suspicion of yellow wall paper, or of Washington and Calvin above his bed.

On Sunday morning the city was practically snow-bound. Paul breakfasted late, and in the afternoon he fell in with a wild San Francisco boy, a freshman at Yale, who said he had run down for a "little flyer" over Sunday. The young man offered to show Paul the night side of the town, and the two boys went off together after dinner, not returning to the hotel until seven o'clock the next morning. They had started out in the confiding warmth of a champagne friendship, but their parting in the elevator was singularly cool. The freshman pulled himself together to make his train, and Paul went to bed. He awoke at two o'clock in the afternoon, very thirsty and dizzy, and rang for ice water, coffee, and the Pittsburgh papers.

On the part of the hotel management, Paul excited no suspicion. There was this to be said for him, that he wore his spoils with dignity and in no way made himself conspicuous. His chief greediness lay in his ears and eyes, and his excesses were not offensive ones. His dearest pleasures were the gray winter twilights in his sitting room; his quiet enjoyment of his flowers, his clothes, his wide divan, his cigarette and his sense of power. He could not remember a time when he had felt so at peace with himself. The mere release from the necessity of petty lying, lying every day and every day, restored his self-respect. He had never lied for pleasure, even at school; but to make himself noticed and admired, to assert his difference from other Cordelia Street boys; and he felt a good deal more manly, more honest, even, now that he had no need for boastful pretensions, now that he could, as his actor friends used to say, "dress the part." It was characteristic that remorse did not occur to him. His golden days went by without a shadow, and he made each as perfect as he could.

On the eighth day after his arrival in New York, he found the whole affair exploited in the Pittsburgh papers, exploited with a wealth of detail which indicated that local news of a sensational nature was at a low ebb. The firm of Denny & Carson announced that the boy's father had refunded the full amount of his theft, and that they had no intention of prosecuting. The Cumberland minister had been interviewed, and

73

expressed his hope of yet reclaiming the motherless lad, and Paul's Sabbath-school teacher declared that she would spare no effort to that end. The rumor had reached Pittsburgh that the boy had been seen in a New York hotel, and his father had gone East to find him and bring him home.

Paul had just come in to dress for dinner; he sank into a chair, weak in the knees, and clasped his head in his hands. It was to be worse than jail, even; the tepid waters of Cordelia Street were to close over him finally and forever. The gray monotony stretched before him in hopeless, unrelieved years; Sabbath-school, Young People's Meeting, the yellow-papered room, the damp dish-towels; it all rushed back upon him with sickening vividness. He had the old feeling that the orchestra had suddenly stopped, the sinking sensation that the play was over. The sweat broke out on his face, and he sprang to his feet, looked about him with his white, conscious smile, and winked at himself in the mirror. With something of the child-ish belief in miracles with which he had so often gone to class, all his lessons unlearned, Paul dressed and dashed whistling down the corridor to the elevator.

He had no sooner entered the dining room and caught the measure of the music, than his remembrance was lightened by his old elastic power of claiming the moment, mounting with it, and finding it all sufficient. The glare and glitter about him, the mere scenic accessories had again, and for the last time, their old potency. He would show himself that he was game, he would finish the thing splendidly. He doubted, more than ever, the existence of Cordelia Street, and for the first time he drank his wine recklessly. Was he not, after all, one of these fortunate beings? Was he not still himself, and in his own place? He drummed a nervous accompaniment to the music and looked about him, telling himself over and over that it had paid.

He reflected drowsily, to the swell of the violin and the chill sweetness of his wine, that he might have done it more wisely. He might have caught an outbound steamer and been well out of their clutches before now. But the other side of the world had seemed too far away and too uncertain then; he could not have waited for it; his need had been too sharp. If he had to choose over again, he would do the same thing to-morrow. He looked affectionately about the dining room, now gilded with a soft mist. Ah, it had paid indeed!

Paul was awakened next morning by a painful throbbing in his head and feet. He had thrown himself across the bed without undressing, and had slept with his shoes on. His limbs and hands were lead heavy, and his tongue and throat were parched. There came upon him one of those fateful attacks of clear-headedness that never occurred except when he was physically exhausted and his nerves hung loose. He lay still and closed his eyes and let the tide of realities wash over him.

His father was in New York; "stopping at some joint or other," he told himself. The memory of successive summers on the front stoop fell upon him like a weight of black water. He had not a hundred dollars left; and he knew now, more than ever, that money was everything, the wall that stood between all he loathed and all he wanted. The thing was winding itself up; he had thought of that on his first glorious day in New York, and had even provided a way to snap the thread. It lay on his dressing-table now; he had got it out last night when he came blindly up from dinner,—but the shiny metal hurt his eyes, and he disliked the look of it, anyway.

He rose and moved about with a painful effort, succumbing now and again to attacks of nausea. It was the old depression exaggerated; all the world had become Cordelia Street. Yet somehow he was not afraid of anything, was absolutely calm; perhaps because he had looked into the dark corner at last, and knew. It was bad enough, what he saw there; but some-how not so bad as his long fear of it had been. He saw every-thing clearly now. He had a feeling that he had made the best of it, that he had lived the sort of life he was meant to live, and for half an hour he sat staring at the revolver. But he told himself that was not the way, so he went downstairs and took a cab to the ferry.

When Paul arrived at Newark, he got off the train and took another cab, directing the driver to follow the Pennsylvania tracks out of the town. The snow lay heavy on the roadways and had drifted deep in the open fields. Only here and there the dead grass or dried weed stalks projected, singularly black, above it. Once well into the country, Paul dismissed the carriage and walked, floundering along the tracks, his mind a medley of irrelevant things. He seemed to hold in his brain an actual picture of everything he had seen that morning. He remembered every feature of both his drivers, the toothless old woman from whom he had bought the red flowers in his coat, the agent from whom he had got his ticket, and all of his fellow-passengers on the ferry. His mind, unable to cope with vital matters near at hand, worked feverishly and deftly at sorting and grouping these images. They made for him a part of the ugliness of the world, of the ache in his head, and the bitter burning on his tongue. He stooped and put a handful of snow into his mouth as he walked, but that, too, seemed hot. When he reached a little hillside, where the tracks ran through a cut some twenty feet below him, he stopped and sat down.

The carnations in his coat were drooping with the cold, he noticed; all their red glory over. It occurred to him that all the flowers he had seen in the show windows that first night must have gone the same way, long before this. It was only one splendid breath they had, in spite of their brave mockery at the winter outside the glass. It was a losing game in the end, it seemed, this revolt against the homilies by which the world is run. Paul took one of the blossoms carefully from his coat and scooped a little hole in the snow, where he covered it up. Then he dozed a while, from his weak condition, seeming insensible to the cold.

The sound of an approaching train woke him, and he started to his feet, remembering only his resolution, and afraid lest he should be too late. He stood watching the approaching locomotive, his teeth chattering, his lips drawn away from them in a frightened smile; once or twice he glanced nervously sidewise, as though he were being watched. When the right moment came, he jumped. As he fell, the folly of his haste occurred to him with merciless clearness, the vastness of what he had left undone. There flashed through his brain, clearer than ever before, the blue of Adriatic water, the yellow of Algerian sands.

He felt something strike his chest,—his body was being thrown swiftly through the air, on and on, immeasurably far and fast, while his limbs gently relaxed. Then, because the picture-making mechanism was crushed, the disturbing visions flashed into black, and Paul dropped back into the immense design of things.

WILBUR DANIEL STEELE

Wilbur Daniel Steele was born in Greensboro, North Carolina, on March 17, 1886, but grew up in Denver, Colorado, where his father had been appointed professor of Biblical literature at the University of Denver. From his earliest youth until his midtwenties Mr. Steele had every intention of becoming a painter. He studied art, in night classes, in a Denver art school while he was attending the University of Denver. After his graduation in 1907, he spent a year at the Boston Museum of Fine Arts and a second at the Académie Julian, Paris.

Up to the time he went abroad he had, as he said, "no premonitions of writing." But while he was living in Paris he attempted a short story, playing hookey from the Académie to write in a café across the street. His aim, even then, was not primarily authorship. "I thought," he said, "that maybe if I could sell it (which I didn't) they might give me the illustration job and thus launch me on my art career."

Back in New York the following year, at the Art Students League, he made another attempt at writing short stories. This time he sold a story to Success Magazine. It was, he recalls, "pretty awful." But it encouraged him to write, and sell, several more. Then that summer, as a member of an artists' colony in Provincetown, Massachusetts, he thought he'd try his hand at writing a Cape Cod

78

story. The result was "White Horse Winter," published in the Atlantic in April 1912. It was a turning point in his life. The story received such critical acclaim that he decided to devote himself to prose fiction rather than to the graphic arts.

His stories began to appear regularly in the Atlantic, Harper's, Scribner's, American Mercury, Pictorial Review. He wrote a novel, Storm (1914). Soon he was being hailed as the outstanding writer of short stories in America. In 1921 the O. Henry Memorial Award Committee presented him with an unprecedented special prize for maintaining the highest level of merit for three years among American short story writers. In 1925 he won the Harper's short story contest with "When Hell Froze." From 1919 to 1931 he received twelve O. Henry Memorial Awards, including three first prizes (one a tie) and one second prize. Seven of his stories were printed in The Best American Short Stories of the year. "How Beautiful with Shoes," published originally in Harper's, August 1932, was included in The Best American Short Stories of 1933 and was later made into a play. His collected stories, Best Stories, were published in 1946.

In addition to his short stories and novels Mr. Steele has written a number of plays, including Post Road (1934), in collaboration with Norma Mitchell, his second wife, which had a successful run on Broadway.

HOW BEAUTIFUL WITH SHOES

By the time the milking was finished, the sow, which had farrowed the past week, was making such a row that the girl spilled a pint of the warm milk down the trough-lead to quiet the animal before taking the pail to the well-house. Then in the quiet she heard a sound of hoofs on the bridge, where the road crossed the creek a hundred yards below the house, and she set the pail down on the ground beside her bare, barn-soiled feet. She picked it up again. She set it down. It was as if she calculated its weight.

That was what she was doing, as a matter of fact, setting off against its pull toward the well-house the pull of that wagon team in the road, with little more of personal will or wish in the matter than has a wooden weather-vane between two currents in the wind. And as with the vane, so with the wooden girl—the added behest of a whip-lash cracking in the distance was enough; leaving the pail at the barn door, she set off in a deliberate, docile beeline through the cow-yard, over the fence, and down in a diagonal across the farm's one tilled field toward the willow brake that walled the road at the dip. And once under way, though her mother came to the kitchen door and called in her high, flat voice, "Amarantha, where you goin', Amarantha?" the girl went on apparently unmoved, as though she had been as deaf as the woman in the doorway;

indeed, if there was emotion in her it was the purely sensuous one of feeling the clods of the furrows breaking softly between her toes. It was springtime in the mountains.

"Amarantha, why don't you answer me, Amarantha?"

For moments after the girl had disappeared beyond the willows the widow continued to call, unaware through long habit of how absurd it sounded, the name which that strange man her husband had put upon their daughter in one of his moods. Mrs. Doggett had been deaf so long she did not realize that nobody else ever thought of it for the broad-fleshed, slow-minded girl, but called her Mary or, even more simply, Mare.

Ruby Herter had stopped his team this side of the bridge, the mules' heads turned into the lane to his father's farm beyond the road. A big-barreled, heavy-limbed fellow with a square, sallow, not unhandsome face, he took out youth in ponderous gestures of masterfulness; it was like him to have cracked his whip above his animals' ears the moment before he pulled them to a halt. When he saw the girl getting over the fence under the willows he tongued the wad of tobacco out of his mouth into his palm, threw it away beyond the road, and drew a sleeve of his jumper across his lips.

"Don't run yourself out o' breath, Mare; I got all night."

"I was comin'." It sounded sullen only because it was matter of fact.

"Well, keep a-comin' and give us a smack." Hunched on the wagon seat, he remained motionless for some time after she had arrived at the hub, and when he stirred it was but to cut a fresh bit of tobacco, as if already he had forgotten why he threw the old one away. Having satisfied his humor, he unbent, climbed down, kissed her passive mouth, and hugged her up to him, roughly and loosely, his hands careless of contours. It was not out of the way; they were used to handling animals, both of them; and it was spring. A slow warmth pervaded the girl, formless, nameless, almost impersonal.

Her betrothed pulled her head back by the braid of her

yellow hair. He studied her face, his brows gathered and his chin out.

"Listen, Mare, you wouldn't leave nobody else hug and kiss you, dang you!"

She shook her head, without vehemence or anxiety.

"Who's that?" She hearkened up the road. "Pull your team out," she added, as a Ford came in sight around the bend above the house, driven at speed. "Geddap!" she said to the mules herself.

But the car came to a halt near them, and one of the five men crowded in it called, "Come on, Ruby, climb in. They's a loony loose out o' Dayville Asylum, and they got him trailed over somewheres on Split Ridge and Judge North phoned up to Slosson's store for ever'body come help circle him—come on, hop the runnin'-board!"

Ruby hesitated, an eye on his team.

"Scared, Ruby?" The driver raced his engine. "They say this boy's a killer."

"Mare, take the team in and tell pa." The car was already moving when Ruby jumped in. A moment after it had sounded on the bridge it was out of sight.

"Amarantha, Amarantha, why don't you come, Amarantha?"

Returning from her errand, fifteen minutes later, Mare heard the plaint lifted in the twilight. The sun had dipped behind the back ridge, and though the sky was still bright with day, the dusk began to smoke up out of the plowed field like a ground-fog. The girl had returned through it, got the milk, and started toward the well-house before the widow saw her.

"Daughter, seems to me you might!" she expostulated without change of key. "Here's some young man friend o' yourn stopped to say howdy, and I been rackin' my lungs out after you. . . . Put that milk in the cool and come!"

Some young man friend? But there was no good to be got from puzzling. Mare poured the milk in the pan in the dark

82

of the low house over the well, and as she came out, stooping, she saw a figure waiting for her, black in silhouette against the yellowing sky.

"Who are you?" she asked, a native timidity making her sound sulky.

"Amarantha!" the fellow mused. "That's poetry." And she knew then that she did not know him.

She walked past, her arms straight down and her eyes front. Strangers always affected her with a kind of muscular terror simply by being strangers. So she gained the kitchen steps, aware by his tread that he followed. There, taking courage at sight of her mother in the doorway, she turned on him, her eyes down at the level of his knees.

"Who are you and what d' y' want?"

He still mused. "Amarantha! Amarantha in Carolina! That makes me happy!"

Mare hazarded one upward look. She saw that he had red hair, brown eyes, and hollows under his cheekbones, and though the green sweater he wore on top of a gray overall was plainly not meant for him, sizes too large as far as girth went, yet he was built so long of limb that his wrists came inches out of the sleeves and made his big hands look even bigger.

Mrs. Doggett complained. "Why don't you introduce us, daughter?"

The girl opened her mouth and closed it again. Her mother, unaware that no sound had come out of it, smiled and nodded, evidently taking to the tall, homely fellow and tickled by the way he could not seem to get his eyes off her daughter. But the daughter saw none of it, all her attention centered upon the stranger's hands.

Restless, hard-fleshed, and chap-bitten, they were like a countryman's hands; but the fingers were longer than the ordinary, and slightly spatulate at their ends, and these ends were slowly and continuously at play among themselves.

The girl could not have explained how it came to her to be frightened and at the same time to be calm, for she was inept with words. It was simply that in an animal way she knew animals, knew them in health and ailing, and when they were ailing she knew by instinct, as her father had known, how to move so as not to fret them.

Her mother had gone in to light up; from beside the lampshelf she called back, "If he's aimin' to stay to supper you should've told me, Amarantha, though I guess there's plenty of the side-meat to go 'round, if you'll bring me in a few more turnips and potatoes, though it is late."

At the words the man's cheeks moved in and out. "I'm very hungry," he said.

Mare nodded deliberately. Deliberately, as if her mother could hear her, she said over her shoulder, "I'll go get the potatoes and turnips, ma." While she spoke she was moving, slowly, softly, at first, toward the right of the yard, where the fence gave over into the field. Unluckily her mother spied her through the window.

"Amarantha, where *are* you goin'?"

"I'm goin' to get the potatoes and turnips." She neither raised her voice nor glanced back, but lengthened her stride. "He won't hurt her," she said to herself. "He won't hurt her; it's me, not her," she kept repeating, while she got over the fence and down into the shadow that lay more than ever like a fog on the field.

The desire to believe that it actually did hide her, the temptation to break from her rapid but orderly walk grew till she could no longer fight it. She saw the road willows only a dash ahead of her. She ran, her feet floundering among the furrows.

She neither heard nor saw him, but when she realized he was with her she knew he had been with her all the while. She stopped, and he stopped, and so they stood, with the dark open of the field all around. Glancing sidewise presently, she saw he was no longer looking at her with those strangely importunate brown eyes of his, but had raised them to the crest of the wooded ridge behind her.

By and by, "What does it make you think of?" he asked. And when she made no move to see, "Turn around and look!" he said, and though it was low and almost tender in its tone, she knew enough to turn.

A ray of the sunset hidden in the west struck through the tops of the topmost trees, far and small up there, a thin, bright hem.

"What does it make you think of, Amarantha? . . . Answer!"

"Fire," she made herself say.

"Or blood."

"Or blood, yeh. That's right, or blood." She had heard a Ford going up the road beyond the willows, and her attention was not on what she said.

The man soliloquized. "Fire and blood, both; spare one or the other, and where is beauty, the way the world is? It's an awful thing to have to carry, but Christ had it. Christ came with a sword. I love beauty, Amarantha. . . . I say, I love beauty!"

"Yeh, that's right, I hear." What she heard was the car stopping at the house.

"Not prettiness. Prettiness'll have to go with ugliness, because it's only ugliness trigged up. But beauty!" Now again he was looking at her. "Do you know how beautiful you are, Amarantha, 'Amarantha sweet and fair'?" Of a sudden, reaching behind her, he began to unravel the meshes of her hairbraid, the long, flat-tipped fingers at once impatient and infinitely gentle. " 'Braid no more that shining hair!' "

Flat-faced Mare Doggett tried to see around those glowing eyes so near to hers, but wise in her instinct, did not try too hard. "Yeh," she temporized. "I mean, no, I mean."

"Amarantha, I've come a long, long way for you. Will you come away with me now?"

"Yeh—that is—in a minute I will, mister—yeh . . ."

"Because you want to, Amarantha? Because you love me as I love you? Answer!"

"Yeh—sure—uh . . . *Ruby!*"

The man tried to run, but there were six against him, coming up out of the dark that lay in the plowed ground. Mare stood where she was while they knocked him down and got a rope around him; after that she walked back toward the house with Ruby and Older Haskins, her father's cousin.

Ruby wiped his brow and felt of his muscles. "Gees, you're lucky we come, Mare. We're no more'n past the town, when they come hollerin' he'd broke over this way."

When they came to the fence the girl sat on the rail for a moment and rebraided her hair before she went into the house, where were making her mother smell ammonia.

Lots of cars were coming. Judge North was coming, somebody said. When Mare heard this she went into her bedroom off the kitchen and got her shoes and put them on. They were brand new two-dollar shoes with cloth tops, and she had only begun to break them in last Sunday; she wished afterwards she had put her stockings on too, for they would have eased the seams. Or else that she had put on the old button pair, even though the soles were worn through.

Judge North arrived. He thought first of taking the loony straight through to Dayville that night, but then decided to keep him in the lock-up at the courthouse till morning and make the drive by day. Older Haskins stayed in, gentling Mrs. Doggett, while Ruby went out to help get the man into the Judge's sedan. Now that she had them on, Mare didn't like to take the shoes off till Older went; it might make him feel small, she thought.

Older Haskins had a lot of facts about the loony.

"His name's Humble Jewett," he told them. "They belong

86

back in Breed County, all them Jewetts, and I don't reckon there's none on 'em that's not a mite unbalanced. He went to college though, worked his way, and he taught somethin' 'rother in some academy-school a spell, till he went off his head all of a sudden and took after folks with an axe. I remember it in the paper at the time. They give out one while how the Principal wasn't goin' to live, and there was others—there was a girl he tried to strangle. That was four–five year back."

Ruby came in guffawing. "Know the only thing they can get 'im to say, Mare? Only God thing he'll say is, 'Amarantha, she's goin' with me.' . . . Mare!"

"Yeh, I know."

The cover of the kettle the girl was handling slid off the stove with a clatter. A sudden sick wave passed over her. She went out to the back, out into the air. It was not till now she knew how frightened she had been.

Ruby went home, but Older Haskins stayed to supper with them, and helped Mare do the dishes afterward; it was nearly nine when he left. The mother was already in bed, and Mare was about to sit down to get those shoes off her wretched feet at last, when she heard the cow carrying on up at the barn, lowing and kicking, and next minute the sow was in it with a horning note. It might be a fox passing by to get at the henhouse, or a weasel. Mare forgot her feet, took a broom-handle they used in boiling clothes, opened the back door, and stepped out. Blinking the lamplight from her eyes, she peered up toward the outbuildings, and saw the gable end of the barn standing like a red arrow in the dark, and the top of a butternut tree beyond it drawn in skeleton traceries, and just then a cock crowed.

She went to the right corner of the house and saw where the light came from, ruddy above the woods down the valley. Returning into the house, she bent close to her mother's ear and shouted, "Somethin's a-fire down to the town, looks like,"

87

then went out again and up to the barn. "Soh! Soh!" she called to the animals. She climbed up and stood on the top rail of the cow-pen fence, only to find she could not locate the flame even there.

Ten rods behind the buildings a mass of rock mounted higher than their ridgepoles, a chopped-off buttress of the back ridge, covered with oak scrub and wild grapes and blackberries, whose thorny ropes the girl beat away from her skirt with the broom-handle as she scrambled up in the wine-colored dark. Once at the top, and the brush held aside, she could see the tongue-tip of the conflagration half a mile away at the town. And she knew by the bearing of the two church steeples that it was the building where the lock-up was that was burning.

There is a horror in knowing animals trapped in a fire, no matter what the animals.

"Oh, my God!" Mare said.

A car went down the road. Then there was a horse galloping. That would be Older Haskins probably. People were out at Ruby's father's farm; she could hear their voices raised. There must have been another car up from the other way, for lights wheeled and shouts were exchanged in the neighborhood of the bridge. Next thing she knew, Ruby was at the house below, looking for her probably.

He was telling her mother. Mrs. Doggett was not used to him, so he had to shout even louder than Mare had to.

"What y' reckon he done, the hellion! he broke the door and killed Lew Fyke and set the courthouse afire! . . . Where's Mare?"

Her mother would not know. Mare called. "Here, up the rock here."

She had better go down. Ruby would likely break his bones if he tried to climb the rock in the dark, not knowing the way. But the sight of the fire fascinated her simple spirit, the fearful element, more fearful than ever now, with the news. "Yes, I'm comin'," she called sulkily, hearing feet in the brush. "You wait; I'm comin'."

When she turned and saw it was Humble Jewett, right behind her among the branches, she opened her mouth to screech. She was not quick enough. Before a sound came out he got one hand over her face and the other arm around her body.

Mare had always thought she was strong, and the loony looked gangling, yet she was so easy for him that he need not hurt her. He made no haste and little noise as he carried her deeper into the undergrowth. Where the hill began to mount it was harder though. Presently he set her on her feet. He let the hand that had been over her mouth slip down to her throat, where the broad-tipped fingers wound, tender as yearning, weightless as caress.

"I was afraid you'd scream before you knew who 'twas, Amarantha. But I didn't want to hurt your lips, dear heart, your lovely, quiet lips."

It was so dark under the trees she could hardly see him, but she felt his breath on her mouth, near to. But then, instead of kissing her, he said, "No! No!" took from her throat for an instant the hand that had held her mouth, kissed its palm, and put it back softly against her skin.

"Now, my love, let's go before they come."

She stood stock still. Her mother's voice was to be heard in the distance, strident and meaningless. More cars were on the road. Nearer, around the rock, there were sounds of tramping and thrashing. Ruby fussed and cursed. He shouted, "Mare, dang you, where are you, Mare?" his voice harsh with uneasy anger. Now, if she aimed to do anything, was the time to do it. But there was neither breath nor power in her windpipe. It was as if those yearning fingers had paralyzed the muscles.

"Come!" The arm he put around her shivered against her shoulder blades. It was anger. "I hate killing. It's a dirty, ugly thing. It makes me sick." He gagged, judging by the sound. But then he ground his teeth. "Come away, my love!"

She found herself moving. Once when she broke a branch underfoot with an instinctive awkwardness he chided her.

89

"Quiet, my heart, else they'll hear!" She made herself heavy. He thought she grew tired and bore more of her weight till he was breathing hard.

Men came up the hill. There must have been a dozen spread out, by the angle of their voices as they kept touch. Always Humble Jewett kept caressing Mare's throat with one hand; all she could do was hang back.

"You're tired and you're frightened," he said at last. "Get down here."

There were twigs in the dark, the overhang of a thicket of some sort. He thrust her in under this, and lay beside her on the bed of groundpine. The hand that was not in love with her throat reached across her; she felt the weight of its forearm on her shoulder and its fingers among the strands of her hair, eagerly, but tenderly, busy. Not once did he stop speaking, no louder than breathing, his lips to her ear.

"*'Amarantha sweet and fair—Ah, braid no more that shining hair . . .'*"

Mare had never heard of Lovelace, the poet; she thought the loony was just going on, hardly listened, got little sense. But the cadence of it added to the lethargy of all her flesh.

"*'Like a clew of golden thread—Most excellently ravelléd . . .'*"

Voices loudened; feet came tramping; a pair went past not two rods away.

"*'. . . Do not then wind up the light—In ribbands, and o'ercloud in night . . .'*"

The search went on up the woods, men shouting to one another and beating the brush.

"*'. . . But shake your head and scatter day!'* I've never loved, Amarantha. They've tried me with prettiness, but prettiness is too cheap, yes, it's too cheap."

Mare was cold, and the coldness made her lazy. All she knew was that he talked on.

"But dogwood blowing in the spring isn't cheap. The earth

90

of a field isn't cheap. Lots of times I've laid down and kissed the earth of a field, Amarantha. That's beauty, and a kiss for beauty." His breath moved up her cheek. He trembled violently. "No, no, not yet!" He got to his knees and pulled her by an arm. "We can go now."

They went back down the slope, but at an angle, so that when they came to the level they passed two hundred yards to the north of the house, and crossed the road there. More and more, her walking was like sleepwalking, the feet numb in their shoes. Even where he had to let go of her, crossing the creek on stones, she stepped where he stepped with an obtuse docility. The voices of the searchers on the back ridge were small in distance when they began to climb the face of Coward Hill, on the opposite side of the valley.

There is an old farm on top of Coward Hill, big hayfields as flat as tables. It had been half-past nine when Mare stood on the rock above the barn; it was toward midnight when Humble Jewett put aside the last branches of the woods and let her out on the height, and half a moon had risen. And a wind blew there, tossing the withered tops of last year's grasses, and mists ran with the wind, and ragged shadows with the mists, and mares'-tails of clear moonlight among the shadows, so that now the boles of birches on the forest's edge beyond the fences were but opal blurs and now cut alabaster. It struck so cold against the girl's cold flesh, this wind, that another wind of shivers blew through her, and she put her hands over her face and eyes. But the madman stood with his eyes wide open and his mouth open, drinking the moonlight and the wet wind.

His voice, when he spoke at last, was thick in his throat.

"Get down on your knees." He got down on his and pulled her after. "And pray!"

Once in England a poet sang four lines. Four hundred years have forgotten his name, but they have remembered his lines. The daft man knelt upright, his face raised to the wild scud, his long wrists hanging to the dead grass. He began simply:

> *"'O western wind, when wilt thou blow*
> *That the small rain down can rain?'"*

The Adam's-apple was big in his bent throat. As simply he finished.

> *"'Christ, that my love were in my arms*
> *And I in my bed again!'"*

Mare got up and ran. She ran without aim or feeling in the power of the wind. She told herself again that the mists would hide her from him, as she had done at dusk. And again, seeing that he ran at her shoulder, she knew he had been there all the while, making a race of it, flailing the air with his long arms for joy of play in the cloud of spring, throwing his knees high, leaping the moon-blue waves of the brown grass, shaking his bright hair; and her own hair was a weight behind her, lying level on the wind. Once a shape went bounding ahead of them for instants; she did not realize it was a fox till it was gone.

She never thought of stopping; she never thought anything, except once, "Oh, my God, I wish I had my shoes off!" And what would have been the good in stopping or in turning another way, when it was only play? The man's ecstasy magnified his strength. When a snake-fence came at them he took the top rail in flight, like a college hurdler, and, seeing the girl hesitate and half turn as if to flee, he would have releaped it without touching a hand. But then she got a loom of buildings, climbed over quickly, before he should jump, and ran along the lane that ran with the fence.

Mare had never been up there, but she knew that the farm and the house belonged to a man named Wyker, a kind of cousin of Ruby Herter's, a violent, bearded old fellow who lived by himself. She could not believe her luck. When she had run half the distance and Jewett had not grabbed her, doubt grabbed her instead. "Oh, my God, go careful!" she told her-self. "Go slow!" she implored herself, and stopped running, to walk.

Here was a misgiving the deeper in that it touched her special knowledge. She had never known an animal so far gone that its instincts failed it; a starving rat will scent the trap sooner than a fed one. Yet, after one glance at the house they approached, Jewett paid it no further attention, but walked with his eyes to the right, where the cloud had blown away, and wooded ridges, like black waves rimmed with silver, ran down away toward the Valley of Virginia.

"I've never lived!" In his single cry there were two things, beatitude and pain.

Between the bigness of the falling world and his eyes the flag of her hair blew. He reached out and let it whip between his fingers. Mare was afraid it would break the spell then, and he would stop looking away and look at the house again. So she did something almost incredible; she spoke.

"It's a pretty—I mean—a beautiful view down that-away."

"God Almighty beautiful, to take your breath away. I knew I'd never loved, Belovéd—" He caught a foot under the long end of one of the boards that covered the well and went down heavily on his hand and knees. It seemed to make no difference. "But I never knew I'd never lived," he finished in the same tone of strong rapture, quadruped in the grass, while Mare ran for the door and grabbed the latch.

When the latch would not give, she lost what little sense she had. She pounded with her fists. She cried with all her might: "Oh—hey—in there—hey—in there!" Then Jewett came and took her gently between his hands and drew her away, and then, though she was free, she stood in something like an awful em-barrassment while he tried shouting.

"Hey! Friend! whoever you are, wake up and let my love and me come in!"

"No!" wailed the girl.

He grew peremptory. "Hey, wake up!" He tried the latch. He passed to full fury in a wink's time; he cursed, he kicked, he beat the door till Mare thought he would break his hands. Withdrawing, he ran at it with his shoulder; it burst at the latch, went slamming in, and left a black emptiness. His anger dissolved in a big laugh. Turning in time to catch her by a wrist, he cried joyously, "Come, my Sweet One!"

"No! No! Please—aw—listen. There ain't nobody there. He ain't to home. It wouldn't be right to go in anybody's house if they wasn't to home, you know that."

His laugh was blither than ever. He caught her high in his arms.

"I'd do the same by his love and him if 'twas my house, I would." At the threshold he paused and thought, "That is, if she was the true love of his heart forever."

The room was the parlor. Moonlight slanted in at the door, and another shaft came through a window and fell across a sofa, its covering dilapidated, showing its wadding in places. The air was sour, but both of them were farm-bred.

"Don't, Amarantha!" His words were pleading in her ear. "Don't be so frightened."

He set her down on the sofa. As his hands let go of her they were shaking.

"But look, I'm frightened too." He knelt on the floor before her, reached out his hands, withdrew them. "See, I'm afraid to touch you." He mused, his eyes rounded. "Of all the ugly things there are, fear is the ugliest. And yet, see, it can be the very beautifulest. That's a strange queer thing."

The wind blew in and out of the room, bringing the thin, little bitter sweetness of new April at night. The moonlight that came across Mare's shoulders fell full upon his face, but hers it left dark, ringed by the aureole of her disordered hair.

"Why do you wear a halo, Love?" He thought about it. "Because you're an angel, is that why?" The swift, untempered logic of the mad led him to dismay. His hands came flying to

94

hers, to make sure they were of earth; and he touched her breast, her shoulders, and her hair. Peace returned to his eyes as his fingers twined among the strands.

"*'Thy hair is as a flock of goats that appear from Gilead . . .'*" He spoke like a man dreaming. "*'Thy temples are like a piece of pomegranate within thy locks.'*"

Mare never knew that he could not see her for the moonlight.

"Do you remember, Love?"

She dared not shake her head under his hand. "Yeh, I reckon," she temporized.

"You remember how I sat at your feet, long ago, like this, and made up a song? And all the poets in all the world have never made one to touch it, have they, Love?"

"Ugh-ugh—never."

"*'How beautiful are thy feet with shoes . . .'* Remember?"

"Oh, my God, what's he sayin' now?" she wailed to herself.

"*'How beautiful are thy feet with shoes, O prince's daughter! the joints of thy thighs are like jewels, the work of the hands of a cunning workman.*

Thy navel is like a round goblet, which wanteth not liquor; thy belly is like an heap of wheat set about with lilies.

Thy two breasts are like two young roes that are twins.'"

Mare had not been to church since she was a little girl, when her mother's black dress wore out. "No, no!" she wailed under her breath. "You're awful to say such awful things." She might have shouted it; nothing could have shaken the man now, rapt in the immortal, passionate periods of Solomon's song.

"*'. . . now also thy breasts shall be as clusters of the vine, and the smell of thy nose like apples.'*"

Hotness touched Mare's face for the first time. "Aw, no, don't talk so!"

"*'And the roof of thy mouth like the best wine for my belovéd . . . causing the lips of them that are asleep to speak.'*"

95

He had ended. His expression changed. Ecstasy gave place to anger, love to hate. And Mare felt the change in the weight of the fingers in her hair.

"What do you mean, I mustn't say it like that?" But it was not to her his fury spoke, for he answered himself straightway. "Like poetry, Mr. Jewett; I won't have blasphemy around my school."

"Poetry! My God! if that isn't poetry—if that isn't music—" . . . "It's Bible, Jewett. What you're paid to teach here is *literature.*"

"Doctor Ryeworth, you're the blasphemer and you're an ignorant man." . . . "And your Principal. And I won't have you going around reading sacred allegory like earthly love."

"Ryeworth, you're an old man, a dull man, a dirty man, and you'd be better dead."

Jewett's hand had slid down from Mare's head. "Then I went to put my fingers around his throat, so. But my stomach turned, and I didn't do it. I went to my room. I laughed all the way to my room. I sat in my room at my table and I laughed. I laughed all afternoon and long after dark came. And then, about ten, somebody came and stood beside me in my room."

" 'Wherefore dost thou laugh, son?'

"Then I knew who He was, He was Christ.

" 'I was laughing about that dirty, ignorant, crazy old fool, Lord.'

" 'Wherefore dost thou laugh?'

"I didn't laugh any more. He didn't say any more. I kneeled down, bowed my head.

" 'Thy will be done! Where is he, Lord?'

" 'Over at the girls' dormitory, waiting for Blossom Sinckley.'

"Brassy Blossom, dirty Blossom . . ."

It had come so suddenly it was nearly too late. Mare tore

at his hands with hers, tried with all her strength to pull her neck away.

"Filthy Blossom! and him an old filthy man, Blossom! and you'll find him in Hell when you reach there, Blossom . . ."

It was more the nearness of his face than the hurt of his hands that gave her power of fright to choke out three words.

"I—ain't—Blossom!"

Light ran in crooked veins. Through the veins she saw his face bewildered. His hands loosened. One fell down and hung; the other he lifted and put over his eyes, took away again and looked at her.

"Amarantha!" His remorse was fearful to see. "What have I done!" His hands returned to hover over the hurts, ravening with pity, grief and tenderness. Tears fell down his cheeks. And with that, dammed desire broke its dam.

"Amarantha, my love, my dove, my beautiful love—"

"And I ain't Amarantha neither, I'm Mary! Mary, that's my name!"

She had no notion what she had done. He was like a crystal crucible that a chemist watches, changing hue in a wink with one adeptly added drop; but hers was not the chemist's eye. All she knew was that she felt light and free of him; all she could see of his face as he stood away above the moonlight were the whites of his eyes.

"Mary!" he muttered. A slight paroxysm shook his frame. So in the transparent crucible desire changed its hue. He retreated farther, stood in the dark by some tall piece of furniture. And still she could see the whites of his eyes.

"Mary! Mary Adorable!" A wonder was in him. "Mother of God!"

Mare held her breath. She eyed the door, but it was too far. And already he came back to go on his knees before her, his shoulders so bowed and his face so lifted that it must have cracked his neck, she thought; all she could see on the face was pain.

"Mary Mother, I'm sick to my death. I'm so tired."

She had seen a dog like that, one she had loosed from a trap after it had been there three days, its caught leg half gnawed free. Something about the eyes.

"Mary Mother, take me in your arms . . ."

Once again her muscles tightened. But he made no move.

". . . and give me sleep."

No, they were worse than the dog's eyes.

"Sleep, sleep! why won't they let me sleep? Haven't I done it all yet, Mother? Haven't I washed them yet of all their sins? I've drunk the cup that was given me; is there another? They've mocked me and reviled me, broken my brow with thorns and my hands with nails, and I've forgiven them, for they knew not what they did. Can't I go to sleep now, Mother?"

Mare could not have said why, but now she was more frightened than she had ever been. Her hands lay heavy on her knees, side by side, and she could not take them away when he bowed his head and rested his face upon them.

After a moment he said one thing more. "Take me down gently when you take me from the Tree."

Gradually the weight of his body came against her shins, and he slept.

The moon streak that entered by the eastern window crept north across the floor, thinner and thinner; the one that fell through the southern doorway traveled east and grew fat. For a while Mare's feet pained her terribly and her legs too. She dared not move them, though, and by and by they did not hurt so much.

A dozen times, moving her head slowly on her neck, she canvassed the shadows of the room for a weapon. Each time her eyes came back to a heavy earthenware pitcher on a stand some feet to the left of the sofa. It would have had flowers in it when Wyker's wife was alive; probably it had not been moved from its dust-ring since she died. It would be a long grab, perhaps too long; still, it might be done if she had her hands.

To get her hands from under the sleeper's head was the task she set herself. She pulled first one, then the other, infinitesimally. She waited. Again she tugged a very, very little. The order of his breathing was not disturbed. But at the third trial he stirred.

"Gently! gently!" His own muttering waked him more. With some drowsy instinct of possession he threw one hand across her wrists, pinning them together between thumb and fingers. She kept dead quiet, shut her eyes, lengthened her breathing, as if she too slept.

There came a time when what was pretense grew to be a peril; strange as it was, she had to fight to keep her eyes open. She never knew whether or not she really napped. But something changed in the air, and she was wide awake again. The moonlight was fading on the doorsill, and the light that runs before dawn waxed in the window behind her head.

And then she heard a voice in the distance, lifted in maundering song. It was old man Wyker coming home after a night, and it was plain he had had some whisky.

Now a new terror laid hold of Mare.

"Shut up, you fool you!" she wanted to shout. "Come quiet, quiet!" She might have chanced it now to throw the sleeper away from her and scramble and run, had his powers of strength and quickness not taken her simple imagination utterly in thrall.

Happily the singing stopped. What had occurred was that the farmer had espied the open door and, even befuddled as he was, wanted to know more about it quietly. He was so quiet that Mare began to fear he had gone away. He had the squirrel-hunter's foot, and the first she knew of him was when she looked and saw his head in the doorway, his hard, soiled, whiskery face half-up-side-down with craning.

He had been to the town. Between drinks he had wandered

in and out of the night's excitement; had even gone a short distance with one search party himself. Now he took in the situation in the room. He used his forefinger. First he held it to his lips. Next he pointed it with a jabbing motion at the sleeper. Then he tapped his own forehead and described wheels. Lastly, with his whole hand, he made pushing gestures, for Mare to wait. Then he vanished as silently as he had appeared.

The minutes dragged. The light in the east strengthened and turned rosy. Once she thought she heard a board creaking in another part of the house, and looked down sharply to see if the loony stirred. All she could see of his face was a temple with freckles on it and the sharp ridge of a cheekbone, but even from so little she knew how deeply and peacefully he slept. The door darkened. Wyker was there again. In one hand he carried something heavy; with the other he beckoned.

"Come jumpin'!" he said out loud.

Mare went jumping, but her cramped legs threw her down half way to the sill; the rest of the distance she rolled and crawled. Just as she tumbled through the door it seemed as if the world had come to an end above her; two barrels of a shotgun discharged into a room make a noise. Afterwards all she could hear in there was something twisting and bumping on the floor-boards. She got up and ran.

Mare's mother had gone to pieces; neighbor women put her to bed when Mare came home. They wanted to put Mare to bed, but she would not let them. She sat on the edge of her bed in her lean-to bedroom off the kitchen, just as she was, her hair down all over her shoulders and her shoes on, and stared away from them, at a place in the wallpaper.

"Yeh, I'll go myself. Lea' me be!"

The women exchanged quick glances, thinned their lips, and left her be. "God knows," was all they would answer to the questionings of those that had not gone in, "but she's gettin' herself to bed."

When the doctor came though he found her sitting just as she had been, still dressed, her hair down on her shoulders and her shoes on.

"What d' y' want?" she muttered and stared at the place in the wallpaper.

How could Doc Paradise say, when he did not know himself?

"I didn't know if you might be—might be feeling very smart, Mary."

"I'm all right. Lea' me be."

It was a heavy responsibility. Doc shouldered it. "No, it's all right," he said to the men in the road. Ruby Herter stood a little apart, chewing sullenly and looking another way. Doc raised his voice to make certain it carried. "Nope, nothing."

Ruby's ears got red, and he clamped his jaws. He knew he ought to go in and see Mare, but he was not going to do it while everybody hung around waiting to see if he would. A mule tied near him reached out and mouthed his sleeve in idle innocence; he wheeled and banged a fist against the side of the animal's head.

"Well, what d' y' aim to do 'bout it?" he challenged its owner.

He looked at the sun then. It was ten in the morning. "Hell, I got work!" he flared, and set off down the road for home. Doc looked at Judge North, and the Judge started after Ruby. But Ruby shook his head angrily. "Lea' me be!" He went on, and the Judge came back.

It got to be eleven and then noon. People began to say, "Like enough she'd be as thankful if the whole neighborhood wasn't camped here." But none went away.

As a matter of fact they were no bother to the girl. She never saw them. The only move she made was to bend her ankles over and rest her feet on edge; her shoes hurt terribly and her feet knew it, though she did not. She sat all the while

101

staring at that one figure in the wallpaper, and she never saw the figure.

Strange as the night had been, this day was stranger. Fright and physical pain are perishable things once they are gone. But while pain merely dulls and telescopes in memory and remains diluted pain, terror looked back upon has nothing of terror left. A gambling chance taken, at no matter what odds, and won was a sure thing since the world's beginning; perils come through safely were never perilous. But what fright does do in retrospect is this—it heightens each sensuous recollection, like a hard, clear lacquer laid on wood, bringing out the color and grain of it vividly.

Last night Mare had lain stupid with fear on groundpine beneath a bush, loud foot-falls and light whispers confused in her ear. Only now, in her room, did she smell the groundpine.

Only now did the conscious part of her brain begin to make words of the whispering.

"*Amarantha,*" she remembered, "*Amarantha sweet and fair.*" That was as far as she could go for the moment, except that the rhyme with "fair" was "hair." But then a puzzle, held in abeyance, brought other words. She wondered what "ravel Ed" could mean. "*Most excellently ravelléd.*" It was left to her mother to bring the end.

They gave up trying to keep her mother out at last. The poor woman's prostration took the form of fussiness.

"Good gracious, daughter, you look a sight. Them new shoes, half ruined; ain't your feet *dead?* And look at your hair, all tangled like a wild one!"

She got a comb.

"Be quiet, daughter; what's ailin' you. Don't shake your head!"

" '*But shake your head and scatter day.*' "

"What you say, Amarantha?" Mrs. Doggett held an ear down.

"Go 'way! Lea' me be!"

Her mother was hurt and left. And Mare ran, as she stared at the wallpaper.

"Christ, that my love were in my arms . . ."

Mare ran. She ran through a wind white with moonlight and wet with "the small rain." And the wind she ran through, it ran through her, and made her shiver as she ran. And the man beside her leaped high over the waves of the dead grasses and gathered the wind in his arms, and her hair was heavy and his was tossing, and a little fox ran before them across the top of the world. And the world spread down around in waves of black and silver, more immense than she had ever known the world could be, and more beautiful.

"God Almighty beautiful, to take your breath away!"

Mare wondered, and she was not used to wondering. "Is it only crazy folks ever run like that and talk that way?"

She no longer ran; she walked; for her breath was gone. And there was some other reason, some other reason. Oh, yes, it was because her feet were hurting her. So, at last, and roundabout, her shoes had made contact with her brain.

Bending over the side of the bed, she loosened one of them mechanically. She pulled it half off. But then she looked down at it sharply, and she pulled it on again.

"How beautiful . . ."

Color overspread her face in a slow wave.

"How beautiful are thy feet with shoes . . ."

"Is it only crazy folks ever say such things?"

"O prince's daughter!"

"Or call you that?"

By and by there was a knock at the door. It opened, and Ruby Herter came in.

"Hello, Mare old girl!" His face was red. He scowled and kicked at the floor. "I'd 'a' been over sooner, except we got a mule down sick." He looked at his dumb betrothed. "Come on, cheer up, forget it! He won't scare you no more, not that boy, not what's left o' him. What you lookin' at, sourface? Ain't you glad to see me?"

Mare quit looking at the wallpaper and looked at the floor. "Yeh," she said.

"That's more like it, babe." He came and sat beside her; reached down behind her and gave her a spank. "Come on, give us a kiss, babe!" He wiped his mouth on his jumper sleeve, a good farmer's sleeve, spotted with milking. He put his hands on her; he was used to handling animals. "Hey, you, warm up a little, reckon I'm goin' to do all the lovin'?"

"Ruby, lea' me be!"

"What!"

She was up, twisting. He was up, purple.

"What's ailin' you, Mare? What you bawlin' about?"

"Nothin'—only go 'way!"

She pushed him to the door and through it with all her strength, and closed it in his face, and stood with her weight against it, crying, "Go 'way! Go 'way! Lea' me be!"

KATHERINE MANSFIELD

Katherine Mansfield was born October 14, 1888, in Wellington, New Zealand, the setting for "The Doll's House" and most of her best stories. Her parents, Harold and Anne Beauchamp, christened this third daughter of theirs "Kathleen Mansfield," after her maternal grandmother, the beloved Granny Dyer, but she dropped the Beauchamp and changed "Kathleen" to "Katherine" early in her career.

When she was five years old, the family moved to the village of Karori, four miles outside of Wellington, where, in the village school, there was a wide social barrier between the Beauchamp girls and most of the other children. When she was nine she was sent to the Wellington Girls' High School, and later, to Miss Swainson's private school.

From an early age she showed an interest in writing. A description of a sea voyage won her a composition prize at Karori, and a little story, "Enna Blake," published in the high school magazine during her first year at the school, showed "promise of great merit," according to an editor's note. At Miss Swainson's she got out a school magazine, writing it herself in longhand.

In 1903, when she was fourteen, she and her two older sisters were sent to Queen's College, London, to finish their education. At Queen's she was, for a time, divided between music and writing as a career—she was taking lessons on the 'cello—but by the spring of 1906, her final year, she wrote to a friend that "in the future I shall give all my time to writing." Five of her stories and a number of her poems had been published in the college magazine.

Back in New Zealand she was desperately unhappy. She worked for a while on a novel, Juliet, abandoned it, and wrote a number of "vignettes," which were published in the Melbourne Native Companion. She finally convinced her parents that she could make her way as a freelance writer if allowed to return to England, and sailed for London in July 1908, with an allowance of one hundred pounds a year. She was nineteen years old.

For the next few years she lived a Bohemian existence, "enamoured," as her future husband, John Middleton Murry, later wrote, "of the idea of experience at all costs." The cost was heavy. She married a singing master eleven years her senior and left him the following day. She became the mistress of a traveling violinist, became pregnant, moved into a pension in Bavaria, where she had a miscarriage. She returned to England and her husband, left him for an affair with another man, left him and sought refuge with a college friend, Ida Baker.

The literary result of those years was a group of brittle stories published in The New Age, an avant-garde magazine edited by A. R. Orage, and reprinted under the title In a German Pension. She was twenty-three. In later years she refused to reissue those stories and destroyed the portions of her diary dealing with this period in her life.

In December 1911, she met John Middleton Murry, then a young critic, who was co-editor and founder of a *little magazine called* Rhythm. *She became the assistant editor of the magazine, publishing in it a number of stories, poems, and critical articles.* Rhythm *and its successor,* The Blue Review, *both collapsed in 1913. By now she was living with Murry. She married him in 1918, when she finally got her divorce.*

In February 1915, an event occurred which altered Miss Mansfield's life as a writer. Her twenty-year-old brother, Leslie, whom she had always called "Chummie," visited her on leave from the British army. They talked endlessly of their childhood in New Zealand, and Miss Mansfield was stirred with a desire to write about her homeland and her youth. This resolve was strengthened by Chummie's death in October. In her Journal *entry on January 22, 1916, she wrote that she was "no longer concerned with the same appearance of things . . . Now I want to write recollections of my own country . . . all the remembered places . . . I shall tell everything."*

The stories she wrote, which return to the scenes of her childhood, are the ones on which her reputation is principally based. The first results of her resolve were "The Wind Blows" and "The Apple Tree," published in Signature, *a little magazine that she and Murry had founded with D. H. Lawrence—it expired after three issues. Then came "The Aloe," published in shortened form as "The Prelude," in 1917.* Bliss and Other Stories, *a compilation of her best stories to date, was published in 1920;* The Garden Party, *in 1922. "The Doll's House," published originally in* The Nation, *February 14, 1922, was reprinted in* The Dove's Nest *(1923).*

Ill health, which had plagued her since she was

twenty, had, by 1917, become tuberculosis, and in her last years she was writing against time. She died on January 9, 1923 at the age of thirty-four. Her collected stories, The Short Stories of Katherine Mansfield, *were published posthumously* (1937), *as were her* Journal (1927) *and several volumes of her letters.*

THE DOLL'S HOUSE

When dear old Mrs. Hay went back to town after staying with the Burnells she sent the children a doll's house. It was so big that the carter and Pat carried it into the courtyard, and there it stayed, propped up on two wooden boxes beside the feed-room door. No harm could come of it; it was summer. And perhaps the smell of paint would have gone off by the time it had to be taken in. For, really, the smell of paint coming from that doll's house ("Sweet of old Mrs. Hay, of course; most sweet and generous!")—but the smell of paint was quite enough to make any one seriously ill, in Aunt Beryl's opinion. Even before the sacking was taken off. And when it was. . . .

There stood the doll's house, a dark, oily, spinach green, picked out with bright yellow. Its two solid little chimneys, glued on to the roof, were painted red and white, and the door, gleaming with yellow varnish, was like a little slab of toffee. Four windows, real windows, were divided into panes by a broad streak of green. There was actually a tiny porch, too, painted yellow, with big lumps of congealed paint hanging along the edge.

But perfect, perfect little house! Who could possibly mind the smell? It was part of the joy, part of the newness.

"Open it quickly, some one!"

Reprinted from *The Short Stories of Katherine Mansfield*, by permission of Alfred A. Knopf, Inc. Copyright 1923, 1937 by Alfred A. Knopf, Inc.

The hook at the side was stuck fast. Pat pried it open with his penknife, and the whole house-front swung back, and—there you were, gazing at one and the same moment into the drawing-room and dining-room, the kitchen and two bedrooms. That is the way for a house to open! Why don't all houses open like that? How much more exciting then peering through the slit of a door into a mean little hall with a hatstand and two umbrellas! That is—isn't it?—what you long to know about a house when you put your hand on the knocker. Perhaps it is the way God opens houses at dead of night when He is taking a quiet turn with an angel. . . .

"O-oh!" The Burnell children sounded as though they were in despair. It was too marvellous; it was too much for them. They had never seen anything like it in their lives. All the rooms were papered. There were pictures on the walls, painted on the paper, with gold frames complete. Red carpet covered all the floors except the kitchen; red plush chairs in the drawing-room, green in the dining-room; tables, beds with real bedclothes, a cradle, a stove, a dresser with tiny plates and one big jug. But what Kezia liked more than anything, what she liked frightfully, was the lamp. It stood in the middle of the dining-room table, an exquisite little amber lamp with a white globe. It was even filled all ready for lighting, though, of course, you couldn't light it. But there was something inside that looked like oil, and that moved when you shook it.

The father and mother dolls, who sprawled very stiff as though they had fainted in the drawing-room, and their two little children asleep upstairs, were really too big for the doll's house. They didn't look as though they belonged. But the lamp was perfect. It seemed to smile at Kezia, to say, "I live here." The lamp was real.

The Burnell children could hardly walk to school fast enough the next morning. They burned to tell everybody, to describe, to—well—to boast about their doll's house before the school-bell rang.

"I'm to tell," said Isabel, "because I'm the eldest. And you two can join in after. But I'm to tell first."

There was nothing to answer. Isabel was bossy, but she was always right, and Lottie and Kezia knew too well the powers that went with being eldest. They brushed through the thick buttercups at the road edge and said nothing.

"And I'm to choose who's to come and see it first. Mother said I might."

For it had been arranged that while the doll's house stood in the courtyard they might ask the girls at school, two at a time, to come and look. Not to stay to tea, of course, or to come traipsing through the house. But just to stand quietly in the courtyard while Isabel pointed out the beauties, and Lottie and Kezia looked pleased. . . .

But hurry as they might, by the time they had reached the tarred palings of the boys' playground the bell had begun to jangle. They only just had time to whip off their hats and fall into line before the roll was called. Never mind. Isabel tried to make up for it by looking very important and mysterious and by whispering behind her hand to the girls near her, "Got something to tell you at playtime."

Playtime came and Isabel was surrounded. The girls of her class nearly fought to put their arms round her, to walk away with her, to beam flatteringly, to be her special friend. She held quite a court under the huge pine trees at the side of the playground. Nudging, giggling together, the little girls pressed up close. And the only two who stayed outside the ring were the two who were always outside, the little Kelveys. They knew better than to come anywhere near the Burnells.

For the fact was, the school the Burnell children went to was not at all the kind of place their parents would have chosen if there had been any choice. But there was none. It was the only school for miles. And the consequence was all the children in the neighborhood, the Judge's little girls, the doctor's daughters, the storekeeper's children, the milkman's, were forced to mix together. Not to speak of there being an equal number of rude, rough little boys as well. But the line had to be drawn somewhere. It was drawn at the Kelveys. Many of the children, including the Burnells, were not allowed even to speak to them. They walked past the Kelveys with their heads in the air, and as they set the fashion in all matters of behaviour, the Kelveys were shunned by everybody. Even the teacher had a special voice for them, and a special smile for the other children when Lil Kelvey came up to her desk with a bunch of dreadfully common-looking flowers.

They were the daughters of a spry, hardworking little washerwoman, who went about from house to house by the day. This was awful enough. But where was Mr. Kelvey? Nobody knew for certain. But everybody said he was in prison. So they were the daughters of a washerwoman and a gaolbird. Very nice company for other people's children! And they looked it. Why Mrs. Kelvey made them so conspicuous was hard to understand. The truth was they were dressed in "bits" given to her by the people for whom she worked. Lil, for instance, who was a stout, plain child, with big freckles, came to school in a dress made from a green art-serge tablecloth of the Burnells', with red plush sleeves from the Logans' curtains. Her hat, perched on top of her high forehead, was a grown-up woman's hat, once the property of Miss Lecky, the postmistress. It was turned up at the back and trimmed with a large scarlet quill. What a little guy she looked! It was impossible not to laugh. And her little sister, our Else, wore a long white dress, rather like a nightgown, and a pair of little boy's boots. But whatever our Else wore she would have looked strange. She was a tiny wishbone of a child, with cropped hair and enormous solemn eyes—a little white owl. Nobody had ever seen her smile; she scarcely ever spoke. She went through life holding on to Lil, with a piece of Lil's skirt screwed up in her hand. Where Lil went our Else followed. In the playground, on the road going to and from school, there was Lil marching in front and our Else holding on behind. Only when she wanted anything, or when she was out of breath, our Else gave Lil a tug, a twitch, and Lil stopped and turned round. The Kelveys never failed to understand each other.

Now they hovered at the edge; you couldn't stop them listening. When the little girls turned round and sneered, Lil, as usual, gave her silly, shamefaced smile, but our Else only looked.

And Isabel's voice, so very proud, went on telling. The carpet made a great sensation, but so did the beds with real bedclothes, and the stove with an oven door.

When she finished Kezia broke in. "You've forgotten the lamp, Isabel."

"Oh, yes," said Isabel, "and there's a teeny little lamp, all made of yellow glass, with a white globe that stands on the dining-room table. You couldn't tell it from a real one."

"The lamp's best of all," cried Kezia. She thought Isabel wasn't making half enough of the little lamp. But nobody paid any attention. Isabel was choosing the two who were to come back with them that afternoon and see it. She chose Emmie Cole and Lena Logan. But when the others knew they were all to have a chance, they couldn't be nice enough to Isabel. One by one they put their arms round Isabel's waist and walked her off. They had something to whisper to her, a secret. "Isabel's *my* friend."

Only the little Kelveys moved away forgotten; there was nothing more for them to hear.

Days passed, and as more children saw the doll's house, the fame of it spread. It became the one subject, the rage. The one question was, "Have you seen Burnells' doll's house? Oh, ain't it lovely!" "Haven't you seen it? Oh, I say!"

Even the dinner hour was given up to talking about it.

The little girls sat under the pines eating their thick mutton sandwiches and big slabs of johnny cake spread with butter. While always, as near as they could get, sat the Kelveys, our Else holding on to Lil, listening too, while they chewed their jam sandwiches out of a newspaper soaked with large red blobs. . . .

"Mother," said Kezia, "can't I ask the Kelveys just once?"

"Certainly not, Kezia."

"But why not?"

"Run away, Kezia; you know quite well why not."

At last everybody had seen it except them. On that day the subject rather flagged. It was the dinner hour. The children stood together under the pine trees, and suddenly, as they looked at the Kelveys eating out of their paper, always by themselves, always listening, they wanted to be horrid to them. Emmie Cole started the whisper.

"Lil Kelvey's going to be a servant when she grows up."

"O-oh, how awful!" said Isabel Burnell, and she made eyes at Emmie.

Emmie swallowed in a very meaning way and nodded to Isabel as she'd seen her mother do on those occasions.

"It's true—it's true—it's true," she said.

Then Lena Logan's little eyes snapped. "Shall I ask her?" she whispered.

"Bet you don't," said Jessie May.

"Pooh, I'm not frightened," said Lena. Suddenly she gave a little squeal and danced in front of the other girls. "Watch! Watch me! Watch me now!" said Lena. And sliding, gliding, dragging one foot, giggling behind her hand, Lena went over to the Kelveys.

Lil looked up from her dinner. She wrapped the rest quickly away. Our Else stopped chewing. What was coming now?

"Is it true you're going to be a servant when you grow up, Lil Kelvey?" shrilled Lena.

Dead silence. But instead of answering, Lil only gave her silly, shamefaced smile. She didn't seem to mind the question at all. What a sell for Lena! The girls began to titter.

Lena couldn't stand that. She put her hands on her hips; she shot forward. "Yah, yer father's in prison!" she hissed, spitefully.

This was such a marvellous thing to have said that the little girls rushed away in a body, deeply, deeply excited, wild with joy. Some one found a long rope, and they began skipping. And never did they skip so high, run in and out so fast or do such daring things as on that morning.

In the afternoon Pat called for the Burnell children with the buggy and they drove home. There were visitors. Isabel and Lottie, who liked visitors, went upstairs to change their pinafores. But Kezia thieved out at the back. Nobody was about; she began to swing on the big white gates of the court-yard. Presently, looking along the road, she saw two little dots. They grew bigger, they were coming towards her. Now she could see that one was in front and one close behind. Now she could see that they were the Kelveys. Kezia stopped swinging. She slipped off the gate as if she was going to run away. Then she hesitated. The Kelveys came nearer, and beside them walked their shadows, very long, stretching right across the road with their heads in the buttercups. Kezia clambered back on the gate; she had made up her mind; she swung out.

"Hullo," she said to the passing Kelveys.

They were so astounded that they stopped. Lil gave her silly smile. Our Else stared.

"You can come and see our doll's house if you want to," said Kezia, and she dragged one toe on the ground. But at that Lil turned red and shook her head quickly.

"Why not?" asked Kezia.

Lil gasped, then she said, "Your ma told our ma you wasn't to speak to us."

"Oh, well," said Kezia. She didn't know what to reply. "It doesn't matter. You can come and see our doll's house all the same. Come on. Nobody's looking."

But Lil shook her head still harder.

"Don't you want to?" asked Kezia.

Suddenly there was a twitch, a tug at Lil's skirt. She turned round. Our Else was looking at her with big, imploring eyes; she was frowning; she wanted to go. For a moment Lil looked at our Else very doubtfully. But then our Else twitched her skirt again. She started forward. Kezia led the way. Like two little stray cats they followed across the courtyard to where the doll's house stood.

"There it is," said Kezia.

There was a pause. Lil breathed loudly, almost snorted; our Else was still as a stone.

"I'll open it for you," said Kezia kindly. She undid the hook and they looked inside.

"There's the drawing-room and the dining-room, and that's the—"

"Kezia!"

Oh, what a start they gave!

"Kezia!"

It was Aunt Beryl's voice. They turned round. At the back door stood Aunt Beryl, staring as if she couldn't believe what she saw.

"How dare you ask the little Kelveys into the courtyard?" said her cold, furious voice. "You know as well as I do, you're not allowed to talk to them. Run away, children, run away at once. And don't come back again," said Aunt Beryl. And she stepped into the yard and shooed them out as if they were chickens.

"Off you go immediately!" she called, cold and proud.

They did not need telling twice. Burning with shame, shrinking together, Lil huddling along like her mother, our

116

Else dazed, somehow they crossed the big courtyard and squeezed through the white gate.

"Wicked, disobedient little girl!" said Aunt Beryl bitterly to Kezia, and she slammed the doll's house to.

The afternoon had been awful. A letter had come from Willie Brent, a terrifying, threatening letter, saying if she did not meet him that evening in Pulman's Bush, he'd come to the front door and ask the reason why! But now that she had frightened those little rats of Kelveys and given Kezia a good scolding, her heart felt lighter. That ghastly pressure was gone. She went back to the house humming.

When the Kelveys were well out of sight of Burnells', they sat down to rest on a big red drain-pipe by the side of the road. Lil's cheeks were still burning; she took off the hat with the quill and held it on her knee. Dreamily they looked over the hay paddocks, past the creek, to the group of wattles where Logan's cows stood waiting to be milked. What were their thoughts?

Presently our Else nudged up close to her sister. But now she had forgotten the cross lady. She put out a finger and stroked her sister's quill; she smiled her rare smile.

"I seen the little lamp," she said, softly.

Then both were silent once more.

ERNEST HEMINGWAY

Ernest M. Hemingway (*he dropped the "M" in 1930*) *was born on July 21, 1899, in Oak Park, Illinois. His father, a physician, was a great lover of the out-of-doors, and especially memorable to Hemingway in his youth were the hours spent with a fishing rod or a gun at the family summer home on Walloon Lake, near Petosky, Michigan. In Oak Park High School he was active in sports—football, swimming, boxing, water polo—but he was also a member of the orchestra and a self-improvement society. Most important, he was "drafted" by one of his teachers to write sport stories for the school's weekly newspaper and soon became one of the enthusiastic editors of the paper, writing, in his senior year, a column imitative of Ring Lardner. He also contributed stories to the* Tabula, *the school literary magazine, his first story appearing in February 1916, when he was sixteen years old.*

By the time he graduated, in 1917, he was committed to a career in writing, and that fall got a job as a cub reporter on the Kansas City Star. *He had just turned eighteen.*

The war interrupted his journalistic career. Turned down by the army because of an eye injury suffered in boxing, he joined the Red Cross Ambulance Corps and was on his way to Italy in May 1918. He was severely wounded in July, and was still a cripple when he was discharged on January 4, 1919. That fall and early winter he buried himself at Petosky, trying, unsuccessfully, to write and sell short stories.

By February 1920, he was back in journalism, this time with the Toronto Star *Weekly and later the* Daily Star, *first as a writer of feature stories at space rates, then as a roving reporter in Europe, with headquarters in Paris. His connection with the* Star *was broken for a brief period when he became editor of a house-organ magazine in Chicago. There he struck up a friendship with Sherwood Anderson, whose* Winesburg, Ohio *(1919) had put its author in the forefront of a group of avant-garde writers. But by December he was on his way to Europe, accompanied by his bride of two months.*

The next few years were an important period of literary apprenticeship. He became an expert journalist and worked hard at his own private attempts at fiction. In Paris, through an introduction from Anderson, he met Gertrude Stein and Ezra Pound, both of whom gave him valuable help and advice. Also, at this time, he was reading widely, studying the style of prose masters like Flaubert, Henry James, Thomas Mann, Turgenev.

In 1922 someone stole a valise containing almost all the manuscripts he had written over the last two years, including a novel, eighteen stories, and thirty poems. Only two stories, which happened to be in the mail at the time, were salvaged. "My Old Man" was one of these. Hemingway published it in 1923 in his first book, Three Stories and Ten Poems, *and although Edward J. O'Brien saw it and included it in the* Best American Short Stories of 1923, *the little pamphlet publication made no splash.*

In Our Time, *a collection of short stories published*

two years later, did receive favorable notice from the critics. But it was not until his first novel, The Sun Also Rises (1926), and the collected stories Men Without Women (1927) that Hemingway emerged as a new star on the literary horizon, the man who had given a new direction to fiction and who was to become the most influential and widely imitated author of his day. The imitation of Hemingway the author extended to an imitation of Hemingway the man, a kind of cult of virility.

Succeeding novels added to his reputation: A Farewell to Arms (1928), For Whom the Bell Tolls (1940), and his final novel, The Old Man and the Sea (1952). In between came novels less enthusiastically received and a number of books of nonfiction. The Fifth Column and the First Forty-Nine Stories (1938) contained his last collected stories.

The Old Man and the Sea won the Pulitzer Prize for 1953. In 1954 Hemingway was awarded the Nobel Prize for Literature "for his powerful style-forming mastery of the art of modern narration."

In 1953, in a letter to a young unpublished writer of nineteen who had sent him a story for criticism, Hemingway wrote: "I can't help you, kid. You write better than I did when I was 19. But the hell of it is you write like me. That is no sin. But you won't get anywhere with it.

"When I was your age I guess I wrote like Kipling. I thought he was the best short story writer that ever lived and I still know some of the short stories are the best but later on I knew I had to break the language down and start new. When you do that it gets to be personal and it sounds personal. . . .

"Why don't you start again at the beginning and read Kipling, i.e., 'The End of the Passage'; 'The Strange Ride of Maraby Jukes'; 'The Mark of the Beast' for three; de Maupassant's 'Boule de Souif' and 'Le Maison Tellier'; Stevie Crane's 'The Open Boat' and 'The Blue Hotel'; Ambrose Bierce's 'An Occurrence at Owl Creek Bridge'; Flaubert's Un Coeur Simple, and read Madame Bovary.

"That will hold you for a while. If you read them then reread them. Read a story of Thomas Mann called 'Disorder and Early Sorrow.' Read Buddenbrooks. . . .

"Then see the things you write about not through my eyes and my ears but through your own with your language conditioned not by me but by the above characters all of whom wrote well. But write it your own way. . . . Nobody but fools ever thought it was an easy trade." Hemingway died on July 2, 1961.

MY OLD MAN

I guess looking at it, now, my old man was cut out for a fat guy, one of those regular little roly-poly fat guys you see around, but he sure never got that way, except a little toward the last, and then it wasn't his fault, he was riding over the jumps only and he could afford to carry plenty of weight then. I remember the way he'd pull on a rubber shirt over a couple of jerseys and a big sweat shirt over that, and get me to run with him in the forenoon in the hot sun. He'd have, maybe, taken a trial trip with one of Razzo's skins early in the morning after just getting in from Torino at four o'clock in the morning and beating it out to the stables in a cab and then with the dew all over everything and the sun just starting to get going, I'd help him pull off his boots and he'd get into a pair of sneakers and all these sweaters and we'd start out.

"Come on, kid," he'd say, stepping up and down on his toes in front of the jock's dressing room, "let's get moving."

Then we'd start off jogging around the infield once, maybe, with him ahead, running nice, and then turn out the gate and along one of those roads with all the trees along both sides of them that run out from San Siro. I'd go ahead of him when we hit the road and I could run pretty good and I'd look around and he'd be jogging easy just behind me and after a little while I'd look around again and he'd begun to sweat. Sweating heavy and he'd just be dogging it along with his eyes on my back, but when he'd catch me looking at him he'd grin and say, "Sweating plenty?" When my old man grinned, nobody could help but grin too. We'd keep right on running out toward the mountains and then my old man would yell, "Hey, Joe!" and I'd look back and he'd be sitting under a tree with a towel he'd had around his waist wrapped around his neck.

I'd come back and sit down beside him and he'd pull a rope out of his pocket and start skipping rope out in the sun with the sweat pouring off his face and him skipping rope out in the white dust with the rope going cloppetty, cloppetty, clop, clop, clop, and the sun hotter, and him working harder up and down a patch of the road. Say, it was a treat to see my old man skip rope, too. He could whirr it fast or lop it slow and fancy. Say, you ought to have seen wops look at us sometimes, when they'd come by, going into town walking along with big white steers hauling the cart. They sure looked as though they thought the old man was nuts. He'd start the rope whirring till they'd stop dead still and watch him, then give the steers a cluck and a poke with the goad and get going again.

When I'd sit watching him working out in the hot sun I sure felt fond of him. He sure was fun and he done his work so hard and he'd finish up with a regular whirring that'd drive the sweat out on his face like water and then sling the rope at the tree and come over and sit down with me and lean back against the tree with the towel and a sweater wrapped around his neck.

"Sure is hell keeping it down, Joe," he'd say and lean back and shut his eyes and breathe long and deep, "it ain't like when you're a kid." Then he'd get up and before he started to cool we'd jog along back to the stables. That's the way it was keeping down to weight. He was worried all the time. Most jocks can just about ride off all they want to. A jock loses about a kilo every time he rides, but my old man was sort of dried out and he couldn't keep down his kilos without all that running.

I remember once at San Siro, Regoli, a little wop, that was riding for Buzoni, came out across the paddock going to the bar for something cool; and flicking his boots with his whip, after he'd just weighed in and my old man had just weighed in too, and came out with the saddle under his arm looking red-faced and tired and too big for his silks and he stood there looking at young Regoli standing up to the outdoors bar, cool and kid-looking, and I said, "What's the matter, Dad?" 'cause I thought maybe Regoli had bumped him or something and he just looked at Regoli and said, "Oh, to hell with it," and went on to the dressing room.

Well, it would have been all right, maybe, if we'd stayed in Milan and ridden at Milan and Torino, 'cause if there ever were any easy courses, it's those two. "Pianola, Joe," my old man said when he dismounted in the winning stall after what the wops thought was a hell of steeple chase. I asked him once. "This course rides itself. It's the pace you're going at, that makes riding the jumps dangerous, Joe. We ain't going any pace here, and they ain't really bad jumps either. But it's the pace always—not the jumps—that makes the trouble."

San Siro was the swellest course I'd ever seen but the old man said it was a dog's life. Going back and forth between Mirafiore and San Siro and riding just about every day in the week with a train ride every other night.

I was nuts about the horses, too. There's something about it, when they come out and go up the track to the post. Sort of dancy and tight looking with the jock keeping a tight hold on them and maybe easing off a little and letting them run a little going up. Then once they were at the barrier it got me worse than anything. Especially at San Siro with that big green infield and the mountains way off and the fat wop starter with his big whip and the jocks fiddling them around and then the barrier snapping up and that bell going off and them all getting off in a bunch and then commencing to string out. You know the way a bunch of skins gets off. If you're up in the stand with a pair of glasses all you see is them plunging off and then that bell goes off and it seems like it rings for a thousand years and then they come sweeping round the turn. There wasn't ever anything like it for me.

But my old man said one day, in the dressing room, when he was getting into his street clothes, "None of these things are horses, Joe. They'd kill that bunch of skates for their hides and hoofs up at Paris." That was the day he'd won the Premio Commercio with Lantorna shooting her out of the field the last hundred meters like pulling a cork out of a bottle.

It was right after the Premio Commercio that we pulled out and left Italy. My old man and Holbrook and a fat wop in a straw hat that kept wiping his face with a handkerchief were having an argument at a table in the Galleria. They were all talking French and the two of them was after my old man about something. Finally he didn't say anything any more but just sat there and looked at Holbrook, and the two of them kept after him, first one talking and then the other, and the fat wop always butting in on Holbrook.

"You go out and buy me a *Sportsman,* will you, Joe?" my old man said, and handed me a couple of soldi without looking away from Holbrook.

So I went out of the Galleria and walked over to in front of the Scala and bought a paper, and came back and stood a little way away because I didn't want to butt in and my old man was sitting back in his chair looking down at his coffee and fooling with a spoon and Holbrook and the big wop were standing and the big wop was wiping his face and shaking his head. And I came up and my old man acted just as though the two of them weren't standing there and said, "Want an ice, Joe?" Holbrook looked down at my old man and said slow and careful, "You son of a bitch," and he and the fat wop went out through the tables.

125

My old man sat there and sort of smiled at me, but his face was white and he looked sick as hell and I was scared and felt sick inside because I knew something had happened and I didn't see how anybody could call my old man a son of a bitch, and get away with it. My old man opened up the *Sportsman* and studied the handicaps for a while and then he said, "You got to take a lot of things in this world, Joe." And three days later we left Milan for good on the Turin train for Paris, after an auction sale out in front of Turner's stables of everything we couldn't get into a trunk and a suit case.

We got into Paris early in the morning in a long, dirty station the old man told me was the Gare de Lyon. Paris was an awful big town after Milan. Seems like in Milan everybody is going somewhere and all the trams run somewhere and there ain't any sort of a mix-up, but Paris is all balled up and they never do straighten it out. I got to like it, though, part of it, anyway, and say, it's got the best race courses in the world. Seems as though that were the thing that keeps it all going and about the only thing you can figure on is that every day the buses will be going out to whatever track they're running at, going right out through everything to the track. I never really got to know Paris well, because I just came in about once or twice a week with the old man from Maisons and he always sat at the Café de la Paix on the Opera side with the rest of the gang from Maisons and I guess that's one of the busiest parts of the town. But, say, it is funny that a big town like Paris wouldn't have a Galleria, isn't it?

Well, we went out to live at Maisons-Lafitte, where just about everybody lives except the gang at Chantilly, with a Mrs. Meyers that runs a boarding house. Maisons is about the swellest place to live I've ever seen in all my life. The town ain't so much, but there's a lake and a swell forest that we used to go off bumming in all day, a couple of us kids, and my old man made me a sling shot and we got a lot of things with it but the best one was a magpie. Young Dick Atkinson shot a rabbit with it one day and we put it under a tree and were all sitting around and Dick had some cigarettes and all of a sudden the rabbit jumped up and beat it into the brush and we chased it but we couldn't find it. Gee, we had fun at Maisons. Mrs. Meyers used to give me lunch in the morning and I'd be gone all day. I learned to talk French quick. It's an easy language.

As soon as we got to Maisons, my old man wrote to Milan for his license and he was pretty worried till it came. He used to sit around the Café de Paris in Maisons with the gang, there were lots of guys he'd known when he rode up at Paris, before the war, lived at Maisons, and there's a lot of time to sit around because the work around a racing stable, for the jocks, that is, is all cleaned up by nine o'clock in the morning. They take the first bunch of skins out to gallop them at 5.30 in the morning and they work the second lot at 8 o'clock. That means getting up early all right and going to bed early, too. If a jock's riding for somebody too, he can't go boozing around because the trainer always has an eye on him if he's a kid and if he ain't a kid he's always got an eye on himself. So mostly if a jock ain't working he sits around the Café de Paris with the gang and they can all sit around about two or three hours in front of some drink like a vermouth and seltz and they talk and tell stories and shoot pool and it's sort of like a club or the Galleria in Milan. Only it ain't really like the Galleria because there everybody is going by all the time and there's everybody around at the tables.

Well, my old man got his license all right. They sent it through to him without a word and he rode a couple of times. Amiens, up country and that sort of thing, but he didn't seem to get any engagement. Everybody liked him and whenever I'd come into the Café in the forenoon I'd find somebody drinking with him because my old man wasn't tight like most of these jockeys that have got the first dollar they made riding at the World's Fair in St. Louis in nineteen ought four. That's what my old man would say when he'd kid George Burns. But it seemed like everybody steered clear of giving my old man any mounts.

We went out to wherever they were running every day with the car from Maisons and that was the most fun of all. I was glad when the horses came back from Deauville and the summer. Even though it meant no more bumming in the woods, 'cause then we'd ride to Enghien or Tremblay or St. Cloud and watch them from the trainers' and jockeys' stand. I sure learned about racing from going out with that gang and the fun of it was going every day.

I remember once out at St. Cloud. It was a big two hundred thousand franc race with seven entries and Kzar a big favorite. I went around to the paddock to see the horses with my old man and you never saw such horses. This Kzar is a great big yellow horse that looks like just nothing but run. I never saw such a horse. He was being led around the paddocks with his head down and when he went by me I felt all hollow inside he was so beautiful. There never was such a wonderful, lean, running built horse. And he went around the paddock putting his feet just so and quiet and careful and moving easy like he knew just what he had to do and not jerking and standing up on his legs and getting wild eyed like you see these selling platers with a shot of dope in them. The crowd was so thick I couldn't see him again except just his legs going by and some yellow and my old man started out through the crowd and I followed him over to the jock's dressing room back in the trees and there was a big crowd around there, too, but the man at the door in a derby nodded to my old man and we got in and everybody was sitting around and getting dressed and pulling shirts over their heads and pulling boots on and it all smelled hot and sweaty and linimenty and outside was the crowd looking in.

The old man went over and sat down beside George Gardner that was getting into his pants and said, "What's the

dope, George?" just in an ordinary tone of voice 'cause there
ain't any use him feeling around because George either can tell
him or he can't tell him.

"He won't win," George says very low, leaning over and
buttoning the bottoms of his breeches.

"Who will?" my old man says, leaning over close so nobody
can hear.

"Kircubbin," George says, "and if he does, save me a couple
of tickets."

My old man says something in a regular voice to George
and George says, "Don't ever bet on anything I tell you,"
kidding like, and we beat it out and through all the crowd that
was looking in, over to the 100 franc mutuel machine. But I
knew something big was up because George is Kzar's jockey.
On the way he gets one of the yellow odds-sheets with the
starting prices on and Kzar is only paying 5 for 10, Cefisidote
is next at 3 to 1 and fifth down the list this Kircubbin at 8 to
1. My old man bets five thousand on Kircubbin to win and
puts on a thousand to place and we went around back of the
grandstand to go up the stairs and get a place to watch the race.

We were jammed in tight and first a man in a long coat
with a gray tall hat and a whip folded up in his hand came out
and then one after another the horses, with the jocks up and
a stable boy holding the bridle on each side and walking along,
followed the old guy. That big yellow horse Kzar came first.
He didn't look so big when you first looked at him until you
saw the length of his legs and the whole way he's built and the
way he moves. Gosh, I never saw such a horse. George Gardner
was riding him and they moved along slow, back of the old
guy in the gray tall hat that walked along like he was a ring
master in a circus. Back of Kzar, moving along smooth and
yellow in the sun, was a good looking black with a nice head
with Tommy Archibald riding him; and after the black was
a string of five more horses all moving along slow in a procession past the grandstand and the pesage. My old man said the

129

black was Kircubbin and I took a good look at him and he was a nice-looking horse, all right, but nothing like Kzar.

Everybody cheered Kzar when he went by and he sure was one swell-looking horse. The procession of them went around on the other side past the pelouse and then back up to the near end of the course and the circus master had the stable boys turn them loose one after another so they could gallop by the stands on their way up to the post and let everybody have a good look at them. They weren't at the post hardly any time at all when the gong started and you could see them way off across the infield all in a bunch starting on the first swing like a lot of little toy horses. I was watching them through the glasses and Kzar was running well back, with one of the bays making the pace. They swept down and around and came pounding past and Kzar was way back when they passed us and this Kircubbin horse in front and going smooth. Gee it's awful when they go by you and then you have to watch them go farther away and get smaller and smaller and then all bunched up on the turns and then come around towards into the stretch and you feel like swearing and god-damming worse and worse. Finally they made the last turn and came into the straightaway with this Kircubbin horse way out in front. Everybody was looking funny and saying "Kzar" in sort of a sick way and them pounding nearer down the stretch, and then something came out of the pack right into my glasses like a horse-headed yellow streak and everybody began to yell "Kzar" as though they were crazy. Kzar came on faster than I'd ever seen anything in my life and pulled up on Kircubbin that was going fast as any black horse could go with the jock flogging hell out of him with the gad and they were right dead neck and neck for a second but Kzar seemed going about twice as fast with those great jumps and that head out—but it was while they were neck and neck that they passed the winning post and when the numbers went up in the slots the first one was 2 and that meant that Kircubbin had won.

I felt all trembly and funny inside, and then we were all jammed in with the people going downstairs to stand in front of the board where they'd post what Kircubbin paid. Honest, watching the race I'd forgot how much my old man had bet on Kircubbin. I'd wanted Kzar to win so damned bad. But now it was all over it was swell to know we had the winner.

"Wasn't it a swell race, Dad?" I said to him.

He looked at me sort of funny with his derby on the back of his head. "George Gardner's a swell jockey, all right," he said. "It sure took a great jock to keep that Kzar horse from winning."

Of course I knew it was funny all the time. But my old man saying that right out like that sure took the kick all out of it for me and I didn't get the real kick back again ever, even when they posted the numbers upon the board and the bell rang to pay off and we saw that Kircubbin paid 67.50 for 10. All round people were saying, "Poor Kzar! Poor Kzar!" And I thought, I wish I were a jockey and could have rode him instead of that son of a bitch. And that was funny, thinking of George Gardner as a son of a bitch because I'd always liked him and besides he'd given us the winner, but I guess that's what he is, all right.

My old man had a big lot of money after that race and he took to coming into Paris oftener. If they raced at Tremblay he'd have them drop him in town on their way back to Maisons and he and I'd sit out in front of the Café de la Paix and watch the people go by. It's funny sitting there. There's streams of people going by and all sorts of guys come up and want to sell you things, and I loved to sit there with my old man. That was when we'd have the most fun. Guys would come by selling funny rabbits that jumped if you squeezed a bulb and they'd come up to us and my old man would kid with them. He could talk French just like English and all those kind of guys knew him 'cause you can always tell a jockey— and then we always sat at the same table and they got used to seeing us there. There were guys selling matrimonial papers and girls selling rubber eggs that when you squeezed them a rooster came out of them and one old wormy-looking guy that went by with post-cards of Paris, showing them to everybody, and, of course, nobody ever bought any, and then he would come back and show the under side of the pack and they would all be smutty post-cards and lots of people would dig down and buy them.

Gee, I remember the funny people that used to go by. Girls around supper time looking for somebody to take them out to eat and they'd speak to my old man and he'd make some joke at them in French and they'd pat me on the head and go on. Once there was an American woman sitting with her kid daughter at the next table to us and they were both eating ices and I kept looking at the girl and she was awfully good looking and I smiled at her and she smiled at me but that was all that ever came of it because I looked for her mother and her every day and I made up ways that I was going to speak to her and I wondered if I got to know her if her mother would let me take her out to Auteuil or Tremblay but I never saw either of them again. Anyway, I guess it wouldn't have been any good, anyway, because looking back on it I remember the way I thought out would be best to speak to her was to say, "Pardon me, but perhaps I can give you a winner at Enghien today?" and, after all, maybe she would have thought I was a tout instead of really trying to give her a winner.

We'd sit at the Café de la Paix, my old man and me, and we had a big drag with the waiter because my old man drank whisky and it cost five francs, and that meant a good tip when the saucers were counted up. My old man was drinking more than I'd ever seen him, but he wasn't riding at all now and besides he said that whisky kept his weight down. But I noticed he was putting it on, all right, just the same. He'd busted away from his old gang out at Maisons and seemed to like just sitting around on the boulevard with me. But he was dropping money every day at the track. He'd feel sort of doleful after the last race, if he'd lost on the day, until we'd get to our table and he'd have his first whisky and then he'd be fine.

He'd be reading the *Paris-Sport* and he'd look over at me and say, "Where's your girl, Joe?" to kid me on account I had told him about the girl that day at the next table. And I'd get red, but I liked being kidded about her. It gave me a good feeling. "Keep your eye peeled for her, Joe," he'd say, "she'll be back."

He'd ask me questions about things and some of the things I'd say he'd laugh. And then he'd get started talking about things. About riding down in Egypt, or at St. Moritz on the ice before my mother died, and about during the war when they had regular races down in the south of France without any purses, or betting or crowd or anything just to keep the breed up. Regular races with the jocks riding hell out of the horses. Gee, I could listen to my old man talk by the hour, especially when he'd had a couple or so of drinks. He'd tell me about when he was a boy in Kentucky and going coon hunting, and the old days in the States before everything went on the bum there. And he'd say, "Joe, when we've got a decent stake, you're going back there to the States and go to school."

"What've I got to go back there to go to school for when everything's on the bum there?" I'd ask him.

"That's different," he'd say and get the waiter over and pay the pile of saucers and we'd get a taxi to the Gare St. Lazare and get on the train out to Maisons.

One day at Auteuil, after a selling steeplechase, my old man bought in the winner for 30,000 francs. He had to bid a little to get him but the stable let the horse go finally and my old man had his permit and his colors in a week. Gee, I felt proud when my old man was an owner. He fixed it up for stable space with Charles Drake and cut out coming in to Paris, and started his running and sweating out again, and him and I were the whole stable gang. Our horse's name was Gilford, he was Irish bred and a nice, sweet jumper. My old man figured that training him and riding him, himself, he was a good investment. I was proud of everything and I thought Gilford was as good a horse as Kzar. He was a good, solid jumper, a bay, with plenty of speed on the flat, if you asked him for it, and he was a nice-looking horse, too.

Gee, I was fond of him. The first time he started with my old man up, he finished third in a 2500 meter hurdle race and when my old man got off him, all sweating and happy in the place stall, and went in to weigh, I felt as proud of him as though it was the first race he'd ever placed in. You see, when a guy ain't been riding for a long time, you can't make yourself really believe that he has ever rode. The whole thing was different now, 'cause down in Milan, even big races never seemed to make any difference to my old man, if he won he wasn't ever excited or anything, and now it was so I couldn't hardly sleep the night before a race and I knew my old man was excited, too, even if he didn't show it. Riding for yourself makes an awful difference.

Second time Gilford and my old man started, was a rainy Sunday at Auteuil, in the Prix du Marat, a 4500 meter steeplechase. As soon as he'd gone out I beat it up in the stand with the new glasses my old man had bought for me to watch them. They started way over at the far end of the course and there was some trouble at the barrier. Something with goggle blinders on was making a great fuss and rearing around and busted the barrier once, but I could see my old man in our black jacket, with a white cross and a black cap, sitting up on Gilford, and patting him with his hand. Then they were off in a jump and out of sight behind the trees and the gong going for dear life and the pari-mutuel wickets rattling down. Gosh, I was so excited, I was afraid to look at them, but I fixed the glasses on the place where they would come out back of the trees and then out they came with the old black jacket going third and they all sailing over the jump like birds. Then they went out of sight again and then they came pounding out and down the hill and all going nice and sweet and easy and taking the fence smooth in a bunch, and moving away from us all solid. Looked as though you could walk across on their backs they were all so bunched and going so smooth. Then they bellied over the big double Bullfinch and something came down. I couldn't see who it was, but in a minute the horse was up and galloping free and the field, all bunched still, sweeping around the long left turn into the straightaway. They jumped the stone wall and came jammed down the stretch toward the big water-jump right in front of the stands. I saw them coming and hollered at my old man as he went by, and he was leading by about a length and riding way out, and light as a monkey, and they were racing for the water-jump. They took off over the big hedge of the water-jump in a pack and then there was a crash, and two horses pulled sideways out off it, and kept on going, and three others were piled up. I couldn't see my old man anywhere. One horse kneed himself up and the jock had hold of the bridle and mounted and went slamming on after the place money. The other horse was up and away by himself, jerking his head and galloping with the bridle rein hanging and the jock staggered over to one side of the track against the fence. Then Gilford rolled over to one side off my old man and got up and started to run on three legs with his front off hoof dangling and there was my old man laying there on the grass flat out with his face up and blood all over the side of his head. I ran down the stand and bumped into a jam of people and got to the rail and a cop grabbed me and held me and two big stretcher-bearers were going out after my old man and around on the other side of the course I saw three horses, strung way out, coming out of the trees and taking the jump.

My old man was dead when they brought him in and while a doctor was listening to his heart with a thing plugged in his ears, I heard a shot up the track that meant they'd killed Gilford. I lay down beside my old man, when they carried the stretcher into the hospital room, and hung onto the stretcher and cried and cried, and he looked so white and gone and so awfully dead, and I couldn't help feeling that if my old man was dead maybe they didn't need to have shot Gilford. His hoof might have got well. I don't know. I loved my old man so much.

Then a couple of guys came in and one of them patted me on the back and then went over and looked at my old man and then pulled a sheet off the cot and spread it over him; and the other was telephoning in French for them to send the ambulance to take him out to Maisons. And I couldn't stop crying, crying and choking, sort of, and George Gardner came in and sat down beside me on the floor and put his arm around me and says, "Come on, Joe, old boy. Get up and we'll go out and wait for the ambulance."

George and I went out to the gate and I was trying to stop bawling and George wiped off my face with his handkerchief and we were standing back a little ways while the crowd was going out of the gate and a couple of guys stopped near us while we were waiting for the crowd to get through the gate and one of them was counting a bunch of mutuel tickets and he said, "Well, Butler got his, all right."

The other guy said, "I don't give a good goddam if he did, the crook. He had it coming to him on the stuff he's pulled."

"I'll say he had," said the other guy, and tore the bunch of tickets in two.

And George Gardner looked at me to see if I'd heard and I had all right and he said, "Don't you listen to what those bums said, Joe. Your old man was one swell guy."

But I don't know. Seems like when they get started they don't leave a guy nothing.

MARTHA FOLEY

Martha Foley was born in Boston, Massachusetts, where she was educated in the Girls' Latin School, 1909 to 1915, and later at Boston University for two years. By 1922 she was in San Francisco, working on the editorial staff of the Journal, launched on a colorful career in journalism that was to occupy her for most of the next decade. From San Francisco she went to Los Angeles as feature editor of the Illustrated Daily News, where one of her duties was handling a column called "The Voice of the People," a letters-to-the-editor column from readers, usually with an axe to grind. When there were no letters, she said, she wrote them herself. In 1925 she was in New York City, as make-up editor, first for the Daily News and later for the Mirror.

Paris in the twenties was the mecca for many American journalists and writers, and Miss Foley decided, in 1927, to toss up her job in New York and go to Paris as a reporter and copy editor for the Paris edition of the New York Herald. Here she met Whit Burnett, who was city editor for the Herald in Paris, and they were married shortly after. The next stop was Vienna, as Central European correspondent for the New York Sun. This, Miss Foley wrote in retrospect, "was a delightful life. I should have been content to let it remain so." What happened next, however, made literary history.

She and Mr. Burnett started a little magazine devoted solely to short stories in order to provide a market for stories of merit the commercial magazines would not publish. Thus Story magazine, one of the most famous of the little magazines, was born in Vienna in the spring of 1931. The first issue was mimeographed with the thought of saving money, but the mimeograph job turned out to be more expensive than printing. Cost being an important factor, the Burnetts decided to make their headquarters at Majorca, off the coast of Spain, the cheapest place in Europe at the time both for living and printing costs. Announced as a bimonthly, Story came out first as a tri-monthly. But its fame spread, the circulation grew, and Miss Foley and her husband decided to move the magazine to New York City. It was established at Fifty-seventh Street and Madison Avenue, its first real offices, in 1933.

While she was a journalist, Miss Foley had published no short stories. With the advent of Story, however, she began to write. "One with Shakespeare," published in Story in 1931, the year it was founded, was chosen by Edward J. O'Brien for The Best Short Stories of 1931, and four more of her stories were subsequently reprinted in this anthology. O'Brien said of her in those days that "no American writer has penetrated more deeply and with more wistful humor into the mind of a young girl."

In 1941 came a new stage in her career. Mr. O'Brien died, leaving a request that she step into his shoes as editor of the anthology he had founded in 1915. It was a difficult decision to make, but Miss Foley finally decided to accept the responsibility and has been editor since.

Miss Foley has lectured on the short story at summer sessions of the University of Colorado, Columbia University, and New York University. Since 1945 she has been a regular lecturer at Columbia University, School of General Studies.

ONE WITH SHAKESPEARE

Yes, Miss Cox was there, sitting at her desk in the almost empty classroom. Elizabeth took in the theme she had written to make up for a class missed because of illness.

A description of people under changing circumstances was the assignment.

Elizabeth had chosen immigrants arriving at a Boston dock. She had got quite excited as she wrote about the black-eyed women and their red and blue dresses, the swarthy men and their earrings, and the brightness of a faraway Mediterranean land slipping off a rocking boat to be lost in the grayness of Boston streets.

Elizabeth had liked writing this theme better than anything she had done since the description of a sunset. Amethyst and rose with a silver ribbon of river. Elizabeth shivered. A silver ribbon—that was lovely. And so was "scarlet kerchief in the night of her hair" in this theme. Words were so beautiful.

Miss Cox read the new theme, a red pencil poised in her authoritative fingers. Miss Cox was so strong. She was strongest of all the teachers in the school. Stronger even than the two men teachers, Mr. Carpenter of physics and Mr. Cattell of math. A beautiful strongness. Thought of Miss Cox made Elizabeth feel as she did when two bright shiny words suddenly sprang together to make a beautiful, a perfect phrase.

Elizabeth was glad she had Miss Cox as an English teacher

Reprinted from *Story Magazine* by permission of Martha Foley.

and not Miss Foster any more. Miss Foster had made the class last year count the number of times certain words occurred in *Poor Richard's Almanac,* to be sure they read the book right through word for word. And the words were all so ugly. Like the picture of Benjamin Franklin. But Miss Cox made you feel the words. As when she read from *The Tale of Two Cities* in her deep singing voice, "This is a far, far better thing than I have ever done." Poor Sydney Carton.

Miss Cox had finished the second page of the theme. She was looking up at Elizabeth, her small dark blue eyes lighting up her glasses.

"Let me give you a pointer, my dear."

Elizabeth automatically looked toward the blackboard ledge at the chalky pointer until the words "my dear" bit into her mind. My dear! Miss Cox had called her "My dear."

"You have a spark of the divine fire," Miss Cox said. "You should make writing your vocation."

Elizabeth flamed. Miss Cox, "my dear," themes about immigrants, blackboards, and desks whirled and fused in the divine fire.

Miss Cox marked "A" in the red pencil at the top of the theme and Elizabeth said "thank you" and went away.

Elizabeth went back to her desk in the IIIA classroom which was in charge of Miss Perry. Miss Perry was her Greek teacher as well as her room teacher. Somehow Miss Perry made Elizabeth hate Greek. Elizabeth liked to think of Greece. White and gold in a blue Aegean. I, Sappho. Wailing Trojan women. Aristotle and Plato and Socrates. Grace and brains, said her father, of the men. But that was outside of Greek class. To Miss Perry, Greece was the aorist of *tithemi* and Xenophon's march in the *Anabasis.* Elizabeth always said to herself as she came into the IIIA room, "I hate Miss Perry, the aorist, and Xenophon. Oh, how I hate them!"

But this morning Elizabeth only pitied Miss Perry. She had no spark of the divine fire, poor thing.

Greek was the first class this morning. Elizabeth didn't care. She should make writing her vocation. That was something Miss Perry could never do. If she were called on for the list of irregular verbs this morning, she would like to tell Miss Perry that. It would explain why she hadn't studied her Greek home-lesson. Why should she be bothered with conjugations when she had to describe blue and red men arriving on an alien shore?

"Now, Miss Morris, will you please give me the principal parts of the verb *to give*."

That was *didomi*. But what was the perfect tense? Divine fire, divine fire.

"If you don't know, you may sit down. But I warn you that unless you do your home-lessons better you are not going to pass this month."

Divine fire, divine fire.

The second hour was study class. Under Miss Pratt with the ugly bulb of a nose, splotchy face, and eternal smile. Miss Pratt taught something or other to the younger girls down in the sixth class. She always smiled at Elizabeth but Elizabeth seldom smiled back. Her smile never means anything, thought Elizabeth.

Elizabeth dumped her books down on her desk in Miss Pratt's room. She opened Vergil at the part she liked—where Aeneas told Dido the story of his wandering while the stars waned and drooped in the sky. It was not her lesson. She had had that months ago. But she liked going back over it, just as she liked the beginning of the first book. Great bearded Aeneas rang out in *arma virumque cano*. That was strong. She would write strong some day. Strong like Vergil, and fine like Swinburne:

> "I will go back to the great sweet mother,
> Mother and lover of men, the sea."

Swinburne had divine fire. Keats. Shelley: "Hail to thee, blithe spirit." And Masefield whose autograph she had bought for five shillings, not to help the British but to have a bit of the man who wrote *The Widow in Bye Street*.

Elizabeth looked out into the school courtyard. Fine green shoots. Yellow on the laburnum. Spring was here. Divine fire, divine fire.

"Miss Morris, haven't you any work to do?" Miss Pratt smiling. Nasty, nasty, smiling. Didn't she know whom she was talking to like that? A great writer. A girl who would be famous. Let her ask Miss Cox. Why, I have a spark of the divine fire. I am one with Shakespeare and Keats, Thackeray and Brontë, and all the other great writers.

Elizabeth plumped her head in her hands and stared at the Latin page. Opposite was an illustration of an old statue, supposed to be Dido. Further on was a pen-an-ink sketch of Dido mounting the funeral pyre. Further on was a sketch of Aeneas nearing Rome. Further on was the vocabulary. Then the end of the book. Elizabeth turned, page by page. She could not study, and if she looked out the window at spring again Miss Pratt would be nasty.

"Please, Miss Pratt, may I go to the library?"

"Must you go to the library? What for?"

"I have a reference in my history lesson to look up in the encyclopedia."

"Very well."

The library was large and quiet—a whole floor above Miss Pratt and the study class. It was divided off into alcoves. History in one. Encyclopedias in another. Languages, sciences. Fiction and poetry were in the farthest end which opened out toward the Fenway. The Fenway with its river and wide sky where Elizabeth liked to walk alone.

Elizabeth had read all the fiction and all the poetry. All of Jane Austen and *The Sorrows of Werther* and lots of other books which had nothing to do with her classes. She was always afraid one of her teachers would come in some day during study class and ask her what she was reading that book for. But that had never happened. And the librarian never paid any attention to her.

Now she went into the fiction and poetry alcove and sat on a small shelf ladder. She looked out the window at the long line of poplars rimming the fens. What would she call them if she were writing about them? Black sentinels against the sky. Oh beautiful, oh beautiful! That was the divine fire.

There was ancient history with Miss Tudor, who had had the smallpox and it showed all over her face; and geometry with Mr. Cattell who had a gray beard and gray eyes and gray clothes and gray manner. Elizabeth liked that—gray manner. That was what the Advanced English Composition called penetrating analysis of character. She would do lots of penetrating analysis when she wrote in earnest.

She would write novels, the greatest, most moving novels ever written, like *Jean Christophe*, Elizabeth was deciding when the bell rang for the end of the history lesson. And in between the novels she would write fine medallions of short stories like Chekhov's, Elizabeth told herself when the bell rang for the end of the geometry lesson. And she would always write lovely poems in between the novels and the short stories, she was thinking when the bell rang for the end of the school day.

Elizabeth walked past Miss Cox's room on her way out of the building. She slowed down her steps as she came to the door. Miss Cox was putting away her things in the drawer of her desk. Elizabeth would dedicate her first book to Miss Cox. "To Miss Eleanor G. Cox this book is gratefully dedicated by the author."

Eileen and Ruth were waiting for Elizabeth at the entrance. Eileen was the cousin of a famous poet and her mother was an Anarchist. Elizabeth liked the thought of anyone being an Anarchist. It sounded so much more beautiful than being a Democrat or a Republican. And Ruth, who was a class ahead, had already had her poems printed in the *Transcript*. Four

143

times. And one of the poems had been reprinted by William Stanley Braithwaite, in his anthology. Oh, they were going to be great and famous, all three.

"Let's walk home and save our fares for fudge sundaes," said Eileen.

"All right, only I am going to have pineapple," said Ruth.

"I'll go with you but I won't have any sundae," Elizabeth said. "I'm going to save my fares this week and buy Miss Cox flowers."

"You have a crush on Miss Cox."

"Perhaps I have and perhaps I haven't. Anyway she said something wonderful to me this morning. She said I had a spark of divine fire and should make writing my vocation."

"Oh, that is wonderful. She never told me that, not even after Mr. Braithwaite took one of my poems for his anthology."

"This is the happiest day of my life. Even when I have written many books and proved Miss Cox's faith in me, I shall always look back to this day. I never expected to be so wonderfully happy."

The three girls, arm in arm, walked through the Fenway.

"I tell you, let's not get sundaes. Since Elizabeth's saving her money, it isn't fair to go in and eat them right before her. Let's you, Ruth, and I buy some of those big frosted doughnuts and some bananas and eat them on the Charles River esplanade. Then Elizabeth can have some too."

"All right, and we can watch the sun set."

"Oh, but that's what isn't fair. To save my money and then eat up what you buy."

"Next time you can give us something."

Elizabeth loved the Charles River. It always hurt her to think that it was on a Charles River bridge that Longfellow should have made up "I stood on the bridge at midnight." Perhaps that wasn't so bad, but so many parodies of the poem had ridiculed the river. Once Elizabeth had written a "Letter to a River." Elizabeth pretended she was away off somewhere like in New York and was writing to the river to tell how much she missed its beauty. She had put so many lovely phrases in it, she thought, and she couldn't understand why the editor of the *Atlantic Monthly* had sent it back to her. But great writers always had many rejections first. That Scottish writer in whose eyes Ruth said she saw his soul, had said in his lecture that to write greatly, one must first suffer greatly.

How she had suffered, thought Elizabeth. Her math and Greek teachers were so cruel to her. She, who had a spark of divine fire, to be treated as they treated her. Tears came to her eyes. And now, when she was tired, she was walking home instead of riding so she could buy Miss Cox flowers. Pink sweetheart roses. Little tight knots of flowers. That was suffering and sacrifice. But it was for love as well as for literature.

"I felt the rhythm of the universe last night," Ruth was saying; "I was sitting on the roof in the dark and I felt the night all around me."

"That makes me think of 'swiftly walk over the western wave, spirit of Night.' But it always bothers me that the wave is to the east in Boston," said Eileen. "Otherwise I like that poem very much."

"The rhythm of the universe? What do you mean?"

"Oh, you know. The way someone said the stars swing round in their courses. And that's why I never, never want to study astronomy. I want only to imagine the stars. That's so much more beautiful than any facts about them can ever be."

"I don't agree with you at all. Why, when you think that the light of the nearest star started coming to you three years ago and what you were doing then and how this minute some star is starting to send you light that may not get to you until far away and old and . . ."

"Stop! Don't give me facts about the stars! You can have those facts about your stars, if you want. But leave me my stars to love as I please."

"Oh, very well. There, now the sky is coloring. See that lovely clear green high up. Pretty soon the deep colors will come. My, these frosted doughnuts are good! Much better than any near where we live."

"There's the first light on the other bank. Over near the Tech building."

That was what it was to have a spark of divine fire. Elizabeth's thoughts flowed on with the darkening river. She could put all this, the river and the sky colors and the lights, into writing. People would feel the loveliness of the world as they had never felt it before. People would no longer walk with their heads bent to the street when there was a sunset to be seen. What have you done to her, masters of men, that her head should be bowed down thus, thus in the deepening twilight and golden angelus? Her father said Noyes wrote maudlin sing-song. It was jingly sometimes but she did like it. And too many heads were bowed down, you masters of men.

"Mother'll scold me if I stay any later," said Eileen.

"And my mother said she wouldn't get me a new dress for the class party if I came home late again."

"Yes, we must all be going. But isn't it nice to think when you wake up at home in bed at night that the river is out here, creeping on and on under the stars?"

"No wonder Miss Cox said you had divine fire. Let's put our banana peels in here. This is Spring Clean-up Week, you know."

"Good night."

"Good night."

"Good night."

Holding the thought of her own greatness close to her, Elizabeth went home. A sliver of moon curled in the sky. That is the moon Shelley, Shakespeare, Spenser and yes, 'way back, Chaucer looked at. And now I am looking at it.

"Mother, Miss Cox says I have a spark of divine fire. I am to be a great writer some day."

146

"Isn't that nice? Did you remember not to wipe your pen point on your petticoat today?"

"Oh, mother, you know that's not a question of remembering. I never do it when I'm thinking about it. But you didn't half listen to what Miss Cox said about me."

"Indeed I did. She said you had a divine spark of fire. That means you'll get another A in English this month on your report card."

"It means more than any old report card. It means my whole life. I'm to be a writer, a great writer."

"But first you must finish school and college. And that means you have to do your mathematics better. Remember how angry your father was about that E in geometry last month."

Elizabeth sighed. She went out on the back porch which looked across the city. Lights pricked the blackness. Like a necklace which had spilled over velvet. Oh, words were lovely.

The moon was still there, a more emphatic sliver now. "Moon of Shelley and Keats and Shakespeare, and my moon," said Elizabeth and went in to dinner.

STEPHEN VINCENT BENÉT

Stephen Vincent Benét was born on July 22, 1898, in Beth-
lehem, Pennsylvania, where his father, Colonel J. Walker
Benét, was stationed at the time. When he was eight years
old, he moved to Benecia Arsenal, California, where his
father had been transferred. Here he spent a happy childhood in a congenial family environment. His father, though
a military man, had a definite leaning toward the arts and
was a lover of good poetry. His older sister, Laura, was
herself a poet. And his older brother, William Rose, a
graduate of Yale, was living at home and writing steadily
in an apprenticeship for a literary career.

When he was twelve years old that idyllic home life
was broken by a distressing term in a military academy,
but the following year he was happily enrolled in Summer-
ville Academy, a coeducational school near Augusta,
Georgia, where his father had been transferred.

Now, at the age of thirteen, his precocious talent for
writing verse began to assert itself. Encouraged by his
brother and by his father, whom he later called "the finest
critic of poetry I have ever known," he won a number of
prizes from St. Nicholas and in May 1915, at the age of
sixteen, sold a poem, "Winged Man," to the New Republic.
That summer, when he had just turned seventeen, he
published a group of six dramatic monologues, Five Men
and Pompey, and had the pleasure of seeing it for sale

at the Yale Co-op when he entered Yale University in September as a freshman.

His college years saw him quickly established as a celebrity. In December of his freshman year Century Magazine published his pirate ballad, "The Hemp," in a lavish four-page spread. He became the leading contributor and editor of the Yale Literary Magazine and Record, the undergraduate periodical devoted to frivolous, and sometimes ribald, verse. He won the Albert S. Cook prize for undergraduate poetry. In October 1918, the Yale University Press issued his second volume of verse, Young Adventure, with a foreword by Chauncey B. Tinker, Sterling Professor of English literature at Yale. By the time he graduated from Yale in 1919 he had published three volumes of poetry and had sold over twenty poems to various magazines.

After a summer writing advertising copy, he returned to Yale for his M.A. degree. The highlight of this year was a course in literary composition under Henry Seidel Canby, long-time editor of the Saturday Review of Literature. Conducted by Canby with a definite vocational slant, this course started Benét on the road to writing prose fiction. He had previously published one story in the college literary magazine. Now he began writing a novel about college life, The Beginning of Wisdom (1921). In July 1920, he sold his first short story to Munsey's.

A $500 fellowship to the Sorbonne enabled him to go to Paris the following year. Here he met Rosemary Carr, and the drive to make money so they could marry started him on a career of writing stories for the big circulation magazines, which he continued to do to the end of his days. "The short story was never exactly my forte," he said at one time. *What he meant was that he was primarily interested in writing poetry, but that he had to write stories to pay the grocery bill. In 1926 a Guggenheim Fellowship gave him the leisure to write* John Brown's Body, *which received the Pulitzer Prize for Poetry in 1929. In 1943, the year of his death,* Western Star, *a long narrative poem dealing with the period of the colonization of America, brought him a second Pulitzer Prize.*

Despite what he said about the short story, he became a master of the form. Between 1922 and 1943 he published more than 120 stories in all the popular magazines. Three of his stories were awarded a first prize by the O. Henry Memorial Award Committee. Six more received O. Henry Awards or were reprinted in The Best American Short Stories *of the year. "The Devil and Daniel Webster," published in 1936, has been called a permanent classic of short story art. "Too Early Spring," published originally in the* Delineator, *June 1933, has been included in a volume of collected stories,* Tales Before Midnight (1939) *and in* Selected Works (1942).

TOO EARLY SPRING

I'm writing this down because I don't ever want to forget the way it was. It doesn't seem as if I could, now, but they all tell you things change. And I guess they're right. Older people must have forgotten or they couldn't be the way they are. And that goes for even the best ones, like Dad and Mr. Grant. They try to understand but they don't seem to know how. And the others make you feel dirty or else they make you feel like a goof. Till, pretty soon, you begin to forget yourself— you begin to think, "Well, maybe they're right and it was that way." And that's the end of everything. So I've got to write this down. Because they smashed it forever—but it wasn't the way they said.

Mr. Grant always says in comp. class: "Begin at the beginning." Only I don't know quite where the beginning was. We had a good summer at Big Lake but it was just the same summer. I worked pretty hard at the practice basket I rigged up in the barn, and I learned how to do the back jackknife. I'll never dive like Kerry but you want to be as all-around as you can. And when I took my measurements, at the end of the summer, I was 5 ft. 9¾ and I'd gained 12 lbs. 6 oz. That isn't bad for going on sixteen and the old chest expansion was O.K. You don't want to get too heavy, because

From *Selected Works of Stephen Vincent Benet* (Holt, Rinehart and Winston, Inc.) Copyright, 1933, by The Butterick Company. Reprinted by permission of Brandt and Brandt.

basketball's a fast game, but the year before was the year when I got my height, and I was so skinny, I got tired. But this year, Kerry helped me practice, a couple of times, and he seemed to think I had a good chance for the team. So I felt pretty set up—they'd never had a Sophomore on it before. And Kerry's a natural athlete, so that means a lot from him. He's a pretty good brother too. Most Juniors at State wouldn't bother with a fellow in High.

It sounds as if I were trying to run away from what I have to write down, but I'm not. I want to remember that summer, too, because it's the last happy one I'll ever have. Oh, when I'm an old man—thirty or forty—things may be all right again. But that's a long time to wait and it won't be the same.

And yet, that summer was different, too, in a way. So it must have started then, though I didn't know it. I went around with the gang as usual and we had a good time. But, every now and then, it would strike me we were acting like awful kids. They thought I was getting the big head, but I wasn't. It just wasn't much fun—even going to the cave. It was like going on shooting marbles when you're in High.

I had sense enough not to try to tag after Kerry and his crowd. You can't do that. But when they all got out on the lake in canoes, warm evenings, and somebody brought a phonograph along, I used to go down to the Point, all by myself, and listen and listen. Maybe they'd be talking or maybe they'd be singing, but it all sounded mysterious across the water. I wasn't trying to hear what they said, you know. That's the kind of thing Tot Pickens does. I'd just listen, with my arms around my knees—and somehow it would hurt me to listen—and yet I'd rather do that than be with the gang.

I was sitting under the four pines, one night, right down by the edge of the water. There was a big moon and they were singing. It's funny how you can be unhappy and nobody know it but yourself.

I was thinking about Sheila Coe. She's Kerry's girl. They fight but they get along. She's awfully pretty and she can swim like a fool. Once Kerry sent me over with her tennis racket and we had quite a conversation. She was fine. And she didn't pull any of this big sister stuff, either, the way some girls will with a fellow's kid brother.

And when the canoe came along, by the edge of the lake, I thought for a moment it was her. I thought maybe she was looking for Kerry and maybe she'd stop and maybe she'd feel like talking to me again. I don't know why I thought that—I didn't have any reason. Then I saw it was just the Sharon kid, with a new kind of bob that made her look grown-up, and I felt sore. She didn't have any business out on the lake at her age. She was just a Sophomore in High, the same as me.

I chunked a stone in the water and it splashed right by the canoe, but she didn't squeal. She just said, "Fish," and chuckled. It struck me it was a kid's trick, trying to scare a kid.

"Hello, Helen," I said. "Where did you swipe the gunboat?"

"They don't know I've got it," she said. "Oh, hello, Chuck Peters. How's Big Lake?"

"All right," I said. "How was camp?"

"It was peachy," she said. "We had a peachy counselor, Miss Morgan. She was on the Wellesley field-hockey team."

"Well," I said, "we missed your society." Of course we hadn't, because they're across the lake and don't swim at our raft. But you ought to be polite.

"Thanks," she said. "Did you do the special reading for English? I thought it was dumb."

"It's always dumb," I said. "What canoe is that?"

"It's the old one," she said. "I'm not supposed to have it out at night. But you won't tell anybody, will you?"

"Be your age," I said. I felt generous. "I'll paddle a while, if you want," I said.

"All right," she said, so she brought it in and I got aboard. She went back in the bow and I took the paddle. I'm not strong on carting kids around, as a rule. But it was better than sitting there by myself.

"Where do you want to go?" I said.

"Oh, back towards the house," she said in a shy kind of voice. "I ought to, really. I just wanted to hear the singing."

"K.O.," I said. I didn't paddle fast, just let her slip. There was a lot of moon on the water. We kept around the edge so they wouldn't notice us. The singing sounded as if it came from a different country, a long way off.

She was a sensible kid, she didn't ask fool questions or giggle about nothing at all. Even when we went by Petters' Cove. That's where the lads from the bungalow colony go and it's pretty well populated on a warm night. You can hear them talking in low voices and now and then a laugh. Once Tot Pickens and a gang went over there with a flashlight, and a big Bohunk chased them for half a mile.

I felt funny, going by there with her. But I said, "Well, it's certainly Old Home Week"—in an offhand tone, because, after all, you've got to be sophisticated. And she said, "People are funny," in just the right sort of way. I took quite a shine to her after that and we talked. The Sharons have only been in town three years and somehow I'd never really noticed her before. Mrs. Sharon's awfully good-looking but she and Mr. Sharon fight. That's hard on a kid. And she was a quiet kid. She had a small kind of face and her eyes were sort of like a kitten's. You could see she got a great kick out of pretending to be grown-up—and yet it wasn't all pretending. A couple of times, I felt just as if I were talking to Sheila Coe. Only more comfortable, because, after all, we were the same age.

Do you know, after we put the canoe up, I walked all the way back home, around the lake? And most of the way, I ran. I felt swell too. I felt as if I could run forever and not stop. It was like finding something. I hadn't imagined anybody could

154

ever feel the way I did about some things. And here was another person, even if it was a girl.

Kerry's door was open when I went by and he stuck his head out, and grinned.

"Well, kid," he said. "Stepping out?"

"Sure. With Greta Garbo," I said, and grinned back to show I didn't mean it. I felt sort of lightheaded, with the run and everything.

"Look here, kid—" he said, as if he was going to say something. Then he stopped. But there was a funny look on his face.

And yet I didn't see her again till we were both back in High. Mr. Sharon's uncle died, back East, and they closed the cottage suddenly. But all the rest of the time at Big Lake, I kept remembering that night and her little face. If I'd seen her in daylight, first, it might have been different. No, it wouldn't have been.

All the same, I wasn't even thinking of her when we bumped into each other, the first day of school. It was raining and she had on a green slicker and her hair was curly under her hat. We grinned and said hello and had to run. But something happened to us, I guess.

I'll say this now—it wasn't like Tot Pickens and Mabel Palmer. It wasn't like Junior David and Betty Page—though they've been going together ever since kindergarten. It wasn't like any of those things. We didn't get sticky and sloppy. It wasn't like going with a girl.

Gosh, there'd be days and days when we'd hardly see each other, except in class. I had basketball practice almost every afternoon and sometimes evenings and she was taking music lessons four times a week. But you don't have to be always twos-ing with a person, if you feel that way about them. You seem to know the way they're thinking and feeling, the way you know yourself.

Now let me describe her. She had that little face and the eyes like a kitten's. When it rained, her hair curled all over the back of her neck. Her hair was yellow. She wasn't a tall girl but she wasn't chunky—just light and well made and quick. She was awfully alive without being nervous—she never bit her fingernails or chewed the end of her pencil, but she'd answer quicker than anyone in the class. Nearly everybody liked her, but she wasn't best friends with any particular girl, the mushy way they get. The teachers all thought a lot of her, even Miss Eagles. Well, I had to spoil that.

If we'd been like Tot and Mabel, we could have had a lot more time together, I guess. But Helen isn't a liar and I'm not a snake. It wasn't easy, going over to her house, because Mr. and Mrs. Sharon would be polite to each other in front of you and yet there'd be something wrong. And she'd have to be fair to both of them and they were always pulling at her. But we'd look at each other across the table and then it would be all right.

I don't know when it was that we knew we'd get married to each other, some time. We just started talking about it, one day, as if we always had. We were sensible, we knew it couldn't happen right off. We thought maybe when we were eighteen. That was two years but we knew we had to be educated. You don't get as good a job, if you aren't. Or that's what people say.

We weren't mushy either, like some people. We got to kissing each other good-by, sometimes, because that's what you do when you're in love. It was cool, the way she kissed you, it was like leaves. But lots of the time we wouldn't even talk about getting married, we'd just play checkers or go over the old Latin, or once in a while go to the movies with the gang. It was really a wonderful winter. I played every game after the first one and she'd sit in the gallery and watch and I'd know she was there. You could see her little green hat or her yellow hair. Those are the class colors, green and gold.

And it's a queer thing, but everybody seemed to be pleased. That's what I can't get over. They liked to see us together. The grown people, I mean. Oh, of course, we got kidded too. And old Mrs. Withers would ask me about "my little sweetheart," in that awful damp voice of hers. But, mostly, they were all right. Even Mother was all right, though she didn't like Mrs. Sharon. I did hear her say to Father, once, "Really, George, how long is this going to last? Sometimes I feel as if I just couldn't stand it."

Then Father chuckled and said to her, "Now, Mary, last year you were worrried about him because he didn't take any interest in girls at all."

"Well," she said, "he still doesn't. Oh, Helen's a nice child— no credit to Eva Sharon—and thank heaven she doesn't giggle. Well, Charles is mature for *his* age too. But he acts so solemn about her. It isn't natural."

"Oh, let Charlie alone," said Father. "The boy's all right. He's just got a one-track mind."

But it wasn't so nice for us after the spring came. In our part of the state, it comes pretty late, as a rule. But it was early this year. The little kids were out with scooters when usually they'd still be having snowfights and, all of a sudden, the radiators in the classrooms smelt dry. You'd got used to that smell for months—and then, there was a day when you hated it again and everybody kept asking to open the windows. The monitors had a tough time, that first week—they always do when spring starts—but this year it was worse than ever because it came when you didn't expect it.

Usually, basketball's over by the time spring really breaks, but this year it hit us while we still had three games to play. And it certainly played hell with us as a team. After Bladesburg nearly licked us, Mr. Grant called off all practice till the day before the St. Matthew's game. He knew we were stale—and they've been state champions two years. They'd have walked all over us, the way we were going.

The first thing I did was telephone Helen. Because that meant that there were six extra afternoons we could have, if she could get rid of her music lessons any way. Well, she said, wasn't it wonderful, her music teacher had a cold? And that seemed just like Fate.

Well, that was a great week and we were so happy. We went to the movies five times and once Mrs. Sharon let us take her little car. She knew I didn't have a driving license but of course I've driven ever since I was thirteen and she said it was all right. She was funny—sometimes she'd be awfully kind and friendly to you and sometimes she'd be like a piece of dry ice. She was that way with Mr. Sharon too. But it was a wonderful ride. We got stuff out of the kitchen—the cook's awfully sold on Helen—and drove way out in the country. And we found an old house, with the windows gone, on top of a hill, and parked the car and took the stuff up to the house and ate it there. There weren't any chairs or tables but we pretended there were.

We pretended it was our house, after we were married. I'll never forget that. She'd even brought paper napkins and paper plates and she set two places on the floor.

"Well, Charles," she said, sitting opposite me, with her feet tucked under, "I don't suppose you remember the days we were both in school."

"Sure," I said—she was always much quicker pretending things than I was—"I remember them all right. That was before Tot Pickens got to be President." And we both laughed.

"It seems very distant in the past to me—we've been married so long," she said, as if she really believed it. She looked at me.

"Would you mind turning off the radio, dear?" she said. "This modern music always gets on my nerves."

"Have we got a radio?" I said.

158

"Of course, Chuck."

"With television?"

"Of course, Chuck."

"Gee, I'm glad," I said. I went and turned it off.

"Of course, if you *want* to listen to the late market reports—" she said just like Mrs. Sharon.

"Nope," I said. "The market—uh—closed firm today. Up twenty-six points."

"That's quite a long way up, isn't it?"

"Well, the country's perfectly sound at heart, in spite of this damfool Congress," I said, like Father.

She lowered her eyes a minute, just like her mother, and pushed away her plate.

"I'm not very hungry tonight," she said. "You won't mind if I go upstairs?"

"Aw, don't be like that," I said. It was too much like her mother.

"I was just seeing if I could," she said. "But I never will, Chuck."

"I'll never tell you you're nervous, either," I said. "I—oh, gosh!"

She grinned and it was all right. "Mr. Ashland and I have never had a serious dispute in our wedded lives," she said—and everybody knows who runs *that* family. "We just talk things over calmly and reach a satisfactory conclusion, usually mine."

"Say, what kind of house have we got?"

"It's a lovely house," she said. "We've got radios in every room and lots of servants. We've got a regular movie projector and a library full of good classics and there's always something in the icebox. I've got a shoe closet."

"A what?"

"A shoe closet. All my shoes are on tipped shelves, like Mother's. And all my dresses are on those padded hangers.

159

And I say to the maid, 'Elise, Madam will wear the new French model today.'"

"What are my clothes on?" I said. "Christmas trees?"

"Well," she said. "You've got lots of clothes and dogs. You smell of pipes and the open and something called Harrisburg tweed."

"I do not," I said. "I wish I had a dog. It's a long time since Jack."

"Oh, Chuck, I'm sorry," she said.

"Oh, that's all right," I said. "He was getting old and his ear was always bothering him. But he was a good pooch. Go ahead."

"Well," she said, "of course we give parties—"

"Cut the parties," I said.

"Chuck! They're grand ones!"

"I'm a homebody," I said. "Give me—er—my wife and my little family and—say, how many kids have we got, anyway?"

She counted on her fingers. "Seven."

"Good Lord," I said.

"Well, I always wanted seven. You can make it three, if you like."

"Oh, seven's all right, I suppose," I said. "But don't they get awfully in the way?"

"No," she said. "We have governesses and tutors and send them to boarding school."

"O.K.," I said. "But it's a strain on the old man's pocketbook, just the same."

"Chuck, will you ever talk like that? Chuck, this is when we're rich." Then suddenly, she looked sad. "Oh, Chuck, do you suppose we ever will?" she said.

"Why, sure," I said.

"I wouldn't mind if it was only a dump," she said. "I could cook for you. I keep asking Hilda how she makes things."

I felt awfully funny. I felt as if I were going to cry.

"We'll do it," I said. "Don't you worry."

160

"Oh, Chuck, you're a comfort," she said.

I held her for a while. It was like holding something awfully precious. It wasn't mushy or that way. I know what that's like too.

"It takes so long to get old," she said. "I wish I could grow up tomorrow. I wish we both could."

"Don't you worry," I said. "It's going to be all right."

We didn't say much, going back in the car, but we were happy enough. I thought we passed Miss Eagles at the turn. That worried me a little because of the driving license. But, after all, Mrs. Sharon had said we could take the car.

We wanted to go back again, after that, but it was too far to walk and that was the only time we had the car. Mrs. Sharon was awfully nice about it but she said, thinking it over, maybe we'd better wait till I got a license. Well, Father didn't want me to get one till I was seventeen but I thought he might come around. I didn't want to do anything that would get Helen in a jam with her family. That shows how careful I was of her. Or thought I was.

All the same, we decided we'd do something to celebrate if the team won the St. Matthew's game. We thought it would be fun if we could get a steak and cook supper out somewhere— something like that. Of course we could have done it easily enough with a gang, but we didn't want a gang. We wanted to be alone together, the way we'd been at the house. That was all we wanted. I don't see what's wrong about that. We even took home the paper plates, so as not to litter things up.

Boy, that was a game! We beat them 36–34 and it took an extra period and I thought it would never end. That two-goal lead they had looked as big as the Rocky Mountains all the first half. And they gave me the full school cheer with nine Peters when we tied them up. You don't forget things like that.

Afterwards, Mr. Grant had a kind of spread for the team at his house and a lot of people came in. Kerry had driven down from State to see the game and that made me feel pretty swell. And what made me feel better yet was his taking me aside and saying, "Listen, kid, I don't want you to get the swelled head, but you did a good job. Well, just remember this. Don't let anybody kid you out of going to State. You'll like it up there." And Mr. Grant heard him and laughed and said, "Well, Peters, I'm not proselytizing. But your brother might think about some of the Eastern colleges." It was all like the kind of dream you have when you can do anything. It was wonderful.

Only Helen wasn't there because the only girls were older girls. I'd seen her for a minute, right after the game, and she was fine, but it was only a minute. I wanted to tell her about that big St. Matthew's forward and—oh, everything. Well, you like to talk things over with your girl.

Father and Mother were swell but they had to go on to some big shindy at the country club. And Kerry was going there with Sheila Coe. But Mr. Grant said he'd run me back to the house in his car and he did. He's a great guy. He made jokes about my being the infant phenomenon of basketball, and they were good jokes too. I didn't mind them. But, all the same, when I'd said good night to him and gone into the house, I felt sort of let down.

I knew I'd be tired the next day but I didn't feel sleepy yet. I was too excited. I wanted to talk to somebody. I wandered around downstairs and wondered if Ida was still up. Well, she wasn't, but she'd left half a chocolate cake, covered over, on the kitchen table, and a note on top of it, "Congratulations to Mister Charles Peters." Well, that was awfully nice of her and I ate some. Then I turned the radio on and got the time signal—eleven—and some snappy music. But still I didn't feel like hitting the hay.

So I thought I'd call up Helen and then I thought—probably she's asleep and Hilda or Mrs. Sharon will answer the phone and be sore. And then I thought—well, anyhow, I could go over and walk around the block and look at her house. I'd get some fresh air out of it, anyway, and it would be a little like seeing her.

So I did—and it was a swell night—cool and a lot of stars— and I felt like a king, walking over. All the lower part of the Sharon house was dark but a window upstairs was lit. I knew it was her window. I went around back of the driveway and whistled once—the whistle we made up. I never expected her to hear.

But she did, and there she was at the window, smiling. She made motions that she'd come down to the side door.

Honestly, it took my breath away when I saw her. She had on a kind of yellow thing over her night clothes and she looked so pretty. Her feet were so pretty in those slippers. You almost expected her to be carrying one of those animals kids like—she looked young enough. I know I oughtn't to have gone into the house. But we didn't think anything about it— we were just glad to see each other. We hadn't had any sort of chance to talk over the game.

We sat in front of the fire in the living room and she went out to the kitchen and got us cookies and milk. I wasn't really hungry, but it was like that time at the house, eating with her. Mr. and Mrs. Sharon were at the country club, too, so we weren't disturbing them or anything. We turned off the lights because there was plenty of light from the fire and Mr. Sharon's one of those people who can't stand having extra lights burning. Dad's that way about saving string.

It was quiet and lovely and the firelight made shadows on the ceiling. We talked a lot and then we just sat, each of us knowing the other was there. And the room got quieter and quieter and I'd told her about the game and I didn't feel excited or jumpy any more—just rested and happy. And then I knew by her breathing that she was asleep and I put my arm around her for just a minute. Because it was wonderful to hear that quiet breathing and know it was hers. I was going to wake her in a minute. I didn't realize how tired I was myself.

And then we were back in that house in the country and it was our home and we ought to have been happy. But something was wrong because there still wasn't any glass in the windows and a wind kept blowing through them and we tried to shut the doors but they wouldn't shut. It drove Helen distracted and we were both running through the house, trying to shut the doors, and we were cold and afraid. Then the sun rose outside the windows, burning and yellow and so big it covered the sky. And with the sun was a horrible, weeping voice. It was Mrs. Sharon's saying, "Oh, my God, oh, my God."

I didn't know what had happened, for a minute, when I woke. And then I did and it was awful. Mrs. Sharon was saying "Oh, Helen—I trusted you . . ." and looking as if she were going to faint. And Mr. Sharon looked at her for a minute and his face was horrible and he said, "Bred in the bone," and she looked as if he'd hit her. Then he said to Helen—

I don't want to think of what they said. I don't want to think of any of the things they said. Mr. Sharon is a bad man. And she is a bad woman, even if she is Helen's mother. All the same, I could stand the things he said better than hers.

I don't want to think of any of it. And it is all spoiled now. Everything is spoiled. Miss Eagles saw us going to that house in the country and she said horrible things. They made Helen sick and she hasn't been back at school. There isn't any way I can see her. And if I could, it would be spoiled. We'd be thinking about the things they said.

I don't know how many of the people know, at school. But Tot Pickens passed me a note. And, that afternoon, I caught him behind his house. I'd have broken his nose if they hadn't pulled me off. I meant to. Mother cried when she heard about it and Dad took me into his room and talked to me. He said you can't lick the whole town. But I will anybody like Tot

Pickens. Dad and Mother have been all right. But they say things about Helen and that's almost worse. They're for me because I'm their son. But they don't understand.

I thought I could talk to Kerry but I can't. He was nice but he looked at me such a funny way. I don't know—sort of impressed. It wasn't the way I wanted him to look. But he's been decent. He comes down almost every weekend and we play catch in the yard.

You see, I just go to school and back now. They want me to go with the gang, the way I did, but I can't do that. Not after Tot. Of course my marks are a lot better because I've got more time to study now. But it's lucky I haven't got Miss Eagles though Dad made her apologize. I couldn't recite to her.

I think Mr. Grant knows because he asked me to his house once and we had a conversation. Not about that, though I was terribly afraid he would. He showed me a lot of his old college things and the gold football he wears on his watch chain. He's got a lot of interesting things.

Then we got talking, somehow, about history and things like that and how times had changed. Why, there were kings and queens who got married younger than Helen and me. Only now we lived longer and had a lot more to learn. So it couldn't happen now. "It's civilization," he said. "And all civilization's against nature. But I suppose we've got to have it. Only sometimes it isn't easy." Well somehow or other, that made me feel less lonely. Before that I'd been feeling that I was the only person on earth who'd ever felt that way.

I'm going to Colorado, this summer, to a ranch, and next year, I'll go East to school. Mr. Grant says he thinks I can make the basketball team, if I work hard enough, though it isn't as big a game in the East as it is with us. Well, I'd like to show them something. It would be some satisfaction. He says not to be too fresh at first, but I won't be that.

It's a boy's school and there aren't even women teachers. And, maybe, afterwards, I could be a professional basketball player or something, where you don't have to see women at all. Kerry says I'll get over that; but I won't. They all sound like Mrs. Sharon to me now, when they laugh.

They're going to send Helen to a convent—I found out that. Maybe they'll let me see her before she goes. But, if we do, it will be all wrong and in front of people and everybody pretending. I sort of wish they don't—though I want to, terribly. When her mother took her upstairs that night—she wasn't the same Helen. She looked at me as if she was afraid of me. And no matter what they do for us now, they can't fix that.

CONRAD PORTER AIKEN

Conrad Porter Aiken was born on August 5, 1889, in Savannah, Georgia, where, as he said, he was "allowed to run wild—no school till nine." Years later he wrote: "That is something for which I have never ceased to be grateful. I can still remember that feeling, every morning, of having before one an infinity of freedom. Very nearly ideal for the boy who very early decided that he wanted to write." His life in Georgia, however, came to an abrupt end in 1900, when he was eleven years old, with the tragic death of both parents (his father killed his mother and then committed suicide). He was sent to Brewster, Massachusetts, to be brought up by a great aunt.

After prep school days at Middlesex School, Concord, Massachusetts, he entered Harvard University in the fall of 1907, a member of the illustrious class that included, among others who were later to make a name for themselves in the world of letters, Robert Benchley, Heywood Broun, Van Wyck Brooks, T. S. Eliot, Walter Lippmann, and Alan Seeger. At Harvard he wrote for the Harvard Monthly and Advocate. He was elected class poet. It was also at Harvard that he became extremely interested in psychoanalysis, and this obsession with the aberrations of the human mind subsequently influenced much of what he wrote. In the spring of his senior year he cut classes for a week to translate a short story by Gautier, "La Morte Amoureuse," *into English verse. The administration not sharing his belief that his action was justified, he was placed on probation. In protest, he dropped out of school, but returned the following year to finish his A.B. degree.*

Since he had an independent income, Mr. Aiken was able to devote himself to the profession of writing after he graduated without worrying about finances. Poetry was always his first love. He had written his first poem at the age of nine. Edgar Allen Poe, he said, was an early influence upon him. Poe's rhythms fascinated him and led him to commit many of Poe's poems to memory before he was thirteen.

His first book of poems, Earth Triumphant and Other Tales in Verse, *was published in 1914, when he was twenty-five, followed in quick succession by four other volumes of poetry.* Selected Poems *won the Pulitzer Prize for 1929, as well as the Shelley Memorial Award.* Collected Poems *won the National Book Award in 1953. In 1958 he was awarded the Gold Medal for Poetry by the National Institute of Arts and Letters. From 1950 to 1952 he held the Chair of Poetry in the Library of Congress. In 1957 he was elected a fellow in the American Academy of Poets.*

Although regarded primarily as a poet and a critic of poetry, Mr. Aiken has written a number of novels and a small body of first-rate short stories. His first novel, Blue Voyage, *was published in 1927.* Great Circle, *published in 1933, elicited such interest from Sigmund Freud that the founder of psychoanalysis is reputed to have offered Mr. Aiken a three months' analysis, free, as an experiment.*

His short stories show the same concern for probing into the human mind. "The Dark City," published originally in Dial, *was reprinted in* The Best American Short Stories of 1922. *Two of his stories, "Impulse" (1933) and "Hello, Tib" (1941), received O. Henry Memorial Awards. His collected stories,* The Short Stories of Conrad Aiken, *were published in 1950. Other volumes of short stories include* Bring! Bring! and Other Stories *(1925),* Costumes by Eros *(1934), and* Among the Lost People *(1934). In 1952 he published an autobiography,* Ushant.

SILENT SNOW, SECRET SNOW

Just why it should have happened, or why it should have happened just when it did, he could not, of course, possibly have said; nor perhaps could it even have occurred to him to ask. The thing was above all a secret, something to be preciously concealed from Mother and Father; and to that very fact it owed an enormous part of its deliciousness. It was like a peculiarly beautiful trinket to be carried unmentioned in one's trouser-pocket—a rare stamp, an old coin, a few tiny gold links found trodden out of shape on the path in the park, a pebble of carnelian, a sea shell distinguishable from all others by an unusual spot or stripe—and, as if it were anyone of these, he carried around with him everywhere a warm and persistent and increasingly beautiful sense of possession. Nor was it only a sense of possession—it was also a sense of protection. It was as if, in some delightful way, his secret gave him a fortress, a wall behind which he could retreat into heavenly seclusion. This was almost the first thing he had noticed about it—apart from the oddness of the thing itself— and it was this that now again, for the fiftieth time, occurred to him, as he sat in the little schoolroom. It was the half hour for geography. Miss Buell was revolving with one finger, slowly, a huge terrestrial globe which had been placed on her desk. The green and yellow continents passed and repassed, questions were asked and answered, and now the little girl in front of him, Deirdre, who had a funny little constellation of freckles on the back of her neck, exactly like the Big Dipper, was standing up and telling Miss Buell that the equator was the line that ran round the middle.

Miss Buell's face, which was old and grayish and kindly, with gray stiff curls beside the cheeks, and eyes that swam very brightly, like little minnows, behind thick glasses, wrinkled itself into a complication of amusements.

"Ah! I see. The earth is wearing a belt, or a sash. Or someone drew a line round it!"

"Oh, no—not that—I mean—"

In the general laughter, he did not share, or only a very little. He was thinking about the Arctic and Antarctic regions, which of course, on the globe, were white. Miss Buell was now telling them about the tropics, the jungles, the steamy heat of equatorial swamps, where the birds and butterflies, and even the snakes, were like living jewels. As he listened to these things, he was already, with a pleasant sense of half-effort, putting his secret between himself and the words. Was it really an effort at all? For effort implied something voluntary, and perhaps even something one did not especially want; whereas this was distinctly pleasant, and came almost of its own accord. All he needed to do was to think of that morning, the first one, and then of all the others—

But it was all so absurdly simple! It had amounted to so little. It was nothing, just an idea—and just why it should have become so wonderful, so permanent, was a mystery—a very pleasant one, to be sure, but also, in an amusing way, foolish. However, without ceasing to listen to Miss Buell, who had now moved up to the north temperate zones, he deliberately invited his memory of the first morning. It was only a moment or two after he had waked up—or perhaps the moment itself. But was there, to be exact, an exact moment? Was one awake all at once? or was it gradual? Anyway, it was after he had

171

stretched a lazy hand up towards the headrail, and yawned, and then relaxed again among his warm covers, all the more grateful on a December morning, that the thing had happened. Suddenly, for no reason, he had thought of the postman, he remembered the postman. Perhaps there was nothing so odd in that. After all, he heard the postman almost every morning in his life—his heavy boots could be heard clumping round the corner at the top of the little cobbled hill-street, and then, progressively nearer, progressively louder, the double knock at each door, the crossings and re-crossings of the street, till finally the clumsy steps came stumbling across to the very door, and the tremendous knock came which shook the house itself.

(Miss Buell was saying "Vast wheat-growing areas in North America and Siberia."

Deirdre had for the moment placed her left hand across the back of her neck.)

But on this particular morning, the first morning, as he lay there with his eyes closed, he had for some reason *waited* for the postman. He wanted to hear him come round the corner. And that was precisely the joke—he never did. He never came. He never had come—*round the corner*—again. For when at last the steps *were* heard, they had already, he was quite sure, come a little down the hill, to the first house; and even so, the steps were curiously different—they were softer, they had a new secrecy about them, they were muffled and indistinct; and while the rhythm of them was the same, it now said a new thing—it said peace, it said remoteness, it said cold, it said sleep. And he had understood the situation at once—nothing could have seemed simpler—there had been snow in the night, such as all winter he had been longing for; and it was this which had rendered the postman's first footsteps inaudible, and the later ones faint. Of course! How lovely! And even now it must be snowing—it was going to be a snowy day—the long white ragged lines were drifting and sifting across

172

the street, across the faces of the old houses, whispering and hushing, making little triangles of white in the corners between cobblestones, seething a little when the wind blew them over the ground to a drifted corner; and so it would be all day, getting deeper and deeper and silenter and silenter.

(Miss Buell was saying "Land of perpetual snow.")

All this time, of course (while he lay in bed), he had kept his eyes closed, listening to the nearer progress of the postman, the muffled footsteps thumping and slipping on the snow-sheathed cobbles; and all the other sounds—the double knocks, a frosty far-off voice or two, a bell ringing thinly and softly as if under a sheet of ice—had the same slightly abstracted quality, as if removed by one degree from actuality—as if everything in the world had been insulated by snow. But when at last, pleased, he opened his eyes, and turned them towards the window, to see for himself this long-desired and now so clearly imagined miracle—what he saw instead was brilliant sunlight on a roof; and when, astonished, he jumped out of bed and stared down into the street, expecting to see the cobbles obliterated by the snow, he saw nothing but the bare bright cobbles themselves.

Queer, the effect this extraordinary surprise had had upon him—all the following morning he had kept with him a sense as of snow falling about him, a secret screen of new snow between himself and the world. If he had not dreamed such a thing—and how could he have dreamed it while awake?—how else could one explain it? In any case, the delusion had been so vivid as to affect his entire behavior. He could not now remember whether it was on the first or the second morning—or was it even the third?—that his mother had drawn attention to some oddness in his manner.

"But my darling—" she had said at the breakfast table—"what has come over you? You don't seem to be listening. . . ."

And how often that very thing had happened since!

(Miss Buell was now asking if anyone knew the difference

between the North Pole and the Magnetic Pole. Deirdre was holding up her flickering brown hand, and he could see the four white dimples that marked the knuckles.)

Perhaps it hadn't been either the second or third morning —or even the fourth or fifth. How could he be sure? How could he be sure just when the delicious *progress* had become clear? Just when it had really *begun?* The intervals weren't very precise. . . . All he now knew was, that at some point or other—perhaps the second day, perhaps the sixth—he had noticed that the presence of the snow was a little more insistent, the sound of it clearer; and, conversely, the sound of the postman's footsteps more indistinct. Not only could he not hear the steps come round the corner, he could not even hear them at the first house. It was below the first house that he heard them; and then, a few days later, it was below the second house that he heard them; and a few days later again, below the third. Gradually, gradually, the snow was becoming heavier, the sound of its seething louder, the cobblestones more and more muffled. When he found, each morning, on going to the window, after the ritual of listening, that the roofs and cobbles were as bare as ever, it made no difference. This was, after all, only what he had expected. It was even what pleased him, what rewarded him: the thing was his own, belonged to no one else. No one else knew about it, not even his mother and father. There, outside, were the bare cobbles; and here, inside, was the snow. Snow growing heavier each day, muffling the world, hiding the ugly, and deadening increasingly—above all—the steps of the postman.

"But my darling—" she had said at the luncheon table— "what has come over you? You don't seem to listen when people speak to you. That's the third time I've asked you to pass your plate. . . ."

How was one to explain this to Mother? or to Father? There was, of course, nothing to be done about it: nothing. All one could do was to laugh embarrassedly, pretend to be a

174

little ashamed, apologize, and take a sudden and somewhat disingenuous interest in what was being done or said. The cat had stayed out all night. He had a curious swelling on his left cheek—perhaps somebody had kicked him, or a stone had struck him. Mrs. Kempton was or was not coming to tea. The house was going to be house cleaned, or "turned out," on Wednesday instead of Friday. A new lamp was provided for his evening work—perhaps it was eye-strain which accounted for this new and so peculiar vagueness of his—Mother was looking at him with amusement as she said this, but with something else as well. A new lamp? A new lamp. Yes Mother, No Mother, Yes Mother. School is going very well. The geometry is very easy. The history is very dull. The geography is very interesting—particularly when it takes one to the North Pole. Why the North Pole? Oh, well, it would be fun to be an explorer. Another Peary or Scott or Shackleton. And then abruptly he found his interest in the talk at an end, stared at the pudding on his plate, listened, waited, and began once more—ah, how heavenly, too, the first beginnings—to hear or feel—for could he actually hear it?—the silent snow, the secret snow.

(Miss Buell was telling them about the search for the Northwest Passage, about Hendrick Hudson, the *Half Moon*.)

This had been, indeed, the only distressing feature of the new experience: the fact that it so increasingly had brought him into a kind of mute misunderstanding, or even conflict, with his father and mother. It was as if he were trying to lead a double life. On the one hand he had to be Paul Hasleman, and keep up the appearance of being that person—dress, wash, and answer intelligently when spoken to—; on the other, he had to explore this new world which had been opened to him. Nor could there be the slightest doubt—not the slightest—that the new world was the profounder and more wonderful of the two. It was irresistible. It was miraculous. Its beauty was simply beyond anything—beyond speech as beyond thought—

utterly incommunicable. But how then, between the two worlds, of which he was thus constantly aware, was he to keep a balance? One must get up, one must go to breakfast, one must talk with Mother, go to school, do one's lessons—and, in all this, try not to appear too much of a fool. But if all the while one was also trying to extract the full deliciousness of another and quite separate existence, one which could not easily (if at all) be spoken of—how was one to manage? How was one to explain? Would it be safe to explain? Would it be absurd? Would it merely mean that he would get into some obscure kind of trouble?

These thoughts came and went, came and went, as softly and secretly as the snow; they were not precisely a disturbance, perhaps they were even a pleasure; he liked to have them; their presence was something almost palpable, something he could stroke with his hand, without closing his eyes, and without ceasing to see Miss Buell and the school-room and the globe and the freckles on Deirdre's neck; nevertheless he did in a sense cease to see, or to see the obvious external world, and substituted for this vision the vision of snow, the sound of snow, and the slow, almost soundless, approach of the postman. Yesterday, it had been only at the sixth house that the postman had become audible; the snow was much deeper now, it was falling more swiftly and heavily, the sound of its seething was more distinct, more soothing, more persistent. And this morning, it had been—as nearly as he could figure—just above the seventh house—perhaps only a step or two above: at most, he had heard two or three footsteps before the knock had sounded. . . . And with each such narrowing of the sphere, each nearer approach of the limit at which the postman was first audible, it was odd how sharply was increased the amount of illusion which had to be carried into the ordinary business of daily life. Each day, it was harder to get out of bed, to go to the window, to look out at the—as always—perfectly empty and snowless street. Each day it was

176

more difficult to go through the perfunctory motions of greeting Mother and Father at breakfast, to reply to their questions, to put his books together and go to school. And at school, how extraordinarily hard to conduct with success simultaneously the public life and the life that was secret. There were times when he longed—positively ached—to tell everyone about it—to burst out with it—only to be checked almost at once by a far-off feeling as of some faint absurdity which was inherent in it—but *was* it absurd?—and more importantly by a sense of mysterious power in his very secrecy. Yes; it must be kept secret. That, more and more, became clear. At whatever cost to himself, whatever pain to others—

(Miss Buell looked straight at him, smiling, and said, "Perhaps we'll ask Paul. I'm sure Paul will come out of his daydream long enough to be able to tell us. Won't you, Paul." He rose slowly from his chair, resting one hand on the brightly varnished desk, and deliberately stared through the snow towards the blackboard. It was an effort, but it was amusing to make it. "Yes," he said slowly, "it was what we now call the Hudson River. This he thought to be the Northwest Passage. He was disappointed." He sat down again, and as he did so Deirdre half turned in her chair and gave him a shy smile, of approval and admiration.)

At whatever pain to others.

This part of it was very puzzling, very puzzling. Mother was very nice, and so was Father. Yes, that was all true enough. He wanted to be nice to them, to tell them everything—and yet, was it really wrong of him to want to have a secret place of his own?

At bedtime, the night before, Mother had said, "If this goes on, my lad, we'll have to see a doctor, we will! We can't have our boy—" But what was it she had said? "Live in another world"? "Live so far away"? The word "far" had been in it, he was sure, and then Mother had taken up a magazine again

177

and laughed a little, but with an expression which wasn't mirthful. He had felt sorry for her. . . .

The bell rang for dismissal. The sound came to him through long curved parallels of falling snow. He saw Deirdre rise, and had himself risen almost as soon—but not quite as soon—as she.

II

On the walk homeward, which was timeless, it pleased him to see through the accompaniment, or counterpoint, of snow, the items of mere externality on his way. There were many kinds of bricks in the sidewalks, and laid in many kinds of patterns. The garden walls too were various, some of wooden palings, some of plaster, some of stone. Twigs of bushes leaned over the walls; the little hard green winter-buds of lilac, on gray stems, sheathed and fat; other branches very thin and fine and black and desiccated. Dirty sparrows huddled in the bushes, as dull in color as dead fruit left in leafless trees. A single starling creaked on a weather vane. In the gutter, beside a drain, was a scrap of torn and dirty newspaper, caught in a little delta of filth: the word ECZEMA appeared in large capitals, and below it was a letter from Mrs. Amelia D. Cravath, 2100 Pine Street, Fort Worth, Texas, to the effect that after being a sufferer for years she had been cured by Caley's Ointment. In the little delta, beside the fan-shaped and deeply runneled continent of brown mud, were lost twigs, descended from their parent trees, dead matches, a rusty horse-chestnut burr, a small concentration of sparkling gravel on the lip of the sewer, a fragment of eggshell, a streak of yellow sawdust which had been wet and now was dry and congealed, a brown pebble, and a broken feather. Further on was a cement sidewalk, ruled into geometrical parallelograms, with a brass inlay at one end commemorating the contractors who had laid it, and, halfway across, an irregular and random

178

series of dog-tracks, immortalized in synthetic stone. He knew these well, and always stepped on them; to cover the little hollows with his own foot had always been a queer pleasure; today he did it once more, but perfunctorily and detachedly, all the while thinking of something else. That was a dog, a long time ago, who had made a mistake and walked on the cement while it was still wet. He had probably wagged his tail, but that hadn't been recorded. Now, Paul Hasleman, aged twelve, on his way home from school, crossed the same river, which in the meantime had frozen into rock. Homeward through the snow, the snow falling in bright sunshine. Homeward?

Then came the gateway with the two posts surmounted by egg-shaped stones which had been cunningly balanced on their ends, as if by Columbus, and mortared in the very act of balance: a source of perpetual wonder. On the brick wall just beyond, the letter H had been stenciled, presumably for some purpose. H? H.

The green hydrant, with a little green-painted chain attached to the brass screw-cap.

The elm tree, with the great gray wound in the bark, kidney-shaped, into which he always put his hand—to feel the cold but living wood. The injury, he had been sure, was due to the gnawings of a tethered horse. But now it deserved only a passing palm, a merely tolerant eye. There were more important things. Miracles. Beyond the thoughts of trees, mere elms. Beyond the thoughts of sidewalks, mere stone, mere brick, mere cement. Beyond the thoughts even of his own shoes, which trod these sidewalks obediently, bearing a burden—far above—of elaborate mystery. He watched them. They were not very well polished; he had neglected them, for a very good reason: they were one of the many parts of the increasing difficulty of the daily return to daily life, the morning struggle. To get up, having at last opened one's eyes, to go to the window, and discover no snow, to wash, to dress, to descend the curving stairs to breakfast—

At whatever pain to others, nevertheless, one must persevere in severance, since the incommunicability of the experience demanded it. It was desirable of course to be kind to Mother and Father, especially as they seemed to be worried, but it was also desirable to be resolute. If they should decide—as appeared likely—to consult the doctor, Doctor Howells, and have Paul inspected, his heart listened to through a kind of dictaphone, his lungs, his stomach—well, that was all right. He would go through with it. He would give them answer for question, too—perhaps such answers as they hadn't expected? No. That would never do. For the secret world must, at all costs, be preserved.

The bird-house in the apple-tree was empty—it was the wrong time of year for wrens. The little round black door had lost its pleasure. The wrens were enjoying other houses, other nests, remoter trees. But this too was a notion which he only vaguely and grazingly entertained—as if, for the moment, he merely touched an edge of it; there was something further on, which was already assuming a sharper importance; something which already teased at the corners of his eyes, teasing also at the corner of his mind. It was funny to think that he so wanted this, so awaited it—and yet found himself enjoying this momentary dalliance with the bird-house, as if for a quite deliberate postponement and enhancement of the approaching pleasure. He was aware of his delay, of his smiling and detached and now almost uncomprehending gaze at the little bird-house: he knew what he was going to look at next: it was his own little cobbled hill-street, his own house, the little river at the bottom of the hill, the grocer's shop with the cardboard man in the window—and now, thinking of all this, he turned his head, still smiling, and looking quickly right and left through the snow-laden sunlight.

And the mist of snow, as he had foreseen, was still on it—a ghost of snow falling in the bright sunlight, softly and steadily floating and turning and pausing, soundlessly meeting the snow

180

that covered, as with a transparent mirage, the bare bright cobbles. He loved it—he stood still and loved it. Its beauty was paralyzing—beyond all words, all experience, all dream. No fairy-story he had ever read could be compared with it— none had ever given him this extraordinary combination of ethereal loveliness with a something else, unnameable, which was just faintly and deliciously terrifying. What was this thing? As he thought of it, he looked upward toward his own bed-room window, which was open—and it was as if he looked straight into the room and saw himself lying half awake in his bed. There he was—at this very instant he was still perhaps actually there—more truly there than standing here at the edge of the cobbled hill-street, with one hand lifted to shade his eyes against the snow-sun. Had he indeed ever left his room, in all this time? since that very first morning? Was the whole progress still being enacted there, was it still the same morning, and him-self not yet wholly awake? And even now, had the postman not yet come round the corner? . . .

This idea amused him, and automatically, as he thought of it, he turned his head and looked toward the top of the hill. There was, of course, nothing there—nothing and no one. The street was empty and quiet. And all the more because of its emptiness it occurred to him to count the houses—a thing which, oddly enough, he hadn't before thought of doing. Of course, he had known there weren't many—many, that is, on his own side of the street, which were the ones that figured in the postman's progress—but nevertheless it came to him as something of a shock to find that there were precisely *six*, above his own house—his own house was the seventh.

Six!

Astonished, he looked at his own house—looked at the door, on which was the number thirteen—and then realized that the whole thing was exactly and logically and absurdly what he ought to have known. Just the same, the realization gave him abruptly, and even a little frighteningly, a sense of hurry. He

181

was being hurried—he was being rushed. For—he knit his brows—he couldn't be mistaken—it was just above the *seventh* house, his *own* house, that the postman had first been audible this very morning. But in that case—in that case—did it mean that tomorrow he would hear nothing? The knock he had heard must have been the knock of their own door. Did it mean—and this was an idea which gave him a really extraordinary feeling of surprise—that he would never hear the postman again?—that tomorrow morning the postman would already have passed the house, in a snow by then so deep as to render his footsteps completely inaudible? That he would have made his approach down the snow-filled street so soundlessly, so secretly, that he, Paul Hasleman, there lying in bed, would not have waked in time, or, waking, would have heard nothing?

But how could that be? Unless even the knocker should be muffled in the snow—frozen tight, perhaps? . . . But in that case—

A vague feeling of disappointment came over him; a vague sadness, as if he felt himself deprived of something which he had long looked forward to, something much prized. After all this, all this beautiful progress, the slow delicious advance of the postman through the silent and secret snow, the knock creeping closer each day, and the footsteps nearer, the audible compass of the world thus daily narrowed, narrowed, narrowed, as the snow soothingly and beautifully encroached and deepened, after all this, was he to be defrauded of the one thing he had so wanted—to be able to count, as it were, the last two or three solemn footsteps, as they finally approached his own door? Was it all going to happen, at the end, so suddenly? or indeed, had it already happened? with no slow and subtle gradations of menace, in which he could luxuriate?

He gazed upward again, toward his own window which flashed in the sun: and this time almost with a feeling that it would be better if he *were* still in bed, in that room; for in that case this must still be the first morning, and there would be six more mornings to come—or, for that matter, seven or eight or nine—how could he be sure?—or even more.

III

After supper, the inquisition began. He stood before the doctor, under the lamp, and submitted silently to the usual thumpings and tappings.

"Now will you please say 'Ah!'?"

"Ah!"

"Now again please, if you don't mind."

"Ah."

"Say it slowly, and hold it if you can—"

"Ah-h-h-h-h-h—"

"Good."

How silly all this was. As if it had anything to do with his throat! Or his heart or lungs!

Relaxing his mouth, of which the corners, after all this absurd stretching, felt uncomfortable, he avoided the doctor's eyes, and stared towards the fireplace, past his mother's feet (in gray slippers) which projected from the green chair, and his father's feet (in brown slippers) which stood neatly side by side on the hearth rug.

"Hm. There is certainly nothing wrong there . . ."

He felt the doctor's eyes fixed upon him, and, as if merely to be polite, returned the look, but with a feeling of justifiable evasiveness.

"Now, young man, tell me,—do you feel all right?"

"Yes, sir, quite all right."

"No headaches? No dizziness?"

"No, I don't think so."

"Let me see. Let's get a book, if you don't mind—yes, thank you, that will do splendidly—and now, Paul, if you'll just read it, holding it as you would normally hold it—"

He took the book and read:

"And another praise have I to tell for this the city our mother, the gift of a great god, a glory of the land most high; the might of horses, the might of young horses, the might of the sea. . . . For thou, son of Cronus, our lord Poseidon, hast throned herein this pride, since in these roads first thou didst show forth the curb that cures the rage of steeds. And the shapely oar, apt to men's hands, hath a wondrous speed on the brine, following the hundred-footed Nereids. . . . O land that art praised above all lands, now is it for thee to make those bright praises seen in deeds."

He stopped, tentatively, and lowered the heavy book.

"No—as I thought—there is certainly no superficial sign of eye-strain."

Silence thronged the room, and he was aware of the focused scrutiny of the three people who confronted him. . . .

"We could have his eyes examined—but I believe it is something else."

"What could it be?" This was his father's voice.

"It's only this curious absent-minded—" This was his mother's voice.

In the presence of the doctor, they both seemed irritatingly apologetic.

"I believe it is something else. Now Paul—I would like very much to ask you a question or two. You will answer them, won't you—you know I'm an old, old friend of yours, eh? That's right! . . ."

His back was thumped twice by the doctor's fat fist,—then the doctor was grinning at him with false amiability, while with one finger-nail he was scratching the top button of his waistcoat. Beyond the doctor's shoulder was the fire, the fingers of flame making light prestidigitation against the sooty fireback, the soft sound of their random flutter the only sound.

"I would like to know—is there anything that worries you?"

The doctor was again smiling, his eyelids low against the little black pupils, in each of which was a tiny white bead of

184

light. Why answer him? why answer him at all? "At whatever
pain to others"—but it was all a nuisance, this necessity for
resistance, this necessity for attention: it was as if one had
been stood up on a brilliantly lighted stage, under a great
round blaze of spotlight; as if one were merely a trained seal,
or a performing dog, or a fish, dipped out of an aquarium and
held up by the tail. It would serve them right if he were
merely to bark or growl. And meanwhile, to miss these last
few precious hours, these hours of which every minute was
more beautiful than the last, more menacing—! He still looked,
as if from a great distance, at the beads of light in the doctor's
eyes, at the fixed false smile, and then, beyond, once more at
his mother's slippers, his father's slippers, the soft flutter of
the fire. Even here, even amongst these hostile presences,
and in this arranged light, he could see the snow, he could
hear it—it was in the corners of the room, where the shadow
was deepest, under the sofa, behind the half-opened door
which led to the dining room. It was gentler here, softer,
its seethe the quietest of whispers, as if, in deference to a
drawing room, it had quite deliberately put on its "manners";
it kept itself out of sight, obliterated itself, but distinctly with
an air of saying, "Ah, but just wait! Wait till we are alone together! Then I will begin to tell you something new! Something white! something cold! something sleepy! something of
cease, and peace, and the long bright curve of space! Tell
them to go away. Banish them. Refuse to speak. Leave them,
go upstairs to your room, turn out the light and get into bed—
I will go with you, I will be waiting for you, I will tell you a
better story than Little Kay of the Skates, or The Snow Ghost
—I will surround your bed, I will close the windows, pile a
deep drift against the door, so that none will ever again be
able to enter. Speak to them! . . ." It seemed as if the little
hissing voice came from a slow white spiral of falling flakes
in the corner by the front window—but he could not be sure.

185

He felt himself smiling, then, and said to the doctor, but without looking at him, looking beyond him still—

"Oh, no, I think not—"

"But are you sure, my boy?"

His father's voice came softly and coldly then—the familiar voice of silken warning.

"You needn't answer at once, Paul—remember we're trying to help you—think it over and be quite sure, won't you?"

He felt himself smiling again, at the notion of being quite sure. What a joke! As if he weren't so sure that reassurance was no longer necessary, and all this cross-examination a ridiculous farce, a grotesque parody! What could they know about it? These gross intelligences, these humdrum minds so bound to the usual, the ordinary? Impossible to tell them about it! Why, even now, even now, with the proof so abundant, so formidable, so imminent, so appallingly present here in this very room, could they believe it?—could even his mother believe it? No—it was only too plain that if anything were said about it, the merest hint given, they would be incredulous—they would laugh—they would say "Absurd!"—think things about him which weren't true. . . .

"Why no, I'm not worried—why should I be?"

He looked then straight at the doctor's low-lidded eyes, looked from one of them to the other, from one bead of light to the other, and gave a little laugh.

The doctor seemed to be disconcerted by this. He drew back in his chair, resting a fat white hand on either knee. The smile faded slowly from his face.

"Well, Paul!" he said, and paused gravely, "I'm afraid you don't take this quite seriously enough. I think you perhaps don't quite realize—don't quite realize—" He took a deep quick breath, and turned, as if helplessly, at a loss for words, to the others. But Mother and Father were both silent—no help was forthcoming.

"You must surely know, be aware, that you have not been quite yourself of late? don't you know that? . . ."

It was amusing to watch the doctor's renewed attempt at a smile, a queer disorganized look, as of confidential embarrassment.

"I feel all right, sir," he said, and again gave the little laugh.

"And we're trying to help you." The doctor's tone sharpened.

"Yes sir, I know. But why? I'm all right. I'm just *thinking*, that's all."

His mother made a quick movement forward, resting a hand on the back of the doctor's chair.

"Thinking?" she said. "But my dear, about what?"

This was a direct challenge—and would have to be directly met. But before he met it, he looked again into the corner by the door, as if for reassurance. He smiled again at what he saw, at what he heard. The little spiral was still there, still softly whirling, like the ghost of a white kitten chasing the ghost of a white tail and making as it did so the faintest of whispers. It was all right! If only he could remain firm, everything was going to be all right.

"Oh, about anything, about nothing,—*you* know the way you do!"

"You mean—day-dreaming?"

"Oh, no—thinking!"

"But thinking about *what*?"

"Anything."

He laughed a third time—but this time, happening to glance upward towards his mother's face, he was appalled at the effect his laughter seemed to have upon her. Her mouth had opened in an expression of horror. . . . This was too bad! Unfortunate! He had known it would cause pain, of course— but he hadn't expected it to be quite so bad as this. Perhaps— perhaps if he just gave them a tiny gleaming hint—?

187

"About the snow," he said.

"What on earth!" This was his father's voice. The brown slippers came a step nearer on the hearth-rug.

"But my dear, what do you mean!" This was his mother's voice.

The doctor merely stared.

"Just *snow*, that's all. I like to think about it."

"Tell us about it, my boy."

"But that's all it is. There's nothing to tell. *You* know what snow is?"

This he said almost angrily, for he felt that they were trying to corner him. He turned sideways so as no longer to face the doctor, and the better to see the inch of blackness between the window-sill and the lowered curtain,—the cold inch of beckoning and delicious night. At once he felt better, more assured.

"Mother—can I go to bed, now, please? I've got a head-ache."

"But I thought you said—"

"It's just come. It's all these questions—! Can I, mother?"

"You can go as soon as the doctor has finished."

"Don't you think this thing ought to be gone into thoroughly, and *now?*" This was Father's voice. The brown slippers again came a step nearer, the voice was the well-known "punishment" voice, resonant and cruel.

"Oh, what's the use, Norman—"

Quite suddenly, everyone was silent. And without precisely facing them, nevertheless he was aware that all three of them were watching him with an extraordinary intensity—staring hard at him—as if he had done something monstrous, or was himself some kind of monster. He could hear the soft irregular flutter of the flames; the cluck-click-cluck-click of the clock; far and faint, two sudden spurts of laughter from the kitchen, as quickly cut off as begun; a murmur of water in the pipes; and then, the silence seemed to deepen, to spread out, to become world-long and worldwide, to become timeless and shapeless, and to center inevitably and rightly, with a slow and sleepy but enormous concentration of all power, on the beginning of a new sound. What this new sound was going to be, he knew perfectly well. It might begin with a hiss, but it would end with a roar—there was no time to lose—he must escape. It mustn't happen here—

Without another word, he turned and ran up the stairs.

IV

Not a moment too soon. The darkness was coming in long white waves. A prolonged sibilance filled the night—a great seamless seethe of wild influence went abruptly across it—a cold low humming shook the windows. He shut the door and flung off his clothes in the dark. The bare black floor was like a little raft tossed in waves of snow, almost overwhelmed, washed under whitely, up again, smothered in curled billows of feather. The snow was laughing: it spoke from all sides at once; it pressed closer to him as he ran and jumped exulting into his bed.

"Listen to us!" it said. "Listen! We have come to tell you the story we told you about. You remember? Lie down. Shut your eyes, now—you will no longer see much—in this white darkness who could see, or want to see? We will take the place of everything. . . . Listen—"

A beautiful varying dance of snow began at the front of the room, came forward and then retreated, flattened out toward the floor, then rose fountain-like to the ceiling, swayed, recruited itself from a new stream of flakes which poured laughing in through the humming window, advanced again, lifted long white arms. It said peace, it said remoteness, it said cold—it said—

But then a gash of horrible light fell brutally across the room from the opening door—the snow drew back hissing—

something alien had come into the room—something hostile. This thing rushed at him, clutched at him, shook him—and he was not merely horrified, he was filled with such a loathing as he had never known. What was this? this cruel disturbance? this act of anger and hate? It was as if he had to reach up a hand toward another world for any understanding of it, —an effort of which he was only barely capable. But of that other world he still remembered just enough to know the exorcising words. They tore themselves from his other life suddenly—

"Mother! Mother! Go away! I hate you!"

And with that effort, everything was solved, everything became all right: the seamless hiss advanced once more, the long white wavering lines rose and fell like enormous whispering sea-waves, the whisper becoming louder, the laughter more numerous.

"Listen!" it said. "We'll tell you the last, the most beautiful and secret story—shut your eyes—it is a very small story—a story that gets smaller and smaller—it comes inward instead of opening like a flower—it is a flower becoming a seed—a little cold seed—do you hear? we are leaning closer to you—"

The hiss was now becoming a roar—the whole world was a vast moving screen of snow—but even now it said peace, it said remoteness, it said cold, it said sleep.

WILLIAM FAULKNER

*William Faulkner was born in New Albany, Mississippi on
September 25, 1897. When he was five years old the family
moved to Oxford, the county seat and home of the University of Mississippi, where he has lived, with few inter-
ruptions, ever since.*

*Although regarded by many critics as America's fore-
most novelist, Mr. Faulkner in his youth showed little
promise of future greatness. He was slow in finding himself, and slower still in developing his unquestioned talent.
His schooling was haphazard and intermittent. A poor
student, he dropped out of high school to work in his
grandfather's bank, but continued to read avidly and to try
his hand at writing verse. In 1918, after fruitless attempts
to enlist in the United States Army, he was accepted by
the Royal Canadian Flying Corps. The war ended while
he was still an air cadet in training, and he was back in
Oxford shortly after his discharge from the service in
December.*

*The following September, 1919, since he was classed
as a "veteran," he was permitted to enroll in the University
of Mississippi as a special student. In November 1920, he
officially withdrew. His brief experience as a college student
was not marked by any academic success. His grades for
his two semesters of English were "D" and "F" (he did
get "A's" in French). But he was regarded as one of the*

campus poets because of his frequent contributions to The Mississippian, *the school newspaper, and the fact that he had published a poem, "L'Apres-Midi d'un Faune," in the* New Republic (*August 6, 1919*). *He wrote one short story for* The Mississippian, *"Landing in Luck."*

After three months in New York City as a book clerk, he was back in Oxford, first engaged in a variety of odd jobs around the campus, and then, from 1922 to 1924, as postmaster of the university post office. Although no longer a student, he continued to write for The Mississippian, *now mainly book reviews. He also contributed a poem and several pen and ink sketches to the 1921 yearbook,* Ole Miss. *Known as "The Count," because he often sported a monocle, he became something of a campus "character." One of his ventures was the Bluebird Insurance Company, which insured students against failing grades. In 1924* The Marble Faun, *a collection of his poems, was privately printed. That same year his eccentricities cost him his job as postmaster.*

He had been saving money for a trip to Europe and decided that now was the time to go, by way of New Orleans. But in New Orleans he met Sherwood Anderson, who quickly became his friend, and a brief visit stretched into six months. It was an important six months. Through Anderson he got a job writing feature stories for the Times Picayune, *sketches he called "Mirrors of Chartres Street." From Anderson came the suggestion to try his hand at a novel. The result was* Soldier's Pay, *written in six weeks, which Anderson recommended to a publisher. He started a second novel,* Mosquitoes, *but in June 1925, left New Orleans for a six months' walking tour through France and Germany.*

He was back in Oxford when Soldier's Pay *appeared in February 1926.* Mosquitoes *came out in 1927. Before its publication he had started* The Sound and the Fury, *his first important novel, which he was three years writing and revising. This, the first of his stories to use the "interior monologue," was also the first of his stories set in the mythical Yoknapatawpha County.* Sartoris *(1929) though published before it, was written later. At first no publisher would touch* The Sound and the Fury. *To earn a living he shoveled coal on the night shift at the Oxford power-plant, writing from midnight to four o'clock on an upturned wheelbarrow, with the whine of a dynamo in his ears. Here he revised* The Sound and the Fury *(1929) and wrote* As I Lay Dying *(1930) and* Sanctuary *(1931).*

Sanctuary *was written as the most shocking story he could devise in a deliberate attempt to make money. And make money it did. It was his first popular success. It introduced him to Hollywood and to financial security. Conservative estimates place the sale of the novel during the next twenty years at over one million copies. Since then Mr. Faulkner has continued to publish regularly, although his reputation, in the United States at least, has waxed and waned. Among his subsequent novels are* Light in August *(1932);* Absalom! Absalom! *(1936);* The Hamlet *(1940);* Intruder in the Dust *(1948);* A Fable *(1954), which won both the Pulitzer Prize and the National Book Award;* The Town *(1957), another Pulitzer Prize winner; and* The Mansion *(1959).*

Mr. Faulkner has written a large number of distinguished short stories, more traditional in form and technique than his novels. Two of his stories, "Barn Burning" (1939) and "A Courtship" (1949), won O. Henry Memorial

Award first prizes. Ten of his other stories won O. Henry awards from 1931 to 1957, and nine more have been reprinted in The Best American Short Stories *of the year. "That Evening Sun Go Down" was published originally in the* American Mercury *for March 1931, reprinted in* The Best American Short Stories of 1931, *and revised and retitled "That Evening Sun" for publication in* These Thirteen (1931), *Mr. Faulkner's first collection of stories. Other collections include* Doctor Martino & Other Stories (1934); Go Down, Moses (1942); Collected Stories of William Faulkner (1950), *which won the National Book Gold Medal; and* Big Woods (1955).

In 1950 Mr. Faulkner became the fourth American to receive the Nobel Prize for Literature. In a famous acceptance speech he indicated his attitude toward the writer's art. "Man will endure," he said, "because he has a soul, a spirit capable of compassion and sacrifice and endurance. The poet's, the writer's duty is to write about these things. It is his privilege to help man endure by lifting his heart, by reminding him of the courage and honor and hope and pride and compassion and pity and sacrifice which has been the glory of his past."

THAT EVENING SUN

Monday is no different from any other weekday in Jefferson now. The streets are paved now, and the telephone and electric companies are cutting down more and more of the shade trees—the water oaks, the maples and locusts and elms—to make room for iron poles bearing clusters of bloated and ghostly and bloodless grapes, and we have a city laundry which makes the rounds on Monday morning, gathering the bundles of clothes into bright-colored, specially made motorcars: the soiled wearing of a whole week now flees apparitionlike behind alert and irritable electric horns, with a long diminishing noise of rubber and asphalt like tearing silk, and even the Negro women who still take in white people's washing after the old custom, fetch and deliver it in automobiles.

But fifteen years ago, on Monday morning the quiet, dusty, shady streets would be full of Negro women with, balanced on their steady, turbaned heads, bundles of clothes tied up in sheets, almost as large as cotton bales, carried so without touch of hand between the kitchen door of the white house and the blackened washpot beside a cabin door in Negro Hollow.

Nancy would set her bundle on the top of her head, then upon the bundle in turn she would set the black straw sailor hat which she wore winter and summer. She was tall, with a high, sad face sunken a little where her teeth were missing.

Sometimes we would go a part of the way down the lane and across the pasture with her, to watch the balanced bundle and the hat that never bobbed nor wavered, even when she walked down into the ditch and up the other side and stooped through the fence. She would go down on her hands and knees and crawl through the gap, her head rigid, uptilted, the bundle steady as a rock or a balloon, and rise to her feet again and go on.

Sometimes the husbands of the washing women would fetch and deliver the clothes, but Jesus never did that for Nancy, even before Father told him to stay away from our house, even when Dilsey was sick and Nancy would come to cook for us.

And then about half the time we'd have to go down the lane to Nancy's cabin and tell her to come on and cook breakfast. We would stop at the ditch, because Father told us to not have anything to do with Jesus—he was a short black man, with a razor scar down his face—and we would throw rocks at Nancy's house until she came to the door, leaning her head around it without any clothes on.

"What yawl mean, chunking my house?" Nancy said. "What you little devils mean?"

"Father says for you to come on and get breakfast," Caddy said. "Father says it's over a half an hour now, and you've got to come this minute."

"I ain't studying no breakfast," Nancy said. "I going to get my sleep out."

"I bet you're drunk," Jason said. "Father says you're drunk. Are you drunk, Nancy?"

"Who says I is?" Nancy said. "I got to get my sleep out. I ain't studying no breakfast."

So after a while we quit chunking the cabin and went back home. When she finally came, it was too late for me to go to school. So we thought it was whiskey until that day they arrested her again and they were taking her to jail and they passed Mr. Stovall. He was the cashier in the bank and a deacon in the Baptist church, and Nancy began to say:

"When you going to pay me, white man? When you going to pay me, white man? It's been three times now since you paid me a cent—" Mr. Stovall knocked her down, but she kept on saying, "When you going to pay me, white man? It's been three times now since—" until Mr. Stovall kicked her in the mouth with his heel and the marshal caught Mr. Stovall back, and Nancy lying in the street, laughing. She turned her head and spat out some blood and teeth and said, "It's been three times now since he paid me a cent."

That was how she lost her teeth, and all that day they told about Nancy and Mr. Stovall, and all that night the ones that passed the jail could hear Nancy singing and yelling. They could see her hands holding to the window bars, and a lot of them stopped along the fence, listening to her and the jailer trying to make her stop. She didn't shut up until almost daylight, when the jailer began to hear a bumping and scraping upstairs and he went up there and found Nancy hanging from the window bar. He said that it was cocaine and not whiskey, because no nigger would try to commit suicide unless he was full of cocaine, because a nigger full of cocaine wasn't a nigger any longer.

The jailer cut her down and revived her; then he beat her, whipped her. She had hung herself with her dress. She had fixed it all right, but when they arrested her she didn't have on anything except a dress and so she didn't have anything to tie her hands with, and she couldn't make her hands let go of the window ledge. So the jailer heard the noise and ran up there and found Nancy hanging from the window, stark naked, her belly already swelling out a little, like a little balloon.

When Dilsey was sick in her cabin and Nancy was cooking for us, we could see her apron swelling out; that was before Father told Jesus to stay away from the house. Jesus was in the kitchen, sitting behind the stove, with his razor scar on his black face like a piece of dirty string. He said it was a watermelon that Nancy had under her dress.

"It never come off of your vine, though," Nancy said.

"Off of what vine?" Caddy said.

"I can cut down the vine it did come off of," Jesus said.

"What makes you want to talk like that before these chillen?" Nancy said. "Whyn't you go on to work? You done et. You want Mr. Jason to catch you hanging around his kitchen, talking that way before these chillen?"

"Talking what way?" Caddy said. "What vine?"

"I can't hang around white man's kitchen," Jesus said. "But white man can hang around mine. White man can come in my house, but I can't stop him. When white man want to come in my house, I ain't got no house. I can't stop him, but he can't kick me outen it. He can't do that."

Dilsey was still sick in her cabin. Father told Jesus to stay off our place. Dilsey was still sick. It was a long time. We were in the library after supper.

"Isn't Nancy through in the kitchen yet?" Mother said. "It seems to me that she has had plenty of time to have finished the dishes."

"Let Quentin go and see," Father said. "Go and see if Nancy is through, Quentin. Tell her she can go on home."

I went to the kitchen. Nancy was through. The dishes were put away and the fire was out. Nancy was sitting in a chair, close to the cold stove. She looked at me.

"Mother wants to know if you are through," I said.

"Yes," Nancy said. She looked at me. "I done finished." She looked at me.

"What is it?" I said. "What is it?"

"I ain't nothing but a nigger," Nancy said. "It ain't none of it my fault."

She looked at me, sitting in the chair before the cold stove, the sailor hat on her head. I went back to the library. It was the cold stove and all, when you think of a kitchen being warm and busy and cheerful. And with a cold stove and the dishes all put away, and nobody wanting to eat at that hour.

"Is she through?" Mother said.

"Yessum," I said.

"What is she doing?" Mother said.

"She's not doing anything. She's through."

"I'll go and see," Father said.

"Maybe she's waiting for Jesus to come and take her home," Caddy said.

"Jesus is gone," I said. Nancy told us how one morning she woke up and Jesus was gone.

"He quit me," Nancy said. "Done gone to Memphis, I reckon. Dodging them city po-lice for a while, I reckon."

"And a good riddance," Father said. "I hope he stays there."

"Nancy's scaired of the dark," Jason said.

"So are you," Caddy said.

"I'm not," Jason said.

"Scairy cat," Caddy said.

"I'm not," Jason said.

"You, Candace!" Mother said. Father came back.

"I am going to walk down the lane with Nancy," he said. "She says that Jesus is back."

"Has she seen him?" Mother said.

"No. Some Negro sent her word that he was back in town. I won't be long."

"You'll leave me alone, to take Nancy home?" Mother said. "Is her safety more precious to you than mine?"

"I won't be long," Father said.

"You'll leave these children unprotected, with that Negro about?"

"I'm going too," Caddy said. "Let me go, Father."

"What would he do with them, if he were unfortunate enough to have them?" Father said.

"I want to go, too," Jason said.

"Jason!" Mother said. She was speaking to Father. You

199

could tell that by the way she said the name. Like she believed that all day Father had been trying to think of doing the thing she wouldn't like the most, and that she knew all the time that after a while he would think of it. I stayed quiet, because Father and I both knew that Mother would want him to make me stay with her if she just thought of it in time. So Father didn't look at me. I was the oldest. I was nine and Caddy was seven and Jason was five.

"Nonsense," Father said. "We won't be long."

Nancy had her hat on. We came to the lane. "Jesus always been good to me," Nancy said. "Whenever he had two dollars, one of them was mine." We walked in the lane. "If I can just get through the lane," Nancy said, "I be all right then."

The lane was always dark. "This is where Jason got scaired on Hallowe'en," Caddy said.

"I didn't," Jason said.

"Can't Aunt Rachel do anything with him?" Father said. Aunt Rachel was old. She lived in a cabin beyond Nancy's by herself. She had white hair and she smoked a pipe in the door, all day long; she didn't work any more. They said she was Jesus' mother. Sometimes she said she was and sometimes she said she wasn't any kin to Jesus.

"Yes you did," Caddy said. "You were scairder than Frony. You were scairder than T.P. even. Scairder than niggers."

"Can't nobody do nothing with him," Nancy said. "He say I done woke up the devil in him and ain't but one thing going to lay it down again."

"Well, he's gone now," Father said. "There's nothing for you to be afraid of now. And if you'd just let white men alone."

"Let what white men alone?" Caddy said. "How let them alone?"

"He ain't gone nowhere," Nancy said. "I can feel him. I can feel him now, in this lane. He hearing us talk, every word, hid somewhere, waiting. I ain't seen him, and I ain't going to see him again but once more, with that razor in his mouth. That razor on that string down his back, inside his shirt. And then I ain't going to be even surprised."

"I wasn't scaired," Jason said.

"If you'd behave yourself, you'd have kept out of this," Father said. "But it's all right now. He's probably in Saint Louis now. Probably got another wife by now and forgot all about you."

"If he has, I better not find out about it," Nancy said. "I'd stand there right over them, and every time he wropped her, I'd cut that arm off. I'd cut his head off and I'd slit her belly and I'd shove—"

"Hush," Father said.

"Slit whose belly, Nancy?" Caddy said.

"I wasn't scaired," Jason said. "I'd walk right down this lane by myself."

"Yah," Caddy said. "You wouldn't dare to put your foot down in it if we were not here too."

II

Dilsey was still sick, so we took Nancy home every night until Mother said, "How much longer is this going on? I to be left alone in this big house while you take home a frightened Negro?"

We fixed a pallet in the kitchen for Nancy. One night we waked up, hearing the sound. It was not singing and it was not crying, coming up the dark stairs. There was a light in Mother's room and we heard Father going down the hall, down the back stairs, and Caddy and I went into the hall. The floor was cold. Our toes curled away from it while we listened to the sound. It was like singing and it wasn't like singing, like the sound that Negroes make.

Then it stopped and we heard Father going down the back stairs, and we went to the head of the stairs. Then the sound began again, in the stairway, not loud, and we could see Nancy's eyes halfway up the stairs, against the wall. They looked like cat's eyes do, like a big cat against the wall, watching us. When we came down the steps to where she was, she quit making the sound again, and we stood there until Father came back up from the kitchen, with his pistol in his hand. He went back down with Nancy and they came back with Nancy's pallet.

We spread the pallet in our room. After the light in Mother's room went off, we could see Nancy's eyes again. "Nancy," Caddy whispered, "are you asleep, Nancy?"

Nancy whispered something. It was oh or no, I don't know which. Like nobody had made it, like it came from nowhere and went nowhere, until it was like Nancy was not there at all; that I had looked so hard at her eyes on the stairs that they had got printed on my eyeballs, like the sun does when you have closed your eyes and there is no sun. "Jesus," Nancy whispered. "Jesus."

"Was it Jesus?" Caddy said. "Did he try to come into the kitchen?"

"Jesus," Nancy said. Like this: Jeeeeeeeeeeeeeeeesus, until the sound went out, like a match or a candle does.

"It's the other Jesus she means," I said.

"Can you see us, Nancy?" Caddy whispered. "Can you see our eyes too?"

"I ain't nothing but a nigger," Nancy said. "God knows. God knows."

"What did you see down there in the kitchen?" Caddy whispered. "What tried to get in?"

"God knows," Nancy said. We could see her eyes. "God knows."

Dilsey got well. She cooked dinner. "You'd better stay in bed a day or two longer," Father said.

"What for?" Dilsey said. "If I had been a day later, this place would be to rack and ruin. Get on out of here now, and let me get my kitchen straight again."

Dilsey cooked supper too. And that night, just before dark, Nancy came into the kitchen.

"How do you know he's back?" Dilsey said. "You ain't seen him."

"Jesus is a nigger," Jason said.

"I can feel him," Nancy said. "I can feel him laying yonder in the ditch."

"Tonight?" Dilsey said. "Is he there tonight?"

"Dilsey's a nigger too," Jason said.

"You try to eat something," Dilsey said.

"I don't want nothing," Nancy said.

"I ain't a nigger," Jason said.

"Drink some coffee," Dilsey said. She poured a cup of coffee for Nancy. "Do you know he's out there tonight? How come you know it's tonight?"

"I know," Nancy said. "He's there, waiting. I know. I done lived with him too long. I know what he is fixing to do fore he know it himself."

"Drink some coffee," Dilsey said. Nancy held the cup to her mouth and blew into the cup. Her mouth pursed out like a spreading adder's, like a rubber mouth, like she had blown all the color out of her lips with blowing the coffee.

"I ain't a nigger," Jason said. "Are you a nigger, Nancy?"

"I hellborn, child," Nancy said. "I won't be nothing soon. I going back where I come from soon."

III

She began to drink the coffee. While she was drinking, holding the cup in both hands, she began to make the sound again. She made the sound into the cup and the coffee sploshed out onto her hands and her dress. Her eyes looked at us and she sat there, her elbows on her knees, holding the cup in both hands, looking at us across the wet cup, making the sound.

"Look at Nancy," Jason said. "Nancy can't cook for us now. Dilsey's got well now."

"You hush up," Dilsey said. Nancy held the cup in both hands, looking at us, making the sound, like there were two of them: one looking at us and the other making the sound. "Whyn't you let Mr. Jason telefoam the marshal?" Dilsey said. Nancy stopped then, holding the cup in her long brown hands. She tried to drink some coffee again, but it sploshed out of the cup, onto her hands and her dress, and she put the cup down. Jason watched her.

"I can't swallow it," Nancy said. "I swallows but it won't go down me."

"You go down to the cabin," Dilsey said. "Frony will fix you a pallet and I'll be there soon."

"Won't no nigger stop him," Nancy said.

"I ain't a nigger," Jason said. "Am I, Dilsey?"

"I reckon not," Dilsey said. She looked at Nancy. "I don't reckon so. What you going to do, then?"

Nancy looked at us. Her eyes went fast, like she was afraid there wasn't time to look, without hardly moving at all. She looked at us, at all three of us at one time. "You member that night I stayed in yawls' room?" she said. She told about how we waked up early the next morning, and played. We had to play quiet, on her pallet, until Father woke up and it was time to get breakfast. "Go and ask your maw to let me stay here tonight," Nancy said. "I won't need no pallet. We can play some more."

Caddy asked Mother. Jason went too. "I can't have Negroes sleeping in the bedrooms," Mother said. Jason cried. He cried until Mother said he couldn't have any dessert for three days if he didn't stop. Then Jason said he would stop if Dilsey would make a chocolate cake. Father was there.

"Why don't you do something about it?" Mother said. "What do we have officers for?"

"Why is Nancy afraid of Jesus?" Caddy said. "Are you afraid of Father, Mother?"

"What could the officers do?" Father said. "If Nancy hasn't seen him, how could the officers find him?"

"Then why is she afraid?" Mother said.

"She says he is there. She says she knows he is there tonight."

"Yet we pay taxes," Mother said. "I must wait here alone in this big house while you take a Negro woman home."

"You know that I am not lying outside with a razor," Father said.

"I'll stop if Dilsey will make a chocolate cake," Jason said. Mother told us to go out and Father said he didn't know if Jason would get a chocolate cake or not, but he knew what Jason was going to get in about a minute. We went back to the kitchen and told Nancy.

"Father said for you to go home and lock the door, and you'll be all right," Caddy said. "All right from what, Nancy? Is Jesus mad at you?" Nancy was holding the coffee cup in her hands again, her elbows on her knees and her hands holding the cup between her knees. She was looking into the cup. "What have you done that made Jesus mad?" Caddy said. Nancy let the cup go. It didn't break on the floor, but the coffee spilled out, and Nancy sat there with her hands still making the shape of the cup. She began to make the sound again, not loud. Not singing and not unsinging. We watched her.

"Here," Dilsey said. "You quit that, now. You get aholt of yourself. You wait here. I going to get Versh to walk home with you." Dilsey went out.

We looked at Nancy. Her shoulders kept shaking, but she quit making the sound. We stood and watched her.

"What's Jesus going to do to you?" Caddy said. "He went away."

Nancy looked at us. "We had fun that night I stayed in yawls' room, didn't we?"

205

"I didn't," Jason said. "I didn't have any fun."

"You were asleep in Mother's room," Caddy said. "You were not there."

"Let's go down to my house and have some more fun," Nancy said.

"Mother won't let us," I said. "It's too late now."

"Don't bother her," Nancy said. "We can tell her in the morning. She won't mind."

"She wouldn't let us," I said.

"Don't ask her now," Nancy said. "Don't bother her now."

"She didn't say we couldn't go," Caddy said.

"We didn't ask," I said.

"If you go, I'll tell," Jason said.

"We'll have fun," Nancy said. "They won't mind, just to my house. I been working for yawl a long time. They won't mind."

"I'm not afraid to go," Caddy said. "Jason is the one that's afraid. He'll tell."

"I'm not," Jason said.

"Yes, you are," Caddy said. "You'll tell."

"I won't tell," Jason said. "I'm not afraid."

"Jason ain't afraid to go with me," Nancy said. "Is you, Jason?"

"Jason is going to tell," Caddy said. The lane was dark. We passed the pasture gate. "I bet if something was to jump out from behind that gate, Jason would holler."

"I wouldn't," Jason said. We walked down the lane. Nancy was talking loud.

"What are you talking so loud for, Nancy?" Caddy said.

"Who; me?" Nancy said. "Listen at Quentin and Caddy and Jason saying I'm talking loud."

"You talk like there was five of us here," Caddy said. "You talk like Father was here too."

"Who; me talking loud, Mr. Jason?" Nancy said.

"Nancy called Jason 'Mister,' " Caddy said.

"Listen how Caddy and Quentin and Jason talk," Nancy said.

"We're not talking loud," Caddy said. "You're the one that's talking like Father—"

"Hush," Nancy said; "hush, Mr. Jason."

"Nancy called Jason 'Mister' aguh—"

"Hush," Nancy said. She was talking loud when we crossed the ditch and stooped through the fence where she used to stoop through with the clothes on her head. Then we came to her house. We were going fast then. She opened the door. The smell of the house was like the lamp and the smell of Nancy was like the wick, like they were waiting for one another to begin to smell. She lit the lamp and closed the door and put the bar up. Then she quit talking loud, looking at us.

"What're we going to do?" Caddy said.

"What do yawl want to do?" Nancy said.

"You said we would have some fun," Caddy said.

There was something about Nancy's house; something you could smell besides Nancy and the house. Jason smelled it, even. "I don't want to stay here," he said. "I want to go home."

"Go home, then," Caddy said.

"I don't want to go by myself," Jason said.

"We're going to have some fun," Nancy said.

"How?" Caddy said.

Nancy stood by the door. She was looking at us, only it was like she had emptied her eyes, like she had quit using them. "What do you want to do?" she said.

"Tell us a story," Caddy said. "Can you tell a story?"

"Yes," Nancy said.

"Tell it," Caddy said. We looked at Nancy. "You don't know any stories."

"Yes," Nancy said. "Yes I do."

She came and sat in a chair before the hearth. There was a little fire there. Nancy built it up, when it was already hot inside. She built a good blaze. She told a story. She talked like her eyes looked, like her eyes watching us and her voice talking to us did not belong to her. Like she was living somewhere else, waiting somewhere else. She was outside the cabin. Her voice was inside and the shape of her, that Nancy that could stoop under a barbed wire fence with a bundle of clothes balanced on her head as though without weight, like a balloon, was there. But that was all. "And so this here queen come walking up to the ditch, where that bad man was hiding. She was walking up to the ditch, and she say, 'If I can just get past this here ditch,' was what she say . . ."

"What ditch?" Caddy said. "A ditch like that one out there? Why did a queen want to go into a ditch?"

"To get to her house," Nancy said. She looked at us. "She had to cross the ditch to get into her house quick and bar the door."

"Why did she want to go home and bar the door?" Caddy said.

IV

Nancy looked at us. She quit talking. She looked at us. Jason's legs stuck straight out of his pants where he sat on Nancy's lap. "I don't think that's a good story," he said. "I want to go home."

"Maybe we had better," Caddy said. She got up from the floor. "I bet they are looking for us right now." She went toward the door.

"No," Nancy said. "Don't open it." She got up quick and passed Caddy. She didn't touch the door, the wooden bar.

"Why not?" Caddy said.

"Come back to the lamp," Nancy said. "We'll have fun. You don't have to go."

"We ought to go," Caddy said. "Unless we have a lot of fun." She and Nancy came back to the fire, the lamp.

"I want to go home," Jason said. "I'm going to tell."

"I know another story," Nancy said. She stood close to the lamp. She looked at Caddy, like when your eyes look up at a stick balanced on your nose. She had to look down to see Caddy, but her eyes looked like that, like when you are balancing a stick.

"I won't listen to it," Jason said. "I'll bang on the floor."

"It's a good one," Nancy said. "It's better than the other one."

"What's it about?" Caddy said. Nancy was standing by the lamp. Her hand was on the lamp, against the light, long and brown.

"Your hand is on that hot globe," Caddy said. "Don't it feel hot to your hand?"

Nancy looked at her hand on the lamp chimney. She took her hand away, slow. She stood there, looking at Caddy, wringing her long hand as though it were tied to her wrist with a string.

"Let's do something else," Caddy said.

"I want to go home," Jason said.

"I got some popcorn," Nancy said. She looked at Caddy and then at Jason and then at me and then at Caddy again. "I got some popcorn."

"I don't like popcorn," Jason said. "I'd rather have candy."

Nancy looked at Jason. "You can hold the popper." She was still wringing her hand; it was long and limp and brown.

"All right," Jason said. "I'll stay a while if I can do that. Caddy can't hold it. I'll want to go home again if Caddy holds the popper."

Nancy built up the fire. "Look at Nancy putting her hands in the fire," Caddy said. "What's the matter with you, Nancy?"

"I got popcorn," Nancy said. "I got some." She took the popper from under the bed. It was broken. Jason began to cry.

"Now we can't have any popcorn," he said.

"We ought to go home anyway," Caddy said. "Come on, Quentin."

"Wait," Nancy said; "wait. I can fix it. Don't you want to help me fix it?"

"I don't think I want any," Caddy said. "It's too late now."

"You help me, Jason," Nancy said. "Don't you want to help me?"

"No," Jason said. "I want to go home."

"Hush," Nancy said; "hush. Watch. Watch me. I can fix it so Jason can hold it and pop the corn." She got a piece of wire and fixed the popper.

"It won't hold good," Caddy said.

"Yes it will," Nancy said. "Yawl watch. Yawl help me shell some corn."

The popcorn was under the bed too. We shelled it into the popper and Nancy helped Jason hold the popper over the fire.

"It's not popping," Jason said. "I want to go home."

"You wait," Nancy said. "It'll begin to pop. We'll have fun then."

She was sitting close to the fire. The lamp was turned up so high it was beginning to smoke. "Why don't you turn it down some?" I said.

"It's all right," Nancy said. "I'll clean it. Yawl wait. The popcorn will start in a minute."

"I don't believe it's going to start," Caddy said. "We ought to start home, anyway. They'll be worried."

"No," Nancy said. "It's going to pop. Dilsey will tell um yawl with me. I been working for yawl long time. They won't mind if yawl at my house. You wait, now. It'll start popping any minute now."

Then Jason got some smoke in his eyes and he began to cry. He dropped the popper into the fire. Nancy got a wet rag and wiped Jason's face, but he didn't stop crying.

"Hush," she said. "Hush." But he didn't hush. Caddy took the popper out of the fire.

"It's burned up," she said. "You'll have to get some more popcorn, Nancy."

"Did you put all of it in?" Nancy said.

"Yes," Caddy said. Nancy looked at Caddy. Then she took the popper and opened it and poured the cinders into her apron and began to sort the grains, her hands long and brown, and we watched her.

"Haven't you got any more?" Caddy said.

"Yes," Nancy said; "yes. Look. This here ain't burnt. All we need to do is—"

"I want to go home," Jason said. "I'm going to tell."

"Hush," Caddy said. We all listened. Nancy's head was already turned toward the barred door, her eyes filled with red lamplight. "Somebody is coming," Caddy said.

Then Nancy began to make that sound again, not loud, sitting there above the fire, her long hands dangling between her knees; all of a sudden water began to come out on her face in big drops, running down her face, carrying in each one a little turning ball of firelight like a spark until it dropped off her chin. "She's not crying," I said.

"I ain't crying," Nancy said. Her eyes were closed. "I ain't crying. Who is it?"

"I don't know," Caddy said. She went to the door and looked out. "We've got to go now," she said. "Here comes Father."

"I'm going to tell," Jason said. "Yawl made me come."

The water still ran down Nancy's face. She turned in her chair. "Listen. Tell him. Tell him we going to have fun. Tell him I take good care of yawl until in the morning. Tell him to let me come home with yawl and sleep on the floor. Tell him I won't need no pallet. We'll have fun. You member last time how we had so much fun?"

"I didn't have fun," Jason said. "You hurt me. You put smoke in my eyes. I'm going to tell."

V

Father came in. He looked at us. Nancy did not get up. "Tell him," she said.

"Caddy made us come down here," Jason said. "I didn't want to."

Father came to the fire. Nancy looked up at him. "Can't you go to Aunt Rachel's and stay?" he said. Nancy looked up at Father, her hands between her knees. "He's not here," Father said. "I would have seen him. There's not a soul in sight."

"He in the ditch," Nancy said. "He waiting in the ditch yonder."

"Nonsense," Father said. He looked at Nancy. "Do you know he's there?"

"I got the sign," Nancy said.

"What sign?"

"I got it. It was on the table when I come in. It was a hog-bone, with blood meat still on it, laying by the lamp. He's out there. When yawl walk out that door, I gone."

"Gone where, Nancy?" Caddy said.

"I'm not a tattletale," Jason said.

"Nonsense," Father said.

"He out there," Nancy said. "He looking through that window this minute, waiting for yawl to go. Then I gone."

"Nonsense," Father said. "Lock up your house and we'll take you on to Aunt Rachel's."

" 'Twon't do no good," Nancy said. She didn't look at Father now, but he looked down at her, at her long, limp, moving hands. "Putting it off won't do no good."

"Then what do you want to do?" Father said.

"I don't know," Nancy said. "I can't do nothing. Just put it off. And that don't do no good. I reckon it belong to me. I reckon what I going to get ain't no more than mine."

"Get what?" Caddy said. "What's yours?"

"Nothing," Father said. "You all must get to bed."

"Caddy made me come," Jason said.

"Go on to Aunt Rachel's," Father said.

"It won't do no good," Nancy said. She sat before the fire, her elbows on her knees, her long hands between her knees.

"When even your own kitchen wouldn't do no good. When even if I was sleeping on the floor in the room with your chillen, and the next morning there I am, and blood—"

"Hush," Father said. "Lock the door and put out the lamp and go to bed."

"I scaired of the dark," Nancy said. "I scaired for it to happen in the dark."

"You mean you're going to sit right here with the lamp lighted?" Father said. Then Nancy began to make the sound again, sitting before the fire, her long hands between her knees. "Ah, damnation," Father said. "Come along, chillen. It's past bedtime."

"When yawl go home, I gone," Nancy said. She talked quieter now, and her face looked quiet, like her hands. "Anyway, I got my coffin money saved up with Mr. Lovelady." Mr. Lovelady was a short, dirty man who collected the Negro insurance, coming around to the cabins or the kitchens every Saturday morning, to collect fifteen cents. He and his wife lived at the hotel. One morning his wife committed suicide. They had a child, a little girl. He and the child went away. After a week or two he came back alone. We would see him going along the lanes and the back streets on Saturday mornings.

"Nonsense," Father said. "You'll be the first thing I'll see in the kitchen tomorrow morning."

"You'll see what you'll see, I reckon," Nancy said. "But it will take the Lord to say what that will be."

VI

We left her sitting before the fire.

"Come and put the bar up," Father said. But she didn't move. She didn't look at us again, sitting quietly there between the lamp and the fire. From some distance down the lane we could look back and see her through the open door.

"What, Father?" Caddy said. "What's going to happen?"

"Nothing," Father said. Jason was on Father's back, so Jason was the tallest of all of us. We went down into the ditch. I looked at it, quiet. I couldn't see much where the moonlight and the shadows tangled.

"If Jesus *is* hid here, he can see us, can't he?" Caddy said.

"He's not there," Father said. "He went away a long time ago."

"You made me come," Jason said, high; against the sky it looked like Father had two heads, a little one and a big one. "I didn't want to."

We went up out of the ditch. We could still see Nancy's house and the open door, but we couldn't see Nancy now, sitting before the fire with the door open, because she was tired. "I just done got tired," she said. "I just a nigger. It ain't no fault of mine."

But we could hear her, because she began just after we came up out of the ditch, the sound that was not singing and not unsinging. "Who will do our washing now, Father?" I said.

"I'm not a nigger," Jason said, high and close above Father's head.

"You're worse," Caddy said, "you are a tattletale. If something was to jump out, you'd be scairder than a nigger."

"I wouldn't," Jason said.

"You'd cry," Caddy said.

"Caddy," Father said.

"I wouldn't!" Jason said.

"Scairy cat," Caddy said.

"Candace!" Father said.

D. H. LAWRENCE

David Henry Lawrence was born in Eastwood, England, a mining town eight miles from Nottingham, on September 11, 1885. His father was an uneducated collier, who had worked in the pits from childhood. His mother, whom he worshipped, and who pressed for her children's advancement in the world, had at one time been a school teacher.

At the local Board School, which he attended along with the sons of other miners, his effeminate manners and penchant for reading set him apart from his school fellows. So did the county scholarship to Nottingham High School that he won at the age of twelve. In the summer of 1901, his three years of high school behind him, he became a clerk in a factory in Nottingham.

That winter he was taken seriously ill with pneumonia, the aftermath of which was a weakened constitution that led to tuberculosis in his later years. Instead of returning to his job as a clerk he became, in the fall of 1902, at the age of seventeen, a pupil-teacher, a kind of apprenticeship for those who lacked a teaching certificate. In 1904 he passed the King's Scholarship Examination for uncertificated teachers with top honors, but not until 1906 did he have enough money to enroll in the Teachers' Training Department of Nottingham University College.

In later life Lawrence said that his two years of college were a "disillusionment," that they lacked the "contact of living men" that he had looked forward to. Certainly he

215

did not distinguish himself in any way. His grades were good, but not outstanding. The only contribution he submitted to the college magazine, a poem called "Study," was rejected. (Ten years later he included it in a volume of poems entitled Amores.) During his second term a short story, "Prelude to a Happy Christmas," which he submitted to the Nottinghamshire Guardian won first prize, three guineas, the first money he earned as a writer.

He submitted the story not in his own name but through Jessie Chambers (the Miriam of Sons and Lovers). She lived two miles outside of Eastwood, on a farm, and he had met her the summer he left high school, when he was sixteen. It was Jessie, Lawrence said at one time, who first fired him with the desire to become a writer. Certainly she read everything he wrote—his poems, the various drafts of a first novel (published as The White Peacock) that he started in 1906—encouraged him, and was responsible for his first publication, in the English Review.

That was in the summer of 1909. Lawrence had been teaching for a year at Croydon, South London, after getting his certificate at Nottingham University, and writing evenings. On her own initiative Jessie copied five of his poems and sent them to Ford Madox Hueffer, editor of the English Review. Hueffer published the poems in the November issue, and a short story, "Goose Fair," the following February. He published three more of his stories in 1911 and 1912. He introduced Lawrence to the London literary circle in which he moved and helped him get The White Peacock published in January 1911. Lawrence, now 25 years old, had made a quick jump from complete obscurity to the status of a published author, regarded by some critics as a "genius."

From 1912 on Lawrence devoted himself exclusively

to freelance writing. The Trespasser (*1912*) *was followed by* Sons and Lovers (*1913*), *his most autobiographical novel. William Heinemann, who had published his first novel, balked at publishing* The Trespasser *because it was* "*too erotic.*" *He later called* Sons and Lovers "*one of the dirtiest books he had ever read.*" *Lawrence was to continue to run into trouble for his frank treatment of sex.* The Rainbow (*1915*) *was suppressed six weeks after its publication.* Women in Love (*1920*) *was privately printed.* Lady Chatterley's Lover, *privately printed in Florence in 1928, was until 1959 banned from the United States.*

Lawrence's private life was as tempestuous as his literary career. In 1912 he fell in love with Frieda von Richthofen Weekley, wife of Ernest Weekley, a former professor of his at Nottingham. She left her husband and three small children to live with Lawrence, marrying him in 1914 when her divorce decree became final. For years they lived a hand-to-mouth existence, in Italy, England, Ceylon, Australia, New Mexico. He had a violent temper, quarreling with anyone and everyone. He died on March 2, 1930.

"*The Rocking-Horse Winner,*" *one of his best-known short stories, was first published in Lady Cynthia Asquith's* The Ghost-Book: Sixteen Stories of the Uncanny, *October 1926. Later it was included in the posthumous collection* Lovely Lady (*1933*). *It was made into a motion picture in 1949 by a British film company.*

The most complete biographical materials about Lawrence are to be found in the three-volume D. H. Lawrence: A Composite Biography, *by Edward Nehls (1957–59).*

THE ROCKING-HORSE
WINNER

There was a woman who was beautiful, who started with all the advantages, yet she had no luck. She married for love, and the love turned to dust. She had bonny children, yet she felt they had been thrust upon her, and she could not love them. They looked at her coldly, as if they were finding fault with her. And hurriedly she felt she must cover up some fault in herself. Yet what it was that she must cover up she never knew. Nevertheless, when her children were present, she always felt the center of her heart go hard. This troubled her, and in her manner she was all the more gentle and anxious for her children, as if she loved them very much. Only she herself knew that at the center of her heart was a hard little place that could not feel love, no, not for anybody. Everybody else said of her: "She is such a good mother. She adores her children." Only she herself, and her children themselves, knew it was not so. They read it in each other's eyes.

There were a boy and two little girls. They lived in a pleasant house, with a garden, and they had discreet servants, and felt themselves superior to anyone in the neighborhood.

Although they lived in style, they felt always an anxiety in the house. There was never enough money. The mother had a small income, and the father had a small income, but not nearly enough for the social position which they had to keep up. The father went into town to some office. But though he had good prospects, these prospects never materialized. There was always the grinding sense of the shortage of money, though the style was always kept up.

At last the mother said: "I will see if *I* can't make something." But she did not know where to begin. She racked her brains, and tried this thing and the other, but could not find anything successful. The failure made deep lines come into her face. Her children were growing up, they would have to go to school. There must be more money, there must be more money. The father, who was always very handsome and expensive in his tastes, seemed as if he never *would* be able to do anything worth doing. And the mother, who had a great belief in herself, did not succeed any better, and her tastes were just as expensive.

And so the house came to be haunted by the unspoken phrase: *There must be more money! There must be more money!* The children could hear it all the time, though nobody said it aloud. They heard it at Christmas, when the expensive and splendid toys filled the nursery. Behind the shining modern rocking-horse, behind the smart doll's house, a voice would start whispering: "There *must* be more money! There *must* be more money!" And the children would stop playing, to listen for a moment. They would look into each other's eyes, to see if they had all heard. And each one saw in the eyes of the other two that they too had heard. "There *must* be more money! There *must* be more money!"

It came whispering from the springs of the still-swaying rocking-horse, and even the horse, bending his wooden, champing head, heard it. The big doll, sitting so pink and smirking in her new pram, could hear it quite plainly, and seemed to be smirking all the more self-consciously because of it. The foolish puppy, too, that took the place of the teddy-bear, he was looking so extraordinarily foolish for no other reason but that he heard the secret whisper all over the house: "There *must* be more money!"

Yet nobody ever said it aloud. The whisper was everywhere, and therefore no one spoke it. Just as no one ever says: "We are breathing!" in spite of the fact that breath is coming and going all the time.

"Mother," said the boy Paul one day, "why don't we keep a car of our own? Why do we always use uncle's, or else a taxi?"

"Because we're the poor members of the family," said the mother.

"But why *are* we, mother?"

"Well—I suppose," she said slowly and bitterly, "it's because your father has no luck."

The boy was silent for some time.

"Is luck money, mother?" he asked, rather timidly.

"No, Paul. Not quite. It's what causes you to have money."

"Oh!" said Paul vaguely. "I thought when Uncle Oscar said *filthy lucker*, it meant money."

"*Filthy lucre* does mean money," said the mother. "But it's lucre, not luck."

"Oh!" said the boy. "Then what *is* luck, mother?"

"It's what causes you to have money. If you're lucky you have money. That's why it's better to be born lucky than rich. If you're rich, you may lose your money. But if you're lucky, you will always get more money."

"Oh! Will you? And is father not lucky?"

"Very unlucky, I should say," she said bitterly.

The boy watched her with unsure eyes.

"Why?" he asked.

"I don't know. Nobody ever knows why one person is lucky and another unlucky."

"Don't they? Nobody at all? Does *nobody* know?"

"Perhaps God. But He never tells."

"He ought to, then. And aren't you lucky either, mother?"

"I can't be, if I married an unlucky husband."

"But by yourself, aren't you?"

"I used to think I was, before I married. Now I think I am very unlucky indeed."

"Why?"

"Well—never mind! Perhaps I'm not really," she said.

The child looked at her to see if she meant it. But he saw, by the lines of her mouth, that she was only trying to hide something from him.

"Well, anyhow," he said stoutly, "I'm a lucky person."

"Why?" said his mother, with a sudden laugh.

He stared at her. He didn't even know why he had said it.

"God told me," he asserted, brazening it out.

"I hope He did, dear!" she said, again with a laugh, but rather bitter.

"He did, mother!"

"Excellent!" said the mother, using one of her husband's exclamations.

The boy saw she did not believe him; or rather, that she paid no attention to his assertion. This angered him somewhat, and made him want to compel her attention.

He went off by himself, vaguely, in a childish way, seeking for the clue to "luck." Absorbed, taking no heed of other people, he went about with a sort of stealth, seeking inwardly for luck. He wanted luck, he wanted it, he wanted it. When the two girls were playing dolls in the nursery, he would sit on his big rocking-horse, charging madly into space, with a frenzy that made the little girls peer at him uneasily. Wildly the horse careered, the waving dark hair of the boy tossed, his eyes had a strange glare in them. The little girls dared not speak to him.

When he had ridden to the end of his mad little journey, he climbed down and stood in front of his rocking-horse, staring fixedly into its lowered face. Its red mouth was slightly open, its big eye was wide and glassy-bright.

"Now!" he would silently command the snorting steed. "Now, take me to where there is luck! Now take me!"

And he would slash the horse on the neck with the little whip he had asked Uncle Oscar for. He *knew* the horse could take him to where there was luck, if only he forced it. So he would mount again and start on his furious ride, hoping at last to get there. He knew he could get there.

"You'll break your horse, Paul!" said the nurse.

"He's always riding like that! I wish he'd leave off!" said his elder sister Joan.

But he only glared down on them in silence. Nurse gave him up. She could make nothing of him. Anyhow, he was growing beyond her.

One day his mother and his Uncle Oscar came in when he was on one of his furious rides. He did not speak to them.

"Hallo, you young jockey! Riding a winner?" said his uncle.

"Aren't you growing too big for a rocking-horse? You're not a very little boy any longer, you know," said his mother.

But Paul only gave a blue glare from his big, rather close-set eyes. He would speak to nobody when he was in full tilt. His mother watched him with an anxious expression on her face.

At last he suddenly stopped forcing his horse into the mechanical gallop and slid down.

"Well, I got there!" he announced fiercely, his blue eyes still flaring, and his sturdy long legs straddling apart.

"Where did you get to?" asked his mother.

"Where I wanted to go," he flared back at her.

"That's right, son!" said Uncle Oscar. "Don't you stop till you get there. What's the horse's name?"

"He doesn't have a name," said the boy.

"Gets on without all right?" asked the uncle.

"Well, he has different names. He was called Sansovino last week."

"Sansovino, eh? Won the Ascot. How did you know his name?"

"He always talks about horse-races with Bassett," said Joan.

The uncle was delighted to find that his small nephew was posted with all the racing news. Bassett, the young gardener, who had been wounded in the left foot in the war and had got his present job through Oscar Cresswell, whose batman he had been, was a perfect blade of the "turf." He lived in the racing events, and the small boy lived with him.

Oscar Cresswell got it all from Bassett.

"Master Paul comes and asks me, so I can't do more than tell him, sir," said Bassett, his face terribly serious, as if he were speaking of religious matters.

"And does he ever put anything on a horse he fancies?"

"Well—I don't want to give him away—he's a young sport, a fine sport, sir. Would you mind asking him himself? He sort of takes a pleasure in it, and perhaps he'd feel I was giving him away, sir, if you don't mind."

Bassett was serious as a church.

The uncle went back to his nephew and took him off for a ride in the car.

"Say, Paul, old man, do you ever put anything on a horse?" the uncle asked.

The boy watched the handsome man closely.

"Why, do you think I oughtn't to?" he parried.

"Not a bit of it! I thought perhaps you might give me a tip for the Lincoln."

The car sped on into the country, going down to Uncle Oscar's place in Hampshire.

"Honor bright?" said the nephew.

"Honor bright, son!" said the uncle.

"Well, then, Daffodil."

"Daffodil! I doubt it, sonny. What about Mirza?"

"I only know the winner," said the boy. "That's Daffodil."

"Daffodil, eh?"

There was a pause. Daffodil was an obscure horse comparatively.

"Uncle!"

"Yes, son?"

"You won't let it go any further, will you? I promised Bassett."

"Bassett be damned, old man! What's he got to do with it?"

"We're partners. We've been partners from the first. Uncle, he lent me my first five shillings, which I lost. I promised him, honor bright, it was only between me and him; only you gave me that ten-shilling note I started winning with, so I thought you were lucky. You won't let it go any further, will you?"

The boy gazed at his uncle from those big, hot, blue eyes, set rather close together. The uncle stirred and laughed uneasily.

"Right you are, son! I'll keep your tip private. Daffodil, eh? How much are you putting on him?"

"All except twenty pounds," said the boy. "I keep that in reserve."

The uncle thought it a good joke.

"You keep twenty pounds in reserve, do you, you young romancer? What are you betting, then?"

"I'm betting three hundred," said the boy gravely. "But it's between you and me, Uncle Oscar! Honor bright?"

The uncle burst into a roar of laughter.

"It's between you and me all right, you young Nat Gould," he said, laughing. "But where's your three hundred?"

"Bassett keeps it for me. We're partners."

"You are, are you! And what is Bassett putting on Daffodil?"

224

"He won't go quite as high as I do, I expect. Perhaps he'll go a hundred and fifty."

"What, pennies?" laughed the uncle.

"Pounds," said the child, with a surprised look at his uncle. "Bassett keeps a bigger reserve than I do."

Between wonder and amusement Uncle Oscar was silent. He pursued the matter no further, but he determined to take his nephew with him to the Lincoln races.

"Now, son," he said, "I'm putting twenty on Mirza, and I'll put five on for you on any horse you fancy. What's your pick?"

"Daffodil, uncle."

"No, not the fiver on Daffodil!"

"I should if it was my own fiver," said the child.

"Good! Good! Right you are! A fiver for me and a fiver for you on Daffodil."

The child had never been to a race-meeting before, and his eyes were blue fire. He pursed his mouth tight and watched. A Frenchman just in front had put his money on Lancelot. Wild with excitement, he flayed his arms up and down, yelling `Lancelot! Lancelot!" in his French accent.

Daffodil came in first, Lancelot second, Mirza third. The child, flushed and with eyes blazing, was curiously serene. His uncle brought him four five-pound notes, four to one.

"What am I to do with these?" he cried, waving them before the boy's eyes.

"I suppose we'll talk to Bassett," said the boy. "I expect I have fifteen hundred now; and twenty in reserve; and this twenty."

His uncle studied him for some moments.

"Look here, son!" he said. "You're not serious about Bassett and that fifteen hundred, are you?"

"Yes, I am. But it's between you and me, uncle. Honor bright?"

"Honor bright all right, son! But I must talk to Bassett."

"If you'd like to be a partner, uncle, with Bassett and me, we could all be partners. Only, you'd have to promise, honor bright, uncle, not to let it go beyond us three. Bassett and I are lucky, and you must be lucky, because it was your ten shillings I started winning with. . . ."

Uncle Oscar took both Bassett and Paul into Richmond Park for an afternoon, and there they talked.

"It's like this, you see, sir," Bassett said. "Master Paul would get me talking about racing events, spinning yarns, you know, sir. And he was always keen on knowing if I'd made or if I'd lost. It's about a year since, now, that I put five shillings on Blush of Dawn for him: and we lost. Then the luck turned, with that ten shillings he had from you: that we put on Singhalese. And since that time, it's been pretty steady, all things considering. What do you say, Master Paul?"

"We're all right when we're sure," said Paul. "It's when we're not quite sure that we go down.

"Oh, but we're careful then," said Bassett.

"But when are you *sure?*" smiled Uncle Oscar.

"It's Master Paul, sir," said Bassett in a secret, religious voice. "It's as if he had it from heaven. Like Daffodil, now, for the Lincoln. That was as sure as eggs."

"Did you put anything on Daffodil?" asked Oscar Cresswell.

"Yes, sir. I made my bit."

"And my nephew?"

Bassett was obstinately silent, looking at Paul.

"I made twelve hundred, didn't I, Bassett? I told uncle I was putting three hundred on Daffodil."

"That's right," said Bassett, nodding.

"But where's the money?" asked the uncle.

"I keep it safe locked up, sir. Master Paul he can have it any minute he likes to ask for it."

"What, fifteen hundred pounds?"

"And twenty! And *forty*, that is, with the twenty he made on the course."

"It's amazing!" said the uncle.

"If Master Paul offers you to be partners, sir, I would, if I were you: if you'll excuse me," said Bassett.

Oscar Cresswell thought about it.

"I'll see the money," he said.

They drove home again, and, sure enough, Bassett came round to the garden-house with fifteen hundred pounds in notes. The twenty pounds reserve was left with Joe Glee, in the Turf Commission deposit.

"You see, it's all right, uncle, when I'm *sure!* Then we go strong, for all we're worth. Don't we, Bassett?"

"We do that, Master Paul."

"And when are you sure?" said the uncle, laughing.

"Oh, well, sometimes I'm *absolutely* sure, like about Daffodil," said the boy; "and sometimes I have an idea; and sometimes I haven't even an idea, have I, Bassett? Then we're careful, because we mostly go down."

"You do, do you! And when you're sure, like about Daffodil, what makes you sure, sonny?"

"Oh, well, I don't know," said the boy uneasily. "I'm sure, you know, uncle; that's all."

"It's as if he had it from heaven, sir," Bassett reiterated.

"I should say so!" said the uncle.

But he became a partner. And when the Leger was coming on Paul was "sure" about Lively Spark, which was a quite inconsiderable horse. The boy insisted on putting a thousand on the horse, Bassett went for five hundred, and Oscar Cresswell two hundred. Lively Spark came in first, and the betting had been ten to one against him. Paul had made ten thousand.

"You see," he said, "I was absolutely sure of him."

Even Oscar Cresswell had cleared two thousand.

"Look here, son," he said, "this sort of thing makes me nervous."

"It needn't, uncle! Perhaps I shan't be sure again for a long time."

227

"But what are you going to do with your money?" asked the uncle.

"Of course," said the boy, "I started it for mother. She said she had no luck, because father is unlucky, so I thought if *I* was lucky, it might stop whispering."

"What might stop whispering?"

"Our house. I *hate* our house for whispering."

"What does it whisper?"

"Why—why"—the boy fidgeted—"why, I don't know. But it's always short of money, you know, uncle."

"I know it, son, I know it."

"You know people send mother writs, don't you, uncle?"

"I'm afraid I do," said the uncle.

"And then the house whispers, like people laughing at you behind your back. It's awful, that is! I thought if I was lucky—"

"You might stop it," added the uncle.

The boy watched him with big blue eyes, that had an uncanny cold fire in them, and he said never a word.

"Well, then!" said the uncle. "What are we doing?"

"I shouldn't like mother to know I was lucky," said the boy.

"Why not, son?"

"She'd stop me."

"I don't think she would."

"Oh!"—and the boy writhed in an odd way—"I *don't* want her to know, uncle."

"All right, son! We'll manage it without her knowing."

They managed it very easily. Paul, at the other's suggestion, handed over five thousand pounds to his uncle, who deposited it with the family lawyer, who was then to inform Paul's mother that a relative had put five thousand pounds into his hands, which sum was to be paid out a thousand pounds at a time, on the mother's birthday, for the next five years.

"So she'll have a birthday present of a thousand pounds for

five successive years," said Uncle Oscar. "I hope it won't make it all the harder for her later."

Paul's mother had her birthday in November. The house had been "whispering" worse than ever lately, and, even in spite of his luck, Paul could not bear up against it. He was very anxious to see the effect of the birthday letter, telling his mother about the thousand pounds.

When there were no visitors, Paul now took his meals with his parents, as he was beyond the nursery control. His mother went into town nearly every day. She had discovered that she had an odd knack of sketching furs and dress materials, so she worked secretly in the studio of a friend who was the chief "artist" for the leading drapers. She drew the figures of ladies in furs and ladies in silk and sequins for the newspaper advertisements. This young woman artist earned several thousand pounds a year, but Paul's mother only made several hundreds, and she was again dissatisfied. She so wanted to be first in something, and she did not succeed, even in making sketches for drapery advertisements.

She was down to breakfast on the morning of her birthday. Paul watched her face as she read her letters. He knew the lawyer's letter. As his mother read it, her face hardened and became more expressionless. Then a cold, determined look came on her mouth. She hid the letter under the pile of others, and said not a word about it.

"Didn't you have anything nice in the post for your birthday, mother?" said Paul.

"Quite moderately nice," she said, her voice cold and absent.

She went away to town without saying more.

But in the afternoon Uncle Oscar appeared. He said Paul's mother had had a long interview with the lawyer, asking if the whole five thousand could not be advanced at once, as she was in debt.

"What do you think, uncle?" said the boy.

"I leave it to you, son."

"Oh, let her have it, then! We can get some more with the other," said the boy.

"A bird in the hand is worth two in the bush, laddie!" said Uncle Oscar.

"But I'm sure to *know* for the Grand National; or the Lincolnshire; or else the Derby. I'm sure to know for *one* of them," said Paul.

So Uncle Oscar signed the agreement, and Paul's mother touched the whole five thousand. Then something very curious happened. The voices in the house suddenly went mad, like a chorus of frogs on a spring evening. There were certain new furnishings, and Paul had a tutor. He was *really* going to Eton, his father's school, in the following autumn. There were flowers in the winter, and a blossoming of the luxury Paul's mother had been used to. And yet the voices in the house, behind the sprays of mimosa and almond-blossom, and from under the piles of iridescent cushions, simply trilled and screamed in a sort of ecstasy: "There *must* be more money! Oh-h-h; there *must* be more money. Oh, now, now-w! Now-w-w—there *must* be more money!—more than ever! More than ever!"

It frightened Paul terribly. He studied away at his Latin and Greek with his tutor. But his intense hours were spent with Bassett. The Grand National had gone by: he had not "known," and had lost a hundred pounds. Summer was at hand. He was in agony for the Lincoln. But even for the Lincoln he didn't "know," and he lost fifty pounds. He became wild-eyed and strange, as if something were going to explode in him.

"Let it alone, son! Don't you bother about it!" urged Uncle Oscar. But it was as if the boy couldn't really hear what his uncle was saying.

"I've got to know for the Derby! I've got to know for the

Derby!" the child reiterated, his big blue eyes blazing with a sort of madness.

His mother noticed how overwrought he was.

"You'd better go to the seaside. Wouldn't you like to go now to the seaside, instead of waiting? I think you'd better," she said, looking down at him anxiously, her heart curiously heavy because of him.

But the child lifted his uncanny blue eyes.

"I couldn't possibly go before the Derby, mother!" he said. "I couldn't possibly!"

"Why not?" she said, her voice becoming heavy when she was opposed. "Why not? You can still go from the seaside to see the Derby with your Uncle Oscar, if that's what you wish. No need for you to wait here. Besides, I think you care too much about these races. It's a bad sign. My family has been a gambling family, and you won't know till you grow up how much damage it has done. But it has done damage. I shall have to send Bassett away, and ask Uncle Oscar not to talk racing to you, unless you promise to be reasonable about it: go away to the seaside and forget it. You're all nerves!"

"I'll do what you like, mother, so long as you don't send me away till after the Derby," the boy said.

"Send you away from where? Just from this house?"

"Yes," he said, gazing at her.

"Why, you curious child, what makes you care about this house so much, suddenly? I never knew you loved it."

He gazed at her without speaking. He had a secret within a secret, something he had not divulged, even to Bassett or to his Uncle Oscar.

But his mother, after standing undecided and a little bit sullen for some moments, said:

"Very well, then! Don't go to the seaside till after the Derby, if you don't wish it. But promise me you won't let your nerves go to pieces. Promise you won't think so much about horse-racing and *events,* as you call them!"

231

"Oh no," said the boy casually. "I won't think much about them, mother. You needn't worry. I wouldn't worry, mother, if I were you."

"If you were me and I were you," said his mother, "I wonder what we *should* do!"

"But you know you needn't worry, mother, don't you?" the boy repeated.

"I should be awfully glad to know it," she said wearily.

"Oh, well, you *can*, you know. I mean, you *ought* to know you needn't worry," he insisted.

"Ought I? Then I'll see about it," she said.

Paul's secret of secrets was his wooden horse, that which had no name. Since he was emancipated from a nurse and a nursery-governess, he had had his rocking-horse removed to his own bedroom at the top of the house.

"Surely you're too big for a rocking-horse!" his mother had remonstrated.

"Well, you see, mother, till I can have a *real* horse, I like to have *some* sort of animal about," had been his quaint answer.

"Do you feel he keeps you company?" she laughed.

"Oh yes! He's very good, he always keeps me company, when I'm there," said Paul.

So the horse, rather shabby, stood in an arrested prance in the boy's bedroom.

The Derby was drawing near, and the boy grew more and more tense. He hardly heard what was spoken to him, he was very frail, and his eyes were really uncanny. His mother had sudden strange seizures of uneasiness about him. Sometimes, for half an hour, she would feel a sudden anxiety about him that was almost anguish. She wanted to rush to him at once, and know he was safe.

Two nights before the Derby, she was at a big party in town, when one of her rushes of anxiety about her boy, her first-born, gripped her heart till she could hardly speak. She fought with the feeling, might and main, for she believed in common sense. But it was too strong. She had to leave the dance and go downstairs to telephone to the country. The children's nursery-governess was terribly surprised and startled at being rung up in the night.

"Are the children all right, Miss Wilmot?"

"Oh yes, they are quite all right."

"Master Paul? Is he all right?"

"He went to bed as right as a trivet. Shall I run up and look at him?"

"No," said Paul's mother reluctantly. "No! Don't trouble. It's all right. Don't sit up. We shall be home fairly soon." She did not want her son's privacy intruded upon.

"Very good," said the governess.

It was about one o'clock when Paul's mother and father drove up to their house. All was still. Paul's mother went to her room and slipped off her white fur cloak. She had told her maid not to wait up for her. She heard her husband downstairs, mixing a whisky and soda.

And then, because of the strange anxiety at her heart, she stole upstairs to her son's room. Noiselessly she went along the upper corridor. Was there a faint noise? What was it?

She stood, with arrested muscles, outside his door, listening. There was a strange, heavy, and yet not loud noise. Her heart stood still. It was a soundless noise, yet rushing and powerful. Something huge, in violent, hushed motion. What was it? What in God's name was it? She ought to know. She felt that she knew the noise. She knew what it was.

Yet she could not place it. She couldn't say what it was. And on and on it went, like a madness.

Softly, frozen with anxiety and fear, she turned the door-handle.

The room was dark. Yet in the space near the window, she heard and saw something plunging to and fro. She gazed in fear and amazement.

Then suddenly she switched on the light, and saw her son,

in his green pyjamas, madly surging on the rocking-horse. The blaze of light suddenly lit him up, as he urged the wooden horse, and lit her up, as she stood, blonde, in her dress of pale green and crystal, in the doorway.

"Paul!" she cried. "Whatever are you doing?"

"It's Malabar!" he screamed in a powerful, strange voice. "It's Malabar!"

His eyes blazed at her for one strange and senseless second, as he ceased urging his wooden horse. Then he fell with a crash to the ground, and she, all her tormented motherhood flooding upon her, rushed to gather him up.

But he was unconscious, and unconscious he remained, with some brain-fever. He talked and tossed, and his mother sat stonily by his side.

"Malabar! It's Malabar! Bassett, Bassett, I *know!* It's Malabar!"

So the child cried, trying to get up and urge the rocking-horse that gave him his inspiration.

"What does he mean by Malabar?" asked the heart-frozen mother.

"I don't know," said the father stonily.

"What does he mean by Malabar?" she asked her brother Oscar.

"It's one of the horses running for the Derby," was the answer.

And, in spite of himself, Oscar Cresswell spoke to Bassett, and himself put a thousand on Malabar: at fourteen to one.

The third day of the illness was critical: they were waiting for a change. The boy, with his rather long, curly hair, was tossing ceaselessly on the pillow. He neither slept nor regained consciousness, and his eyes were like blue stones. His mother sat, feeling her heart had gone, turned actually into a stone.

In the evening, Oscar Cresswell did not come, but Bassett sent a message, saying could he come up for one moment, just one moment? Paul's mother was very angry at the intrusion, but on second thought she agreed. The boy was the same. Perhaps Bassett might bring him to consciousness.

The gardener, a shortish fellow with a little brown moustache and sharp little brown eyes, tiptoed into the room, touched his imaginary cap to Paul's mother, and stole to the bedside, staring with glittering, smallish eyes at the tossing, dying child.

"Master Paul!" he whispered. "Master Paul! Malabar came in first all right, a clean win. I did as you told me. You've made over seventy thousand pounds, you have; you've got over eighty thousand. Malabar came in all right, Master Paul."

"Malabar! Malabar! Did I say Malabar, mother? Did I say Malabar? Do you think I'm lucky, mother? I knew Malabar, didn't I? Over eighty thousand pounds! I call that lucky, don't you, mother? Over eighty thousand pounds! I knew, didn't I know I knew? Malabar came in all right. If I ride my horse till I'm sure, then I tell you, Bassett, you can go as high as you like. Did you go for all you were worth, Bassett?"

"I went a thousand on it, Master Paul."

"I never told you, mother, that if I can ride my horse, and *get there*, then I'm absolutely sure—oh, absolutely! Mother, did I ever tell you? I *am* lucky!"

"No, you never did," said his mother.

But the boy died in the night.

And even as he lay dead, his mother heard her brother's voice saying to her: "My God, Hester, you're eighty-odd thousand to the good, and a poor devil of a son to the bad. But, poor devil, poor devil, he's best gone out of a life where he rides his rocking-horse to find a winner."

JOHN STEINBECK

John Steinbeck was born on February 27, 1902, and brought up in Salinas, California. His interest in writing goes back as far as he can remember. At four, he recalls, he discovered with delight that high *rhymed with* fly, *and the discovery led to a fascination with words that he never lost. As a student in Salinas High School he wrote for the school paper,* El Gabilan, *but his interests were not limited to literary activities. He was a member of the basketball team and the track team. He graduated in 1919 president of his class. During high school he also worked on the farms and ranches in the valley and in a big sugar refinery nearby.*

In the fall of 1919 he entered Stanford University as a special student. He was, he told the registrar, interested not in a degree, but only in certain subjects. In the spring of 1920 he withdrew and did not return until the fall of 1922. This time, however, he remained in residence until 1925. In the intervals between his appearances on campus he worked at various jobs in the Salinas Valley and also started writing in earnest. Finally, in 1925, he decided that writing should be his career and that New York City was the place to pursue it. And so he headed east, by way of a freighter through the Panama Canal.

He stopped off in Panama for a while to absorb atmosphere for a contemplated book on Henry Morgan the pirate (later published as Cup of Gold, *1929). In New York he worked for a brief period as a cub reporter for the* Journal, *quit, and got a job carrying bricks with a construction crew building Madison Square Garden. When that job ended, he tried freelancing for a time, but soon headed back to California.*

That winter (1928) he took a job as caretaker for a house in the High Sierras near Lake Tahoe while he finished Cup of Gold. *Actually, this was his fourth book; he had destroyed three earlier novels. On the strength of being a published author, he got married in 1930 and went to live in Pacific Grove. But recognition and financial success were a long time coming.* Pastures of Heaven (1932) *and* To a God Unknown (1933) *got good reviews, but did not sell.* Tortilla Flat (1935) *was a modest success. It paid his debts and gave him financial security to write* In Dubious Battle (1936). *This novel brought him an award from the Commonwealth Club of California for the best novel of the year by a Californian, but little money.*

Of Mice and Men (1937) *was his first big success. He was thirty-five years old when it was published. A Book-of-the-Month Club selection, it was a best seller for months and was dramatized in collaboration with George Kaufman. It had a successful Broadway run in 1938.*

In 1939 Mr. Steinbeck published the novel that made him famous: Grapes of Wrath. *He had started working on it two years before, shortly after he had written a series of articles on the migrant workers for the San Francisco* News *(October 1936). He did not think the novel would be popular; it made publishing history.*

Firmly established as a major writer, Mr. Steinbeck continued to publish regularly, with a break during World

War II, *when he worked for a time at special writing assignments for the United States Army Air Force and later as overseas war correspondent for the New York* Herald Tribune. *Among his better known works since the war are* The Moon Is Down *(1942),* Cannery Row *(1945),* The Wayward Bus *(1947),* East of Eden *(1952),* Sweet Thursday *(1954) and his latest,* The Winter of Our Discontent *(1961). He became interested in the theater, and among other productions wrote* Pipe Dream, *a musical produced by Rodgers and Hammerstein in 1955.*

Four of his short stories have received O. Henry Memorial Awards from 1934 to 1950. "The Promise" (1938) was awarded third prize. His only collection of short stories, The Long Valley *(1938), contains "The Great Mountains," published originally in the* North American Review *in December 1933.*

THE GREAT MOUNTAINS

In the humming heat of a midsummer afternoon the little boy Jody listlessly looked about the ranch for something to do. He had been to the barn, had thrown rocks at the swallows' nests under the eaves until every one of the little mud houses broke open and dropped its lining of straw and dirty feathers. Then at the ranch house he baited a rat trap with stale cheese and set it where Doubletree Mutt, that good big dog, would get his nose snapped. Jody was not moved by an impulse of cruelty; he was bored with the long hot afternoon. Doubletree Mutt put his stupid nose in the trap and got it smacked, and shrieked with agony and limped away with blood on his nostrils. No matter where he was hurt, Mutt limped. It was just a way he had. Once when he was young, Mutt got caught in a coyote trap, and always after that he limped, even when he was scolded.

When Mutt yelped, Jody's mother called from inside the house, "Jody! Stop torturing that dog and find something to do."

Jody felt mean then, so he threw a rock at Mutt. Then he took his slingshot from the porch and walked up toward the brush line to try to kill a bird. It was a good slingshot, with store-bought rubbers, but while Jody had often shot at birds, he had never hit one. He walked up through the vegetable patch, kicking his bare toes into the dust. And on the way he found the perfect slingshot stone, round and slightly flattened and heavy enough to carry through the air. He fitted it into the leather pouch of his weapon and proceeded to the brush line. His eyes narrowed, his mouth worked strenuously; for the first time that afternoon he was intent. In the shade of the sagebrush the little birds were working, scratching in the leaves, flying restlessly a few feet and scratching again. Jody pulled back the rubbers of the sling and advanced cautiously. One little thrush paused and looked at him and crouched, ready to fly. Jody sidled nearer, moving one foot slowly after the other. When he was twenty feet away, he carefully raised the sling and aimed. The stone whizzed; the thrush started up and flew right into it. And down the little bird went with a broken head. Jody ran to it and picked it up.

"Well, I got you," he said.

The bird looked much smaller dead than it had alive. Jody felt a little mean pain in his stomach, so he took out his pocket-knife and cut off the bird's head. Then he disemboweled it, and took off its wings; and finally he threw all the pieces into the brush. He didn't care about the bird, or its life, but he knew what older people would say if they had seen him kill it; he was ashamed because of their potential opinion. He decided to forget the whole thing as quickly as he could, and never to mention it.

The hills were dry at this season, and the wild grass was golden, but where the spring-pipe filled the round tub and the tub spilled over, there lay a stretch of fine green grass, deep and sweet and moist. Jody drank from the mossy tub and washed the bird's blood from his hands in cold water. Then he lay on his back in the grass and looked up at the dumpling summer clouds. By closing one eye and destroying perspective he brought them down within reach so that he could put up his fingers and stroke them. He helped the gentle wind push them down the sky; it seemed to him that they went faster for his help. One fat white cloud he helped clear to the mountain rims and pressed it firmly over, out of sight. Jody wondered what it was seeing, then. He sat up the better to look at the great mountains where they went piling back, growing darker and more savage until they finished with one jagged ridge, high up against the west. Curious secret mountains; he thought of the little he knew about them.

"What's on the other side?" he asked his father once.

"More mountains, I guess. Why?"

"And on the other side of them?"

"More mountains. Why?"

"More mountains on and on?"

"Well, no. At last you come to the ocean."

"But what's in the mountains?"

"Just cliffs and brush and rocks and dryness."

"Were you ever there?"

"No."

"Has anybody ever been there?"

"A few people, I guess. It's dangerous, with cliffs and things. Why, I've read there's more unexplored country in the mountains of Monterey County than any place in the United States." His father seemed proud that this should be so.

"And at last the ocean?"

"At last the ocean."

"But," the boy insisted, "but in between? No one knows?"

"Oh, a few people do, I guess. But there's nothing there to get. And not much water. Just rocks and cliffs and greasewood. Why?"

"It would be good to go."

"What for? There's nothing there."

Jody knew something was there, something very wonderful because it wasn't known, something secret and mysterious. He could feel within himself that this was so. He said to his mother, "Do you know what's in the big mountains?"

She looked at him and then back at the ferocious range, and she said, "Only the bear, I guess."

"What bear?"

"Why the one that went over the mountain to see what he could see."

Jody questioned Billy Buck, the ranch hand, about the possibility of ancient cities lost in the mountains, but Billy agreed with Jody's father.

"It ain't likely," Billy said. "There'd be nothing to eat unless a kind of people that can eat rocks live there."

That was all the information Jody ever got, and it made the mountains dear to him, and terrible. He thought often of the miles of ridge after ridge until at last there was the sea. When the peaks were pink in the morning they invited him among them: and when the sun had gone over the edge in the evening and the mountains were a purple-like despair, then Jody was afraid of them; then they were so impersonal and aloof that their very imperturbability was a threat.

Now he turned his head toward the mountains of the east, the Gabilans, and they were jolly mountains, with hill ranches in their creases, and with pine trees growing on the crests. People lived there, and battles had been fought against the Mexicans on the slopes. He looked back for an instant at the Great Ones and shivered a little at the contrast. The foothill cup of the home ranch below him was sunny and safe. The house gleamed with white light and the barn was brown and warm. The red cows on the farther hill ate their way slowly toward the north. Even the dark cypress tree by the bunkhouse was usual and safe. The chickens scratched about in the dust of the farmyard with quick waltzing steps.

Then a moving figure caught Jody's eye. A man walked slowly over the brow of the hill, on the road from Salinas, and he was headed toward the house. Jody stood up and moved

242

down toward the house too, for if someone was coming, he wanted to be there to see. By the time the boy had got to the house the walking man was only halfway down the road, a lean man, very straight in the shoulders. Jody could tell he was old only because his heels struck the ground with hard jerks. As he approached nearer, Jody saw that he was dressed in blue jeans and in a coat of the same material. He wore clodhopper shoes and an old flat-brimmed Stetson hat. Over his shoulder he carried a gunny sack, lumpy and full. In a few moments he had trudged close enough so that his face could be seen. And his face was as dark as dried beef. A mustache, blue-white against the dark skin, hovered over his mouth, and his hair was white, too, where it showed at his neck. The skin of his face had shrunk back against the skull until it defined bone, not flesh, and made the nose and chin seem sharp and fragile. The eyes were large and deep and dark, with eyelids stretched tightly over them. Irises and pupils were one, and very black, but the eyeballs were brown. There were no wrinkles in the face at all. This old man wore a blue denim coat buttoned to the throat with brass buttons, as all men do who wear no shirts. Out of the sleeves came strong bony wrists and hands gnarled and knotted and hard as peach branches. The nails were flat and blunt and shiny.

The old man drew close to the gate and swung down his sack when he confronted Jody. His lips fluttered a little and a soft impersonal voice came from between them.

"Do you live here?"

Jody was embarrassed. He turned and looked at the house, and he turned back and looked toward the barn where his father and Billy Buck were. "Yes," he said, when no help came from either direction.

"I have come back," the old man said. "I am Gitano, and I have come back."

Jody could not take all this responsibility. He turned abruptly, and ran into the house for help, and the screen door banged after him. His mother was in the kitchen poking out the clogged holes of a colander with a hairpin, and biting her lower lip with concentration.

"It's an old man," Jody cried excitedly. "It's an old *paisano* man, and he says he's come back."

His mother put down the colander and stuck the hairpin behind the sink board. "What's the matter now?" she asked patiently.

"It's an old man outside. Come on out."

"Well, what does he want?" She untied the strings of her apron and smoothed her hair with her fingers.

"I don't know. He came walking."

His mother smoothed down her dress and went out, and Jody followed her. Gitano had not moved.

"Yes?" Mrs. Tiflin asked.

Gitano took off his old black hat and held it with both hands in front of him. He repeated, "I am Gitano, and I have come back."

"Come back? Back where?"

Gitano's whole straight body leaned forward a little. His right hand described the circle of the hills, the sloping fields and the mountains, and ended at his hat again. "Back to the rancho. I was born here, and my father, too."

"Here?" she demanded. "This isn't an old place."

"No, there," he said, pointing to the western ridge. "On the other side there, in a house that is gone."

At last she understood. "The old 'dobe that's washed almost away, you mean?"

"Yes, *señora*. When the rancho broke up they put no more lime on the 'dobe, and the rains washed it down."

Jody's mother was silent for a little, and curious home-sick thoughts ran through her mind, but quickly she cleared them out. "And what do you want here now, Gitano?"

"I will stay here," he said quietly, "until I die."

"But we don't need an extra man here."

"I can not work hard any more, *señora*. I can milk a cow, feed chickens, cut a little wood; no more. I will stay here." He indicated the sack on the ground beside him. "Here are my things."

She turned to Jody. "Run down to the barn and call your father."

Jody dashed away, and he returned with Carl Tiflin and Billy Buck behind him. The old man was standing as he had been, but he was resting now. His whole body had sagged into a timeless repose.

"What is it?" Carl Tiflin asked. "What's Jody so excited about?"

Mrs. Tiflin motioned to the old man. "He wants to stay here. He wants to do a little work and stay here."

"Well, we can't have him. We don't need any more men. He's too old. Billy does everything we need."

They had been talking over him as though he did not exist, and now, suddenly, they both hesitated and looked at Gitano and were embarrassed.

He cleared his throat. "I am too old to work. I come back where I was born."

"You weren't born here," Carl said sharply.

"No. In the 'dobe house over the hill. It was all one rancho before you came."

"In the mud house that's all melted down?"

"Yes, I and my father. I will stay here now on the rancho."

"I tell you you won't stay," Carl said angrily. "I don't need an old man. This isn't a big ranch. I can't afford food and doctor bills for an old man. You must have relatives and friends. Go to them. It is like begging to come to strangers."

"I was born here," Gitano said patiently and inflexibly.

Carl Tiflin didn't like to be cruel, but he felt he must. "You can eat here tonight," he said. "You can sleep in the little room of the old bunkhouse. We'll give you your breakfast in

245

the morning, and then you'll have to go along. Go to your friends. Don't come to die with strangers."

Gitano put on his black hat and stooped for the sack. "Here are my things," he said.

Carl turned away. "Come on, Billy, we'll finish down at the barn. Jody, show him the little room in the bunkhouse."

He and Billy turned back toward the barn. Mrs. Tiflin went into the house, saying over her shoulder, "I'll send some blankets down."

Gitano looked questioningly at Jody. "I'll show you where it is," Jody said.

There was a cot with a shuck mattress, an apple box holding a tin lantern, and a backless rocking-chair in the little room of the bunkhouse. Gitano laid his sack carefully on the floor and sat down on the bed. Jody stood shyly in the room, hesitating to go. At last he said,

"Did you come out of the big mountains?"

Gitano shook his head slowly. "No, I worked down the Salinas Valley."

The afternoon thought would not let Jody go. "Did you ever go into the big mountains back there?"

The old dark eyes grew fixed, and their light turned inward on the years that were living in Gitano's head. "Once— when I was a little boy. I went with my father."

"Way back, clear into the mountains?"

"Yes."

"What was there?" Jody cried. "Did you see any people or any houses?"

"No."

"Well, what was there?"

Gitano's eyes remained inward. A little wrinkled strain came between his brows.

"What did you see in there?" Jody repeated.

"I don't know," Gitano said. "I don't remember."

"Was it terrible and dry?"

"I don't remember."

In his excitement, Jody had lost his shyness. "Don't you remember anything about it?"

Gitano's mouth opened for a word, and remained open while his brain sought the word. "I think it was quiet—I think it was nice."

Gitano's eyes seemed to have found something back in the years, for they grew soft and a little smile seemed to come and go in them.

"Didn't you ever go back in the mountains again?" Jody insisted.

"No."

"Didn't you ever want to?"

But now Gitano's face became impatient. "No," he said in a tone that told Jody he didn't want to talk about it any more. The boy was held by a curious fascination. He didn't want to go away from Gitano. His shyness returned.

"Would you like to come down to the barn and see the stock?" he asked.

Gitano stood up and put on his hat and prepared to follow.

It was almost evening now. They stood near the watering trough while the horses sauntered in from the hillsides for an evening drink. Gitano rested his big twisted hands on the top rail of the fence. Five horses came down and drank, and then stood about, nibbling at the dirt or rubbing their sides against the polished wood of the fence. Long after they had finished drinking an old horse appeared over the brow of the hill and came painfully down. It had long yellow teeth; its hoofs were flat and sharp as spades, and its ribs and hip-bones jutted out under its skin. It hobbled up to the trough and drank water with a loud sucking noise.

"That's old Easter," Jody explained. "That's the first horse my father ever had. He's thirty years old." He looked up into Gitano's old eyes for some response.

"No good any more," Gitano said.

Jody's father and Billy Buck came out of the barn and walked over.

"Too old to work," Gitano repeated. "Just eats and pretty soon dies."

Carl Tiflin caught the last words. He hated his brutality toward old Gitano, and so he became brutal again.

"It's a shame not to shoot Easter," he said. "It'd save him a lot of pains and rheumatism." He looked secretly at Gitano, to see whether he noticed the parallel, but the big bony hands did not move, nor did the dark eyes turn from the horse. "Old things ought to be put out of their misery," Jody's father went on. "One shot, a big noise, one big pain in the head maybe, and that's all. That's better than stiffness and sore teeth."

Billy Buck broke in. "They got a right to rest after they worked all their life. Maybe they like to just walk around."

Carl had been looking steadily at the skinny horse. "You can't imagine now what Easter used to look like," he said softly. "High neck, deep chest, fine barrel. He could jump a five-bar gate in stride. I won a flat race on him when I was fifteen years old. I could of got two hundred dollars for him any time. You wouldn't think how pretty he was." He checked himself, for he hated softness. "But he ought to be shot now," he said.

"He's got a right to rest," Billy Buck insisted.

Jody's father had a humorous thought. He turned to Gitano. "If ham and eggs grew on a side-hill I'd turn you out to pasture too," he said. "But I can't afford to pasture you in my kitchen."

He laughed to Billy Buck about it as they went on toward the house. "Be a good thing for all of us if ham and eggs grew on the side-hills."

Jody knew how his father was probing for a place to hurt Gitano. He had been probed often. His father knew every place in the boy where a word would fester.

"He's only talking," Jody said. "He didn't mean it about

248

shooting Easter. He likes Easter. That was the first horse he ever owned."

The sun sank behind the high mountains as they stood there, and the ranch was hushed. Gitano seemed to be more at home in the evening. He made a curious sharp sound with his lips and stretched one of his hands over the fence. Old Easter moved stiffly to him, and Gitano rubbed the lean neck under the mane.

"You like him?" Jody asked softly.

"Yes—but he's no damn good."

The triangle sounded at the ranch house. "That's supper," Jody cried. "Come on up to supper."

As they walked up toward the house Jody noticed again that Gitano's body was as straight as that of a young man. Only by a jerkiness in his movements and by the scuffling of his heels could it be seen that he was old.

The turkeys were flying heavily into the lower branches of the cypress tree by the bunkhouse. A fat sleek ranch cat walked across the road carrying a rat so large that its tail dragged on the ground. The quail on the side-hills were still sounding the clear water call.

Jody and Gitano came to the back steps and Mrs. Tiflin looked out through the screen door at them.

"Come running, Jody. Come in to supper, Gitano."

Carl and Billy Buck had started to eat at the long oilcloth-covered table. Jody slipped into his chair without moving it, but Gitano stood holding his hat until Carl looked up and said, "Sit down, sit down. You might as well get your belly full before you go on." Carl was afraid he might relent and let the old man stay, and so he continued to remind himself that this couldn't be.

Gitano laid his hat on the floor and diffidently sat down. He wouldn't reach for food. Carl had to pass it to him. "Here, fill yourself up." Gitano ate very slowly, cutting tiny pieces of meat and arranging little pats of mashed potato on his plate.

249

The situation would not stop worrying Carl Tiflin. "Haven't you got any relatives in this part of the country?" he asked.

Gitano answered with some pride, "My brother-in-law is in Monterey. I have cousins there, too."

"Well, you can go and live there, then."

"I was born here," Gitano said in gentle rebuke.

Jody's mother came in from the kitchen, carrying a large bowl of tapioca pudding.

Carl chuckled to her, "Did I tell you what I said to him? I said if ham and eggs grew on the side-hills I'd put him out to pasture, like old Easter."

Gitano stared unmoved at his plate.

"It's too bad he can't stay," said Mrs. Tiflin.

"Now don't you start anything," Carl said crossly.

When they had finished eating, Carl and Billy Buck and Jody went into the living-room to sit for a while, but Gitano, without a word of farewell or thanks, walked through the kitchen and out the back door. Jody sat and secretly watched his father. He knew how mean his father felt.

"This country's full of these old *paisanos*," Carl said to Billy Buck.

"They're damn good men," Billy defended them. "They can work older than white men. I saw one of them a hundred and five years old, and he could still ride a horse. You don't see any white men as old as Gitano walking twenty or thirty miles."

"Oh, they're tough all right," Carl agreed. "Say, are you standing up for him too? Listen, Billy," he explained, "I'm having a hard enough time keeping this ranch out of the Bank of Italy without taking on anybody else to feed. You know that, Billy."

"Sure, I know," said Billy. "If you was rich, it'd be different."

"That's right, and it isn't like he didn't have relatives to go to. A brother-in-law and cousins right in Monterey. Why should I worry about him?"

Jody sat quietly listening, and he seemed to hear Gitano's gentle voice and its unanswerable, "But I was born here." Gitano was mysterious like the mountains. There were ranges back as far as you could see, but behind the last range piled up against the sky there was a great unknown country. And Gitano was an old man, until you got to the dull dark eyes. And in behind them was some unknown thing. He didn't ever say enough to let you guess what was inside, under the eyes. Jody felt himself irresistibly drawn toward the bunkhouse. He slipped from his chair while his father was talking and he went out the door without making a sound.

The night was very dark and far-off noises carried in clearly. The hamebells of a wood team sounded from way over the hill on the country road. Jody picked his way across the dark yard. He could see a light through the window of the little room of the bunkhouse. Because the night was secret he walked quietly up to the window and peered in. Gitano sat in the rocking-chair and his back was toward the window. His right arm moved slowly back and forth in front of him. Jody pushed the door open and walked in. Gitano jerked upright and, seizing a piece of deerskin, he tried to throw it over the thing in his lap, but the skin slipped away. Jody stood overwhelmed by the thing in Gitano's hand, a lean and lovely rapier with a golden basket hilt. The blade was like a thin ray of dark light. The hilt was pierced and intricately carved.

"What is it?" Jody demanded.

Gitano only looked at him with resentful eyes, and he picked up the fallen deerskin and firmly wrapped the beautiful blade in it.

Jody put out his hand. "Can't I see it?"

Gitano's eyes smoldered angrily and he shook his head. "Where'd you get it? Where'd it come from?"

251

Now Gitano regarded him profoundly, as though he pondered. "I got it from my father."

"Well, where'd he get it?"

Gitano looked down at the long deerskin parcel in his hand. "I don' know?"

"Didn't he ever tell you?"

"No."

"What do you do with it?"

Gitano looked slightly surprised. "Nothing. I just keep it."

"Can't I see it again?"

The old man slowly unwrapped the shining blade and let the lamplight slip along it for a moment. Then he wrapped it up again. "You go now. I want to go to bed." He blew out the lamp almost before Jody had closed the door.

As he went back toward the house, Jody knew one thing more sharply than he had ever known anything. He must never tell anyone about the rapier. It would be a dreadful thing to tell anyone about it, for it would destroy some fragile structure of truth. It was a truth that might be shattered by division.

On the way across the dark yard Jody passed Billy Buck. "They're wondering where you are," Billy said.

Jody slipped into the living-room, and his father turned to him. "Where have you been?"

"I just went out to see if I caught any rats in my new trap."

"It's time you went to bed," his father said.

Jody was first at the breakfast table in the morning. Then his father came in, and last, Billy Buck. Mrs. Tiflin looked in from the kitchen.

"Where's the old man, Billy?" she asked.

"I guess he's out walking," Billy said. "I looked in his room and he wasn't there."

"Maybe he started early to Monterey," said Carl. "It's a long walk."

"No," Billy explained. "His sack is in the little room."

After breakfast Jody walked down to the bunkhouse. Flies were flashing about in the sunshine. The ranch seemed especially quiet this morning. When he was sure no one was watching him, Jody went into the little room, and looked into Gitano's sack. An extra pair of long cotton underwear was there, an extra pair of jeans and three pairs of worn socks. Nothing else was in the sack. A sharp loneliness fell on Jody. He walked slowly back toward the house. His father stood on the porch talking to Mrs. Tiflin.

"I guess old Easter's dead at last," he said. "I didn't see him come down to water with the other horses."

In the middle of the morning Jess Taylor from the ridge ranch rode down.

"You didn't sell that old gray crowbait of yours, did you, Carl?"

"No, of course not. Why?"

"Well," Jess said. "I was out this morning early, and I saw a funny thing. I saw an old man on an old horse, no saddle, only a piece of rope for a bridle. He wasn't on the road at all. He was cutting right up straight through the brush. I think he had a gun. At least I saw something shine in his hand."

"That's old Gitano," Carl Tiflin said. "I'll see if any of my guns are missing." He stepped into the house for a second. "Nope, all here. Which way was he heading, Jess?"

"Well, that's the funny thing. He was heading straight back into the mountains."

Carl laughed. "They never get too old to steal," he said. "I guess he stole old Easter."

"Want to go after him, Carl?"

"Hell no, just save me burying that horse. I wonder where he got the gun. I wonder what he wants back there."

Jody walked up through the vegetable patch, toward the brush line. He looked searchingly at the towering mountains—ridge after ridge after ridge until at last there was the ocean.

For a moment he thought he could see a black speck crawling up the farthest ridge. Jody thought of the rapier and of Gitano. And he thought of the great mountains. A longing caressed him, and it was so sharp that he wanted to cry to get it out of his breast. He lay down in the green grass near the round tub at the brush line. He covered his eyes with his crossed arms and lay there a long time, and he was full of a nameless sorrow.

KATHERINE ANNE PORTER

Katherine Anne Porter was born at Indian Creek, near San Antonio, Texas, on May 15, 1894, and spent her childhood in Texas and Louisiana. Educated in a number of private schools in the South, she was, in her own words, "precocious, nervous, rebellious, unteachable," making life uncomfortable both for herself and for those around her.

Writing has always been the one absorbing passion of her life. She began writing stories at the age of three, when she first learned to print words, and she continued to write as she grew older, not with any particular audience in mind, but simply in an attempt to master the craft of fiction. Most of what she has written has never seen publication. "I have written and destroyed manuscripts quite literally by the trunkful," she said at one time. Since her youth she has also been an avid reader, particularly of the English classics and the classics in translation. Familiarity with the classics, she believes, is essential for anyone who wants to write.

When she chose literature as a profession (she would insist that she had no choice in the matter) she was under no illusion that she could support herself by it. She made her living as a hack writer, turning out political articles, reviewing books, acting as "ghost" writer for others. In 1952 she published some of the best of these occasional pieces, written "by request, with limitations of space, a date fixed for finishing, on a chosen subject or theme," under the title The Days Before. These served, she said, "to get me a living, such as it was, so that I might be able to write my stories in their own time and way."

Miss Porter has always moved about a good deal, and it was a sojourn in Mexico, where she went in 1920 to study the native arts of the Mexicans, that led to her first published story, "María Concepción," in Century, December 1922. Accused of having a "taste for the exotic, for foreign flavors," she retaliated by saying, "I write about Mexico because that is my familiar country. . . . The artist can do no more than deal with familiar and beloved things, from which he could not, and, above all, would not escape."

Eight years later, when "María Concepción" was published, along with five other stories, in Flowering Judas, Miss Porter was immediately hailed as an outstanding craftsman, a finished artist in the writing of prose fiction. Subsequent publications have added to her reputation.

The immediate result of this first volume of stories in 1930 was a Guggenheim Fellowship for creative writing the following year, which enabled her to go to Paris to write. She received a second Guggenheim in 1938. Her literary output over the years has been slim. In 1935 she brought out a second edition of Flowering Judas, adding four more stories; two of the four, "Theft" and "The Cracked Looking Glass," had appeared in The Best American Short Stories for 1930 and 1933. In 1939 she published Pale Horse, Pale Rider, a group of three novelettes. It was awarded the Gold Medal for Literature by the Society for Libraries of New York University. The Leaning Tower and Other Stories (1944) contains, among others, the *stories drawn from childhood, including "The Circus." A novel has been promised for some time.*

Miss Porter has been writer-in-residence and guest lecturer in a number of colleges and universities, including Stanford University (1949), the University of Chicago (1951), the University of Michigan (1953), the University of Virginia (1958), and Washington and Lee (1959). She was a Fulbright Lecturer at the University of Liege, Belgium, in 1955, and Fellow of Regional American Literature in the Library of Congress, 1944. She has gone to Hollywood upon occasion to work on movie scenarios. She is a former vice-president of the National Institute of Arts and Letters.

THE CIRCUS

The long planks set on trestles rose one above the other to a monstrous height and stretched dizzyingly in a wide oval ring. They were packed with people—"lak fleas on a dog's ear," said Dicey, holding Miranda's hand firmly and looking about her with disapproval. The white billows of enormous canvas sagged overhead, held up by three poles set evenly apart down the center. The family, when seated, occupied almost a whole section on one level.

On one side of them in a long row sat Father, sister Maria, brother Paul, Grandmother; great-aunt Keziah, cousin Keziah, and second-cousin Keziah, who had just come down from Kentucky on a visit; uncle Charles Breaux, cousin Charles Breaux, and aunt Marie-Anne Breaux. On the other side sat small cousin Lucie Breaux, big cousin Paul Gay, great-aunt Sally Gay (who took snuff and was therefore a disgrace to the family); two strange, extremely handsome young men who might be cousins but who were certainly in love with cousin Miranda Gay; and cousin Miranda Gay herself, a most dashing young lady with crisp silk skirts, a half dozen of them at once, a lovely perfume and wonderful black curly hair above enormous wild gray eyes, "like a colt's," Father said. Miranda hoped to be exactly like her when she grew up. Hanging to

Dicey's arm she leaned out and waved to cousin Miranda, who waved back smiling, and the strange young men waved to her also. Miranda was most fearfully excited. It was her first circus; it might also be her last because the whole family had combined to persuade Grandmother to allow her to come with them. "Very well, this once," Grandmother said, "since it's a family reunion."

This once! This once! She could not look hard enough at everything. She even peeped down between the wide crevices of the piled-up plank seats, where she was astonished to see odd-looking, roughly dressed little boys peeping up from the dust below. They were squatted in little heaps, staring up quietly. She looked squarely into the eyes of one, who returned her a look so peculiar she gazed and gazed, trying to understand it. It was a bold grinning stare without any kind of friendliness in it. He was a thin, dirty little boy with a floppy old checkerboard cap pulled over crumpled red ears and dust-colored hair. As she gazed he nudged the little boy next to him, whispered, and the second little boy caught her eye. This was too much. Miranda pulled Dicey's sleeve. "Dicey, what are those little boys doing down there?" "Down where?" asked Dicey, but she seemed to know already, for she bent over and looked through the crevice, drew her knees together and her skirts around her, and said severely: "You jus mind yo' own business and stop throwin' yo' legs around that way. Don't you pay any mind. Plenty o' monkeys right here in the show widout you studyin dat kind."

An enormous brass band seemed to explode right at Miranda's ear. She jumped, quivered, thrilled blindly and almost forgot to breathe as sound and color and smell rushed together and poured through her skin and hair and beat in her head and hands and feet and pit of her stomach. "Oh," she called out in her panic, closing her eyes and seizing Dicey's hand hard. The flaring lights burned through her lids, a roar of laughter like rage drowned out the steady raging of the drums and horns. She opened her eyes . . . A creature in a blousy white overall with ruffles at the neck and ankles, with bone-white skull and chalk-white face, with tufted eyebrows far apart in the middle of his forehead, the lids in a black sharp angle, a long scarlet mouth stretching back into sunken cheeks, turned up at the corners in a perpetual bitter grimace of pain, astonishment, not smiling, pranced along a wire stretched down the center of the ring, balancing a long thin pole with little wheels at either end. Miranda thought at first he was walking on air, or flying, and this did not surprise her; but when she saw the wire, she was terrified. High above their heads the inhuman figure pranced, spinning the little wheels. He paused, slipped, the flapping white leg waved in space; he staggered, wobbled, slipped sidewise, plunged, and caught the wire with frantic knee, hanging there upside down, the other leg waving like a feeler above his head; slipped once more, caught by one frenzied heel, and swung back and forth like a scarf. . . . The crowd roared with savage delight, shrieks of dreadful laughter like devils in delicious torment. . . . Miranda shrieked too, with real pain, clutching at her stomach with her knees drawn up. . . . The man on the wire, hanging by his foot, turned his head like a seal from side to side and blew sneering kisses from his cruel mouth. Then Miranda covered her eyes and screamed, the tears pouring over her cheeks and chin.

"Take her home," said her father, "get her out of here at once," but the laughter was not wiped from his face. He merely glanced at her and back to the ring. "Take her away, Dicey," called the Grandmother, from under her half-raised crepe veil. Dicey, rebelliously, very slowly, without taking her gaze from the white figure swaying on the wire, rose, seized the limp, suffering bundle, prodded and lumped her way over knees and feet, through the crowd, down the levels of the scaffolding, across a space of sandy tanbark, out through a flap in the tent. Miranda was crying steadily with an occasional hiccough. A dwarf was standing in the entrance, wearing a little woolly beard, a pointed cap, tight red breeches, long shoes with turned-up toes. He carried a thin white wand. Miranda almost touched him before she saw him, her distorted face with its open mouth and glistening tears almost level with his. He leaned forward and peered at her with kind, not-human golden eyes, like a near-sighted dog: then made a horrid grimace at her, imitating her own face. Miranda struck at him in sheer ill temper, screaming. Dicey drew her away quickly, but not before Miranda had seen in his face, suddenly, a look of haughty, remote displeasure, a true grown-up look. She knew it well. It chilled her with a new kind of fear: she had not believed he was really human.

"Raincheck, get your raincheck!" said a very disagreeable-looking fellow as they passed. Dicey turned toward him almost in tears herself. "Mister, caint you see I won't be able to git back? I got this young un to see to. . . . What good dat lil piece of paper goin to do *me?*" All the way home she was cross, and grumbled under her breath: little ole meany . . . little ole scare-cat . . . gret big baby . . . never go nowhere . . . never see nothin . . . come on here now, hurry up—always ruinin everything for othah folks . . . won't let anybody rest a minute, won't let anybody have any good times . . . come on here now, you wanted to go home and you're going there . . . snatching Miranda along, vicious but cautious, careful not to cross the line where Miranda could say outright: "Dicey did this or said this to me . . ." Dicey was allowed a certain freedom up to a point.

The family trooped into the house just before dark and scattered out all over it. From every room came the sound of chatter and laughter. The other children told Miranda what she had missed: wonderful little ponies with plumes and bells on their bridles, ridden by darling little monkeys in velvet jackets and peaked hats . . . trained white goats that danced . . . a baby elephant that crossed his front feet and leaned against his cage and opened his mouth to be fed, *such a baby!* . . . more clowns, funnier than the first one even . . . beautiful ladies with bright yellow hair, wearing white silk tights with red satin sashes, had performed on white trapezes; they also had hung by their toes, but how gracefully, like flying birds! Huge white horses had lolloped around and round the ring with men and women dancing on their backs! One man had swung by his teeth from the top of the tent and another had put his head in a lion's mouth. Ah, what she had not missed! Everybody had been enjoying themselves while she was missing her first big circus and spoiling the day for Dicey. Poor Dicey. Poor dear Dicey. The other children who hadn't thought of Dicey until that moment, mourned over her with sad mouths, their malicious eyes watching Miranda squirm. Dicey had been looking forward for weeks to this day! And then Miranda must get scared—"Can you *imagine* being afraid of that funny old clown?" each one asked the other, and then they smiled pityingly on Miranda. . . .

Then too, it had been a very important occasion in another way: it was the first time Grandmother had ever allowed herself to be persuaded to go to the circus. One could not gather, from her rather generalized opinions, whether there had been no circuses when she was young, or there had been and it was not proper to see them. At any rate for her usual sound reasons, Grandmother had never approved of circuses, and though she would not deny she had been amused somewhat, still there had been sights and sounds in this one which she maintained were, to say the least, not particularly edifying to the young. Her son Harry, who came in while the children made an early supper, looked at their illuminated faces, all the brothers and sisters and visiting cousins, and said, "This basket of young doesn't seem to be much damaged." His mother said, "The fruits of their present are in a future so far off, neither of us may live to know whether harm has been done or not. That is the trouble," and she went on ladling out hot milk to pour over their buttered toast. Miranda was sitting silent, her underlip drooping. Her father smiled at her. "You missed it, Baby," he said softly, "and what good did that do you?"

Miranda burst again into tears: had to be taken away at last, and her supper was brought up to her. Dicey was exasperated and silent. Miranda could not eat. She tried, as if she were really remembering them, to think of the beautiful wild beings in white satin and spangles and red sashes who danced and frolicked on the trapezes; of the sweet little furry ponies and the lovely pet monkeys in their comical clothes. She fell asleep, and her invented memories gave way before her real ones, the bitter terrified face of the man in blowsy white falling to his death—ah, the cruel joke!—and the terrible grimace of the unsmiling dwarf. She screamed in her sleep and sat up crying for deliverance from her torments.

Dicey came, her cross, sleepy eyes half-closed, her big dark mouth pouted, thumping the floor with her thick bare feet. "I *swear*," she said, in a violent hoarse whisper. "What the matter with you? You need a good spankin, I *swear*! Wakin everybody up like this . . ."

Miranda was completely subjugated by her fears. She had a way of answering Dicey back. She would say, "Oh, hush up, Dicey." Or she would say, "I don't have to mind *you*. I don't have to mind anybody but my grandmother," which was provokingly true. And she would say, "You don't know what you're talking about." The day just past had changed that. Miranda sincerely did not want anybody, not even Dicey, to be cross with her. Ordinarily she did not care how cross she made the harassed adults around her. Now if Dicey must be cross, she still did not really care, if only Dicey might not turn out the lights and leave her to the fathomless terrors of the darkness where sleep could overtake her once more. She hugged Dicey with both arms, crying, "Don't, don't leave me. *Don't* be so angry! I c-c-can't b-bear it!"

263

Dicey lay down beside her with a long moaning sigh, which meant that she was collecting her patience and making up her mind to remember that she was a Christian and must bear her cross. "Now you go to sleep," she said, in her usual warm being-good voice. "Now you jes shut yo eyes and go to sleep. I ain't going to leave you. Dicey ain't mad at nobody . . . *no*body in the whole worl'. . . ."

JOHN O'HARA

John O'Hara was born in Pottsville, Pennsylvania, on January 31, 1905, the oldest child in a family of seven. His father was a well-to-do surgeon, and Mr. O'Hara was brought up accustomed to every convenience, if not luxury. In 1924 he graduated from the Niagara Preparatory School, after having twice been expelled from other private academies, and was preparing to enter Yale University when disaster struck. His father died suddenly; the estate he left turned out to be surprisingly small; and Yale University was out of the question.

Instead, Mr. O'Hara took a job as reporter for the Pottsville Journal, *tossed it up after a short while, and headed west. For the next few years he drifted from job to job: ship's steward, clerk in a railway freight office, guard in an amusement park, reader of gas meters, press agent. Eventually he came to New York City, where he was, for a while, secretary to Heywood Broun. Leaving Broun's employ, he worked for various New York newspapers and magazines as rewrite man, dramatic critic, football editor, religious editor, radio editor. He went to Pittsburgh as editor of the* Bulletin-Index, *but by August 1933, he was back in New York City, trying to make a living as a freelance writer of short stories, submitted mainly to the* New Yorker, *which published a number of his stories.*

In December 1933, he started working on a novel,

using the bed in his hall bedroom as a desk, typing away, as has always been his custom, late at night, after spending the early evening out somewhere talking to people. When he had 25,000 words of the novel written he sent identical letters to three publishing houses, offering the novel to the one that would subsidize him while he finished writing it. All three expressed their interest, and the next day he signed an agreement with one of them guaranteeing him $50 a week for three months, at which time he promised the completed novel.

This was Appointment in Samarra, *published in 1934, when he was twenty-nine years old. It stamped him immediately as a member of the "hard-boiled school of fiction." It had a mixed reception from the critics because of what Henry Seidel Canby, editor of the* Saturday Review of Literature, *called its "thoroughgoing vulgarity," despite the brilliance of the prose. But it was an immediate popular success. Paramount Studios offered him a lucrative contract as a writer of movie scripts, and Mr. O'Hara's days of penury were over.*

For the next six years he worked for one movie studio after another, and went back and forth between Hollywood and New York City. A rapid writer, impatient of revision, he continued to turn out novels and short stories in rapid succession. Butterfield 8 *(1935) and* Hope of Heaven *(1938) were his next novels.* The Doctor's Son and Other Stories *(1935),* Files on Parade *(1939), and* Pal Joey *(1940) were collections of short stories. The latter, stories about a second-rate night club crooner, appeared originally in the* New Yorker. *He later turned these stories into a musical comedy with Rodgers and Hart that won the New York Critics Circle and Donaldson awards*

for the best musical in 1952. "Do You Like It Here?"
appeared originally in the New Yorker, *September 8, 1939,*
and was reprinted in Short Stories from the New Yorker
(1940). Pipe Night *(1945) and* Hellbox *(1947) are two*
other volumes of his collected stories.

Ten North Frederick *(1955) won the National Book*
Award for the year. Since then he has written From the
Terrace *(1958) and* Ourselves to Know *(1960).*

Mr. O'Hara insists that his newspaper experience,
particularly as a rewrite man, taught him how to say a
thing right the first time.

DO YOU LIKE IT HERE?

The door was open. The door had to be kept open during study period, so there was no knock, and Roberts was startled when a voice he knew and hated said, "Hey, Roberts. Wanted in Van Ness's office." The voice was Hughes'.

"What for?" said Roberts.

"Why don't you go and find out what for, Dopey?" said Hughes.

"Phooey on you," said Roberts.

"Phooey on *you*," said Hughes, and left.

Roberts got up from the desk. He took off his eyeshade and put on a tie and coat. He left the light burning.

Van Ness's office, which was *en suite* with his bedroom, was on the ground floor of the dormitory, and on the way down Roberts wondered what he had done. It got so after a while, after going to so many schools, that you recognized the difference between being "wanted in Somebody's office" and "Somebody wants to see you." If a master wanted to see you on some minor matter, it didn't always mean that you had to go to his office, but if it was serious, they always said, "You're wanted in Somebody's office." That meant Somebody would be in his office, waiting for you, waiting specially for you. Roberts didn't know why this difference existed, but it did, all right. Well, all he could think of was that he had been smoking in the shower room, but Van Ness never paid much attention to that. Everybody smoked in the shower room, and Van Ness never did anything about it unless he just happened to catch you.

For minor offenses Van Ness would speak to you when he made his rounds of the rooms during study period. He would walk slowly down the corridor, looking in at each room to see that the proper occupant, and no one else, was there; and when he had something to bawl you out about, something unimportant, he would consult a list he carried, and he would stop in and bawl you out about it and tell you what punishment went with it. That was another detail that made the summons to the office a little scary.

Roberts knocked on Van Ness's half-open door and a voice said, "Come in."

Van Ness was sitting at his typewriter, which was on a small desk beside the large desk. He was in a swivel chair and when he saw Roberts he swung around, putting himself behind the large desk, like a damn judge.

He had his pipe in his mouth and he seemed to look over the steel rims of his spectacles. The light caught his Phi Beta Kappa key, which momentarily gleamed as though it had diamonds in it.

"Hughes said you wanted me to report here," said Roberts.

"I did," said Van Ness. He took his pipe out of his mouth and began slowly to knock the bowl empty as he repeated, "I did." He finished emptying his pipe before he again spoke. He took a long time about it, and Roberts, from his years of experience, recognized that as torture tactics. They always made you wait to scare you. It was sort of like the third degree. The horrible damn thing was that it always did scare you a little, even when you were used to it.

Van Ness leaned back in his chair and stared through his glasses at Roberts. He cleared his throat. "You can sit down," he said.

269

"Yes, sir," said Roberts. He sat down and again Van Ness made him wait.

"Roberts, you've been here now how long—five weeks?"

"A little over. About six."

"About six weeks," said Van Ness. "Since the seventh of January. Six weeks. Strange. Strange. Six weeks, and I really don't know a thing about you. Not much, at any rate. Roberts, tell me a little about yourself."

"How do you mean, Mister?"

"How do I mean? Well—about your life, before you decided to honor us with your presence. Where you came from, what you did, why you went to so many schools, so on."

"Well, I don't know."

"Oh, now. Now, Roberts. Don't let your natural modesty overcome the autobiographical urge. Shut the door."

Roberts got up and closed the door.

"Good," said Van Ness. "Now, proceed with this—uh—dossier. Give me the—huh—huh—*lowdown* on Roberts, Humphrey, Second Form, McAllister Memorial Hall, et cetera."

Roberts, Humphrey, sat down and felt the knot of his tie. "Well, I don't know. I was born at West Point, New York. My father was a first lieutenant then and he's a major now. My father and mother and I lived in a lot of places because he was in the Army and they transferred him. Is that the kind of stuff you want, Mister?"

"Proceed, proceed. I'll tell you when I want you to—uh—halt." Van Ness seemed to think that was funny, that "halt."

"Well, I didn't go to a regular school till I was ten. My mother got a divorce from my father and I went to school in San Francisco. I only stayed there a year because my mother got married again and we moved to Chicago, Illinois."

"Chicago, Illinois! Well, a little geography thrown in, eh, Roberts? Gratuitously. Thank you. Proceed."

"Well, so then we stayed there about two years and then

270

we moved back East, and my stepfather is a certified public accountant and we moved around a lot."

"Peripatetic, eh, Roberts?"

"I guess so. I don't exactly know what that means." Roberts paused.

"Go on, go on."

"Well, so I just went to a lot of schools, some day and some boarding. All that's written down on my application blank here. I had to put it all down on account of my credits."

"Correct. A very imposing list it is, too, Roberts, a very imposing list. Ah, to travel as you have. Switzerland. How I've regretted not having gone to school in Switzerland. Did you like it there?"

"I was only there about three months. I liked it all right, I guess."

"And do you like it here, Roberts?"

"Sure."

"You do? You're sure of that? You wouldn't want to change anything?"

"Oh, I wouldn't say that, not about any school."

"Indeed," said Van Ness. "With your vast experience, naturally you would be quite an authority on matters educational. I suppose you have many theories as to the strength and weaknesses inherent in the modern educational systems."

"I don't know. I just—I don't know. Some schools are better than others. At least I like some better than others."

"Of course. Of course." Van Ness seemed to be thinking about something. He leaned back in his swivel chair and gazed at the ceiling. He put his hands in his pants pockets and then suddenly he leaned forward. The chair came down and Van Ness's belly was hard against the desk and his arm was stretched out on the desk, full length, fist closed.

"Roberts! Did you ever see this before? Answer me!" Van Ness's voice was hard. He opened his fist, and in it was a wristwatch.

271

Roberts looked down at the watch. "No, I don't think so," he said. He was glad to be able to say it truthfully.

Van Ness continued to hold out his hand, with the wrist-watch lying in the palm. He held out his hand a long time, fifteen seconds at least, without saying anything. Then he turned his hand over and allowed the watch to slip onto the desk. He resumed his normal position in the chair. He picked up his pipe, slowly filled it, and lit it. He shook the match back and forth long after the flame had gone. He swung around a little in his chair and looked at the wall, away from Roberts. "As a boy I spent six years at this school. My brothers, my two brothers, went to this school. My *father* went to this school. I have a deep and abiding and lasting affection for this school. I have been a member of the faculty of this school for more than a decade. I like to think that I am part of this school, that in some small measure I have assisted in its progress. I like to think of it as more than a mere steppingstone to higher education. At this very moment there are in this school the sons of men who were my classmates. I have not been without my opportunities to take a post at this and that college or university, but I choose to remain here. Why? Why? Because I love this place. I love this place, Roberts. I cherish its traditions. I cherish its good name." He paused, and turned to Roberts. "Roberts, there is no room here for a thief!"

Roberts did not speak.

"There is no room here for a thief, I said!"

"Yes, sir."

Van Ness picked up the watch without looking at it. He held it a few inches above the desk. "This miserable watch was stolen last Friday afternoon, more than likely during the basketball game. As soon as the theft was reported to me I immediately instituted a search for it. My search was unsuccessful. Sometime Monday afternoon the watch was put here, here in my room. When I returned here after classes Monday afternoon, this watch was lying on my desk. Why?

Because the contemptible rat who stole it knew that I had instituted the search, and like the rat he is, he turned yellow and returned the watch to me. Whoever it is, he kept an entire dormitory under a loathsome suspicion. I say to you, I do not know who stole this watch or who returned it to my rooms. But by God, Roberts, I'm going to find out, if it's the last thing I do. If it's the last thing I do. That's all, Roberts. You may go." Van Ness sat back, almost breathless.

Roberts stood up. "I give you my word of honor, I—"

"I said you may go!" said Van Ness.

Roberts was not sure whether to leave the door open or to close it, but he did not ask. He left it open.

He went up the stairs to his room. He went in and took off his coat and tie, and sat on the bed. Over and over again, first violently, then weakly, he said it, "The bastard, the dirty bastard."

JEROME WEIDMAN

Jerome Weidman was born August 4, 1913, on the lower East Side of New York City, the son of Joseph and Anne (Falkovitz) Weidman, both immigrants from Central Europe. His childhood, he writes, was a very happy one. "My knowledge of family tensions and sibling frictions came from observing the families of my friends. My parents seemed by instinct to understand and practice what several decades of books on child psychology have since codified and urged on the modern parent. They liked their children, and their children liked them."

He had a host of friends and playmates, most of them, like himself, children of immigrants from various parts of Europe. And the lower East Side was a wonderful place to play. "The East River, which flowed almost under our windows, was, to me and the rest of these kids not unlike, I see now, the Mississippi to Mark Twain. We played on the docks, on the barges, swam in the river, and lived cheek by jowl with the sight of ships, the sound of ships, and the men who work on ships."

An extremely good student, he graduated from De Witt Clinton High School valedictorian of his class and was offered his choice of three college scholarships. Unfortunately, none of these included money for living expenses. His family had struggled to send him and his sister through high school, his mother taking in part-time work from a necktie factory in the neighborhood to supplement the money that his father earned as an operator in a men's clothing shop. Athough he felt fairly sure of being able to work his way through college, he was also certain that he could not do so and still send money to his parents. And so he got a job in New York, as a combination office boy, stenographer, and junior auditor, with a firm on Seventh Avenue. The salary was twelve dollars a week.

His closest friends all went off to college, and suddenly he found himself, at seventeen, all alone. He had been a good athlete, popular socially, something of a leader in a close group. "I do not think," he writes, "that my friends meant to drop me, or were even aware that they were dropping me, but drop me they did. Geography and other interests, I am sure, were responsible, but I was not in a mood to analyze at that time." One day, feeling particularly depressed, he decided to "write out the act of betrayal" on the part of one of his former friends. He says of the act, "I don't know why. Perhaps I wanted a private record of my friend's perfidy. I certainly did not do it as a literary exercise." The result astonished him. "As soon as I finished writing about it, the pain of the act vanished, and was replaced by a feeling of accomplishment that I don't think I would be exaggerating to describe as pleasure."

He was totally unaware of the literary implications of what he had done, but two years later, when he was nineteen, he embarked quite consciously upon a writing career. Again, the impulse to write came as a reaction to depression, but this time in a quite different way. On January 1, 1932, taking stock of his prospects in life, and feeling particularly sorry for himself, he decided that the thing to *do was to commit suicide. The next day, however, he became intrigued with the account of an incident related by one of the girls in the office. She had told it so ineptly that he had the urge to write it down and bring out the inherent drama in the situation. He did, and sold it to the* American Spectator *for $10. Elated, he wrote seven more stories in seven consecutive days. The* American Spectator *bought three of them, other editors bought the rest, and Mr. Weidman was launched on a literary career that has seen two hundred of his stories published in magazines throughout the United States, Canada, Europe, and even Asia and Australia.*

College ambitions were later fulfilled by attendance at City College of New York and Washington Square College. He studied law at New York University (1934–37), was admitted to the bar, but never practiced, for in 1937 his first novel, I Can Get It for You Wholesale, *was so successful that he decided to devote full time to writing.*

"The Horse That Could Whistle Dixie," written in the days when most of his efforts went into depicting "heels" of both sexes, was published originally as "Pony Ride." It was the title story in a collection of his stories published in 1939. His most recent collection is My Father Sits in the Dark *(1961). Three of his short stories have won O. Henry Memorial Awards; another was included in* The Best American Short Stories of 1943.

Among his dozen novels, The Enemy Camp *(1958) was a Book-of-the-Month Club selection. Fiorello, a romantic musical comedy, based on the life of former mayor La Guardia of New York City, with George Abbott as coauthor, received the Pulitzer Prize in 1959.*

THE HORSE THAT
COULD WHISTLE "DIXIE"

The pony track at the zoo lay in a hollow between the Small Mammals and the Flying Cages. There was a charge for those who wanted to ride the ponies, but there was no charge for watching, so even the people who couldn't afford to pay for rides stopped to let the children look and give themselves a rest after the walk from the Boston Post Road entrance and the exhausting business of hauling their young through the Small Mammal House and past the shrieking birds in the Flying Cages. A long, smooth iron rail that was just the right height for leaning on enclosed the track. The track itself was a large oval about a hundred yards from tip to tip, with a bridle path that went all the way round, hugging the iron rail and circling a floral centerpiece. At one end of the oval stood a tiny brick structure which housed a refreshment stand and the ticket office. In front of the house, inside the oval, was a small paddock with a dozen hitching posts, and here the children clustered.

The ponies not in use were tethered to the hitching posts. They were handsome little animals with shaggy coats, long manes, and saddles that seemed to have been designed for the specific purpose of being called "cute," a word much used by the spectators around the track. All the ponies looked tired; their sides heaved and their twitching nostrils hung close to the gravel that covered the paddock. Each hitching post had a nameplate that read "Dopey," "Grumpy," "Dixie," "Josie," and so on, and each pony had an attendant, a boy of about sixteen, wearing khaki breeches, a brown suede windbreaker, and a numbered metal badge. They all looked bored stiff.

Tickets cost ten cents and were good for one ride on a pony's back or in a small wickerwork cart intended for children who were afraid to sit in a saddle. It didn't matter whether a child knew how to ride or not—the boys in the suede windbreakers took care of that. They pocketed the tickets handed them by the parent, hoisted the child onto the pony, and walked along holding the child in place until the trip around the track was completed. Most children scorned the pony cart and wouldn't ride at all if they couldn't ride in a saddle. One of the things that contributed to the boredom of the boy attendants was the number of timid parents who were constantly finding this out.

A fat man with a derby and an expensive cigar with a raveled end leaned on the rail with both arms, chewing his cigar and watching with deep interest the movement of the ponies and the disputes of the parents and children. Between his legs, peering through the crisscrossed wires of the fence, was a small boy in a dark-blue chinchilla coat with brass buttons and several interesting approximations of naval insignia. The boy was fascinated by the ponies as his father was, but they seemed to affect him in a different way. He jumped around excitedly between his father's legs and moved from side to side in short, ecstatic leaps. The man kept him within bounds with gentle nudges of his knees. Occasionally, when the boy grew too excited for the confines of his father's legs, the man would give him a sharp poke with his knee that would knock the boy back into prescribed territory. The man was enjoying himself too thoroughly to look down at his son when he did this.

Every time a parent with a ticket tried to urge a child into the wickerwork cart, the fat man on the rail would begin to chuckle. He knew what was going to happen. The child would rebel and insist on riding in a saddle. If the fight grew good and loud, with the child screaming while the embarrassed parent tried to quiet him, the fat man would look delighted as he rattled his derby into a more comfortable position on his head and dusted ashes from the frayed end of his cigar. He would glance to his right and his left at the people who were leaning on the rail beside him, and say with an admiring grin, "Them kids, damn it, they got more guts than their old man."

He said this seven or eight times, and for a while the people on the rail kept changing, so he always had a new audience. Finally, when he said it once more, he realized that the man on his left had been there for about ten minutes. This embarrassed the fat man and he turned quickly to the man on his right. He got as far as "Them kids, damn it, they got more guts" before he saw that the man on his right had also been there long enough to have heard this observation at least three times. The fat man scowled and plugged one corner of his mouth with the battered cigar. "Come on, Timmy," he said through the other corner. "How about a ride?"

The small boy between his legs didn't hear him. He had his hands twined tightly in the metal of the fence and he was hopping with joy because of what he was seeing. His father reached down, seized his hand, and yanked him free of the fence. The boy looked startled, but he didn't cry. He probably didn't have time to cry. He was trying desperately to recover his balance as his father hauled him along, his thin, naked legs, with black shoes and blue socks at the ends of them, twinkling up and down and his free arm sawing the air. The two

279

disappeared into the structure that housed the ticket office. Several moments later they came out through the other end, inside the oval. The small boy had recovered his balance and the fat man had recovered his composure. But the boy had lost the expression of glee that he had worn when he was outside peering in. Being so close to the ponies was different from looking at them through the wire fence. He walked warily behind his father, turning his small face to right and left in quick, short glances. His father led him to the hitching post labelled "Dixie." The attendant, who had been lounging against the pony's side, straightened up and looked alert.

"Ride, sir?"

"Whaddaya *think* I want?" the fat man said jovially as he handed him a ticket. "The horse should whistle me a tune?"

The attendant paid no attention to the witticism. He slipped the ticket into his pocket and reached down for the child. But the small boy seemed to become suddenly aware of his danger. He shied away. The attendant didn't even look surprised. His look of boredom merely deepened and he put more accuracy into his second clutch. He slipped his hands deftly under the child's arms and started to lift him. The boy released a bellow of fear and a series of violent kicks. The attendant set him down promptly. The fat man looked surprised.

"Timmy!" he said sternly. "What's the matter with you?" Then, to the bored attendant, "Go ahead, son. Put him on."

This time the bellowing and the kicking started before the attendant's hands reached the boy. If his father hadn't been holding on to him, Timmy would have been well on his way to the Flying Cages. He was really frightened.

"Looks like he's scared of the horse, Mister." The attendant pointed to the wickerwork cart nearby. "How about a ride around in that?"

The fat man flushed scarlet. "Who says he's scared?" he snapped, and his jowls quivered.

The startled attendant opened his eyes wide. "All I said, Mister, I said the kid looks—"

"Never mind how he looks," the fat man said angrily. "You guys, you're paid to drive them around. Nothing else. You got your ticket. Put him on and drive him around." The attendant's face grew red, too, and he opened his mouth to say something. But he glanced about him first. The little scene had attracted the attention of the people outside the rail and the parents inside who were waiting for children to finish their rides. Everybody, including the other attendants, was looking on with interest.

"Yes, sir," the attendant said through tight lips. He reached for Timmy again, but the boy yelled with fright and hid himself behind his father, where he started to cry, his small body shaking and one fist burrowing into his eye. The attendant straightened up with a shrug. "Sorry, Mister, but I can't—"

"Hold the horse," the fat man ordered.

"What's that?" the attendant asked in a surprised voice.

"Tzimatter, can't you hear? I said hold the horse."

The attendant's lips grew tighter, but he reached over and took the pony's bridle with one hand and stroked its neck with the other. The fat man dipped down for his son. The boy, still crying with fright, dodged his father's grasp. One of the men leaning on the rail laughed. The fat man's red face seemed to swell with anger. He grabbed his son, swung him up in an arc, and brought him down with a thump in the saddle. The pony reared and the boy screamed with terror. He rocked dangerously for a moment, but the attendant stepped to his side and put one arm around him.

"Listen, Mister," the attendant said in a low voice, "if the kid's scared, there's no sense—"

"He's not scared," the fat man almost shouted. "Go ahead and give him his ride."

The attendant shrugged and unhitched the pony. Just as they started, the boy's inarticulate terror found voice.

281

"Pa!" he screamed. "Pa! Pa! Paaaaa!"

The attendant hesitated and looked back, but the fat man waved him on angrily. "Give him the ride, I said, didn't I?"

The pony, with the boy walking along beside it, moved off. The fat man watched it for a moment, and then he glanced around. Several people leaning on the rail were watching the moving pony. Two or three men were watching him. He dropped his eyes and busied himself with trying to relight his cigar. This was a hopeless task because the end was too frayed, but he worked at it until he recovered his composure. Then he walked abruptly into the small house. When he came out again, the pony was rounding the bend at the far end of the track. The fat man went to the hitching post and waited. Anyone could see the boy's terror was still with him, but he had stopped screaming. He was clutching tightly at the attendant's arm and whimpering. His eyes were glued on the hitching post and it seemed as though he would be able to hold his small, tense body together just long enough to make it. As they reached the post and the attendant put his arms under the boy's shoulders to lift him off the pony, the fat man stepped forward.

"Take him around again," he said curtly, holding out a ticket. The attendant stared at him in amazement. The fat man poked the ticket under his nose angrily. "I said take him around again."

The attendant took the ticket, and as he put it in his pocket the small boy seemed to realize what was happening. He broke into a fit of screaming and kicking that caused the pony to hop about nervously.

"Listen, Mister," the attendant said as he tried to quiet the plunging pony and keep the screaming boy in the saddle, "the kid's scared stiff. Can't you see he don't want—"

"You got your ticket, didn't you?" the fat man said savagely. "Well, give him the ride you got paid for. And leave out the advice."

Once more the pony carried the terrified child around the track. By this time everybody leaning on the rail or standing inside was watching the fat man and his son, but nobody was laughing. There was nothing funny about the sound of the small boy's hysterical whimpering or the sight of the father's flushed, sullen face. When the pony completed the circuit and reached the hitching post, the fat man shoved another ticket forward.

"Take him around again," he said.

The attendant looked at him with an angry sneer on his face, but he took the ticket. The small boy's whimpering rose a note or two, but died down as the pony started on its third trip. The people on the rail looked at one another and made room for newcomers who were being attracted by the strange sight. By the time the pony reached the hitching post again, a small crowd had gathered.

"Once more," the fat man said grimly, holding out a ticket.

The attendant took it and looked pleadingly at the crowd. Several people were scowling in a tentative, puzzled way, but nobody moved forward to interrupt. There was something formidable about the fat man in the derby, whose jaw was set so fiercely that thick ridges of muscle showed through the heavy jowls. The pony started around again.

The people on the rail were now whispering to each other nervously. Even the bored attendants were gathered in an excited knot at one side of the paddock. The fat man paid no attention to them. He chewed his cigar with slow, grinding movements of his jaws and watched his son. As the pony approached the hitching post for the fourth time, the man moved forward. The small boy wasn't making a sound. His wide, tense eyes stared out of his head, which was sunk in the collar of his brass-buttoned chinchilla coat. With his hands still clutching desperately at the attendant's arm, he was now a whipped, silent mass of tear-stained, quivering fright. The fat man didn't have any more tickets.

283

"All right," he said. "Take him off."

The attendant lifted the boy from the saddle and set him down on the ground. The child staggered, but he managed to remain upright. The insides of his naked knees were a bright, glowing pink where they had been irritated by the movement of the saddle and the pony's flanks and his own terrified efforts to grip the saddle. The fat man took the boy's hand and marched him firmly toward the gate in the wire fence. He kept the stub of his cigar tilted toward the sky and he stared straight ahead as he walked. The people who had been watching fell back before him. Just as he reached the gate, a fussy little old lady in a black fur coat stepped out of the crowd.

"That boy's knees," she said in shrill, indignant tones. "Look what you've done to that boy's knees! You ought to be ashamed of yourself. You take that boy to a drugstore right away and have them put—"

The fat man's free arm shot out. It faltered just before it reached the little old lady and then it brushed her aside, gently but firmly. The cigar stub jiggled up and down.

"Madam," the fat man said through his clenched teeth, "would you mind minding your own damn business?"

WALLACE E. STEGNER

Wallace E. Stegner was born on a farm near Lake Mills, Iowa, on February 18, 1909, but grew up in the wide open spaces of the West: North Dakota; Redmond, Washington; Eastend, Saskatchewan; Great Falls, Montana; Salt Lake City, Utah. For five years, between the ages of five and ten, he lived in Eastend, a frontier town near the American border, the setting for "Chip Off the Old Block." Here, in this "really rough and unregenerate frontier hamlet," as he called it, he earned his first money at the age of ten by shooting small game with a 12-gauge shotgun. Mr. Stegner once called those years in Saskatchewan more important to him than any other five years of his life, a tribute to the influence of one's childhood.

He attended high school in Salt Lake City, and worked his way through the University of Utah by selling rugs and linoleum and by keeping books in a pool hall for his meals. The urge to write fiction was with him in college, stimulated, in part, by Vardis Fisher, the Mormon author, who was teaching at the University during his first two years there. After graduating in 1930, at the age of twenty-one, he went to the University of Iowa for graduate study and part-time teaching. His thesis for his M.A. degree (1932) was a group of short stories. He finished his Ph.D. in 1935, with time out for an interval spent in California *and a teaching job at Augustana College, Rock Island, Illinois.*

In 1935 he returned to his alma mater, the University of Utah, as an instructor in English, writing fiction in his spare time and getting several stories published. Then, in 1937, at the age of twenty-eight, he won the Little, Brown and Company novelette contest with Remembering Laughter. *Immediately he resigned from the University and went to Paris with his wife (he had married in 1934) to devote full time to writing.* The Potter's House (1938) *was the result of that year in France. By the fall of 1938 he was back in teaching, this time at the University of Wisconsin, and he has remained in teaching ever since. From 1939 to 1945 he taught at Harvard University. Since 1945 he has been professor of English and Director of the Creative Writing Center at Stanford University.*

Mr. Stegner has continued, over the years, to publish short stories, novels, historical articles, and critical and technical articles on the art of fiction. Many of his short stories have won special recognition. "The Blue Winged Teal" received the O. Henry Memorial First Prize Award in 1950, and two other stories, "Two Rivers" (1942) and "Beyond the Glass Mountain" (1948), took second prize. Six of his stories, including "Chip Off the Old Block," published originally in the Virginia Quarterly Review, *October 1942, have appeared in the* Best American Short Stories *of the year. His collected stories have been published in* The Women on the Wall (1950) *and* The City of the Living (1956). *Among his novels,* The Big Rock Candy Mountain (1945) *has been, perhaps, the most widely popular, both with the critics and with the public at large. His most recent novel,* A Shooting Star, *set in*

California, was a Literary Guild Selection in 1961. One Nation (*with editors of* Look) *won the Houghton-Mifflin Life in America Award in 1945 and shared the* Saturday Review of Literature *Anisfield-Wolfe award in the same year.*

In 1950 and again in 1952 Mr. Stegner was awarded a Guggenheim Fellowship for creative writing.

For a number of years he has been co-editor (with Richard Scowcroft) of an annual collection of short stories written by students in the writing seminar at Stanford University. With Mr. Scowcroft and Boris Ilyina, he is the author of a book on the art of prose fiction, The Writer's Art (*1950*). *He has written half a dozen articles on various aspects of short story writing for* The Writer, *the* Atlantic Monthly, *and the* Saturday Review of Literature.

CHIP OFF THE OLD BLOCK

Sitting alone looking at the red eyes of the parlor heater, Chet thought how fast things happened. One day the flu hit. Two days after that his father left for Montana to get a load of whisky to sell for medicine. The next night he got back in the midst of a blizzard with his hands and feet frozen, bringing a sick homesteader he had picked up on the road; and now this morning all of them, the homesteader, his father, his mother, his brother Bruce, were loaded in a sled and hauled to the schoolhouse-hospital. It was scary how fast they all got it, even his father, who seldom got anything and was tougher than boiled owl. Everybody, he thought with some pride, but him. His mother's words as she left were a solemn burden on his mind. "You'll have to hold the fort, Chet. You'll have to be the man of the house." And his father, sweat on his face even in the cold, his frozen hands held tenderly in his lap, saying, "Better let the whisky alone. Put it away somewhere till we get back."

So he was holding the fort. He accepted the duty soberly. In the two hours since his family had left he had swept the floors, milked old Red and thrown down hay for her, brought in scuttles of lignite. And sitting now in the parlor he knew he was scared. He heard the walls tick and the floors creak.

Every thirty seconds he looked up from his book, and finally he yawned, stretched, laid the book down, and took a stroll through the whole house, cellar to upstairs, as if for exercise. But his eyes were sharp, and he stepped back a little as he threw open the doors of bedrooms and closets. He whistled a little between his teeth and looked at the calendar in the hall to see what day it was. November 4, 1918.

A knock on the back door sent him running. It was the young man named Vickers who had taken his family away. He was after beds and blankets for the schoolhouse. Chet helped him knock the beds down and load them on the sled. He would sleep on the couch in the parlor; it was warmer there, anyway; no cold floors to worry about.

In the kitchen, making a list of things he had taken, Vickers saw the keg, the sacked cases of bottles, the pile of whisky-soaked straw sheaths from the bottles that had been broken on the trip. "Your dad doesn't want to sell any of that, does he?" he said.

Chet thought briefly of his father's injunction to put the stuff away. But gee, the old man had frozen his hands and feet and caught the flu getting it, and now when people came around asking. . . . "Sure," he said. "That's what he bought it for, flu medicine."

"What've you got?"

"Rye and bourbon," Chet said. "There's some Irish, but I think he brought that special for somebody." He rummaged among the sacks. "Four dollars a bottle, I think it is," he said, and looked at Vickers to see if that was too much. Vickers didn't blink. "Or is it four-fifty?" Chet said.

Vicker's face was expressionless. "Sure it isn't five? I wouldn't want to cheat you." He took out his wallet, and under his eyes Chet retreated. "I'll go look," he said. "I think there's a list."

He stood in the front hall for a minute or two before he

came back. "Four-fifty," he said casually. "I thought probably it was."

Vickers counted out twenty-seven dollars. "Give me six rye," he said. With the sack in his hand he stood in the back door and looked at Chet and laughed. "What are you going to do with that extra three dollars?"

Chet felt his heart stop while he might have counted ten. His face began to burn. "What three dollars?"

"Never mind," Vickers said. "I was just ragging you. Got all you need to eat here?"

"I got crocks of milk," Chet said. He grinned at Vickers in relief, and Vickers grinned back. "There's bread Ma baked the other day, and spuds. If I need any meat I can go shoot a rabbit."

"Oh." Vicker's eyebrows went up. "You're a hunter, eh?"

"I shot rabbits all last fall for Mrs. Rieger," Chet said. "She's 'nemic and has to eat rabbits and prairie chickens and stuff. She lent me the shotgun and bought the shells."

"Mmm," Vickers said. "I guess you can take care of yourself. How old are you?"

"Twelve."

"That's old enough," said Vickers. "That's pretty old, in fact. Well, Mervin, if you need anything you call the school and I'll see that you get it."

"My name isn't Mervin," Chet said. "It's Chet."

"Okay," Vickers said. "Don't get careless with the fires."

"What do you think I am?" Chet said in scorn. He raised his hand stiffly as Vickers went out. A little tongue of triumph licked up in him. That three bucks would look all right, all right. Next time he'd know better than to change the price, too. He took the bills out of his pocket and counted them. Twenty-seven dollars was a lot of dough. He'd show Ma and Pa whether he could hold the fort or not.

But holding the fort was tiresome. By two o'clock he was bored stiff, and the floors were creaking again in the silence.

Then he remembered suddenly that he was the boss of the place. He could go or come as he pleased, as long as the cow was milked and the house kept warm. He thought of the two traps he had set in muskrat holes under the river bank. The blizzard and the flu had made him forget to see to them. And he might take Pa's gun and do a little hunting.

"Well," he said in the middle of the parlor rug, "I guess I will."

For an hour and a half he prowled the river brush. Over on the path toward Heathcliff's he shot a snowshoe rabbit, and the second of his traps yielded a stiffly frozen muskrat. The weight of his game was a solid satisfaction as he came up the dugway swinging the rabbit by its feet, the muskrat by its plated tail.

Coming up past the barn, he looked over towards Van Dam's, then the other way, toward Chapman's, half hoping that someone might be out, and see him. He whistled loudly, sang a little into the cold afternoon air, but the desertion of the whole street, the unbroken fields of snow where ordinarily there would have been dozens of sled tracks and fox-and-goose paths, let a chill in upon his pride. He came up the back steps soberly and opened the door.

The muskrat's slippery tail slid out of his mitten and the frozen body thumped on the floor. Chet opened his mouth, shut it again, speechless with surprise and shock. Two men were in the kitchen. His eyes jumped from the one by the whisky keg to the other, sitting at the table drinking whisky from a cup. The one drinking he didn't know. The other was Louis Treat, a halfbreed who hung out down at the stable and sometimes worked a little for the Half-Diamond Bar. All Chet knew about him was that he could braid horsehair ropes and sing a lot of dirty songs.

"Aha!" said Louis Treat. He smiled at Chet and made a rubbing motion with his hands. "We 'ave stop to get warm. You 'ave been hunting?"

"Yuh," Chet said automatically. He stood where he was, his eyes swinging between the two men. The man at the table raised his eyebrows at Louis Treat.

"Ees nice rabbit there," Louis said. His bright black button eyes went over the boy. Chet lifted the rabbit and looked at the frozen beads of blood on the white fur. "Yuh," he said. He was thinking about what his father always said. You could trust an Indian, if he was your friend, and you could trust a white man sometimes, if money wasn't involved, and you could trust a Chink more than either, but you couldn't trust a halfbreed.

Louis' voice went on, caressingly. "You 'ave mushrat too, eh? You lak me to 'elp you peel thees mushrat?" His hand, dipping under the sheepskin and into his pants pocket, produced a long-bladed knife that jumped open with the pressure of his thumb on a button.

Chet dropped the rabbit and took off his mitts. "No thanks," he said. "I can peel him."

Shrugging, Louis put the knife away. He turned to thump the bung hard into the keg, and nodded at the other man, who rose. "Ees tam we go," Louis said. "We 'ave been told to breeng thees wisky to the 'ospital."

"Who told you?" Chet's insides grew tight, and his mind was setting like plaster of Paris. If Pa was here he'd scatter these thieves all the way to Chapman's. But Pa wasn't here. He watched Louis Treat. You could never trust a halfbreed.

"The doctor, O'Malley," Louis said. Keeping his eye on Chet, he jerked his head at the other man. "Ere, you tak' the other end."

His companion, pulling up his sheepskin collar, stooped and took hold of the keg. Chet, with no blood in his face and no breath in his lungs, hesitated a split second and then jumped. Around the table, in the dining room door, he was out of their reach, and the shotgun was pointed straight at their

292

chests. With his thumb he cocked both barrels, click, click.

Louis Treat swore. "Put down that gun!"

"No, sir!" Chet said. "I won't put it down till you drop that keg and get out of here!"

The two men looked at each other. Louis set his end gently back on the chair, and the other did the same. "We 'ave been sent," Louis said. "You do not understan' w'at I mean."

"I understand all right," Chet said. "If Doctor O'Malley had wanted that, he'd've sent Mr. Vickers for it this morning."

The second man ran his tongue over his teeth and spat on the floor. "Think he knows how to shoot that thing?"

Chet's chest expanded. The gun trembled so that he braced it against the frame of the door. "I shot that rabbit, didn't I?" he said.

The halfbreed's teeth were bared in a bitter grin. "You are a fool," he said.

"And you're a thief!" Chet said. He covered the two carefully as they backed out, and when they were down the steps he slammed and bolted the door. Then he raced for the front hall, made sure that door was locked, and peeked out the front window. The two were walking side by side up the irrigation ditch toward town, pulling an empty box sled. Louis was talking furiously with his hands.

Slowly and carefully Chet uncocked the gun. Ordinarily he would have unloaded, but not now, not with thieves like those around. He put the gun above the mantel, looked in the door of the stove, threw in a half-scuttle of lignite, went to the window again to see if he could see the two men. Then he looked at his hands. They were shaking. So were his knees. He sat down suddenly on the couch, unable to stand.

For days the only people he saw were those who came to buy whisky. They generally sat a while in the kitchen and talked about the flu and the war, but they weren't much company. Once Miss Landis, his schoolteacher, came apologetically and furtively with a two-quart fruit jar under her coat, and he charged her four dollars a quart for bulk rye out of the keg. His secret hoard of money mounted to eighty-five dollars, to a hundred and eight.

When there was none of that business (he had even forgotten by now that his father had told him not to meddle with it), he moped around the house, milked the cow, telephoned to the hospital to see how his folks were. One day his dad was pretty sick. Two days later he was better, but his mother had had a relapse because they were so short of beds they had had to put Brucie in with her. The milk crocks piled up in the cellarway, staying miraculously sweet, until he told the schoolhouse nurse over the phone about all the milk he had, and then Doctor O'Malley sent down old Gundar Moe to pick it up for the sick people.

Sometimes he stood on the porch on sunny, cold mornings and watched Lars Poulsen's sled go out along the road on the way to the graveyard, and the thought that maybe Mom or Bruce or Pa might die and be buried out there on the knoll by the sandhills made him swallow and go back inside where he couldn't see how deserted the street looked, and where he couldn't see the sled and the steaming gray horses move out toward the south bend of the river. He resolved to be a son his parents could be proud of, and sat down at the piano determined to learn a piece letter-perfect. But the dry silence of the house weighed on him; before long he would be lying with his forehead on the keyboard, his finger picking on one monotonous note. That way he could concentrate on how different it sounded with his head down, and forgot to be afraid.

And at night, when he lay on the couch and stared into the sleepy red eyes of the heater, he heard noises that walked the house, and there were crosses in the lamp chimneys when he lighted them, and he knew that someone would die.

On the fifth day he sat down at the dining room table determined to write a book. In an old atlas he hunted up a promising locale. He found a tributary of the Amazon called the Tapajos, and firmly, his lips together in concentration, he wrote his title across the top of a school tablet: "The Curse of the Tapajos." All that afternoon he wrote enthusiastically. He created a tall, handsome young explorer and a halfbreed guide obscurely like Louis Treat. He plowed through steaming jungles, he wrestled pythons and other giant serpents which he spelled "boy constructors." All this time he was looking for the Lost City of Gold. And when the snakes got too thick even for his taste, and when he was beginning to wonder himself why the explorer didn't shoot the guide, who was constantly trying to poison the flour or stab his employer in his tent at midnight, he let the party come out on a broad pampa and see in the distance, crowning a golden hill, the lost city for which they searched. And then suddenly the explorer reeled and fell, mysteriously stricken, and the halfbreed guide, smiling with sinister satisfaction, disappeared quietly into the jungle. The curse of the Tapajos, which struck everyone who found that lost city, had struck again. But the young hero was not dead . . .

Chet gnawed his pencil and stared across the room. It was going to be hard to figure out how his hero escaped. Maybe he was just stunned, not killed. Maybe a girl could find him there, and nurse him back to health. . . .

He rose, thinking, and wandered over to the window. A sled came across the irrigation ditch and pulled on over to Chance's house. Out of it got Mr. Chance and Mrs. Chance and Ed and Harvey Chance. They were well, then. People were starting to come home cured. He rushed to the telephone and called the hospital. No, the nurse said, his family weren't well yet; they wouldn't be home for three or four days at least. But they were all better. How was he doing? Did he need anything?

No, Chet said, he didn't need anything.

But at least he wasn't the only person on the street any more. That night after milking he took a syrup pail of milk to the Chances. They were all weak, all smiling. Mrs. Chance cried every time she spoke, and they were awfully grateful for the milk. He promised them, over their protests, that he would bring them some every day, and chop wood and haul water for them until they got really strong. Mr. Chance, who had the nickname of Dictionary because he strung off such jaw-breaking words, told him he was a benefactor and a Samaritan, and called upon his own sons to witness this neighborly kindness and be edified and enlarged. Chet went home in the dark, wondering if it might not be a good idea, later in his book somewhere, to have his explorer find a bunch of people, or maybe just a beautiful and ragged girl, kept in durance vile by some tribe of pigmies or spider men or something, and have him rescue them and confound their captors.

On the afternoon of the eighth day Chet sat in the kitchen at Chance's. His own house had got heavier and heavier to bear, and there wasn't much to eat there but milk and potatoes, and both stores were closed because of the flu. So he went a good deal to Chance's, doing their chores and talking about the hospital, and listening to Mr. Chance tell about the Death Ward where they put people who weren't going to get well. The Death Ward was the eighth-grade room, his own room, and he and Ed Chance speculated on what it would be like to go back to that room where so many people had died— Mrs. Rieger, and old Gypsy Davy from Poverty Flat, and John Chapman, and a lot of people. Mrs. Chance sat by the stove and when anyone looked at her or spoke to her she shook her head and smiled and the tears ran down. She didn't seem unhappy about anything; she just couldn't help crying.

Mr. Chance said over and over that there was certainly going to be a multitude of familiar faces missing after this thing was over. The town would never be the same. He wouldn't be surprised if the destitute and friendless were found in every home in town, adopted and cared for by friends. They might have to build an institution to house the derelict and the bereaved.

He pulled his sagging cheeks and said to Chet, "Mark my words, son, you are one of the fortunate. In that hospital I said to myself a dozen times, 'Those poor Mason boys are going to lose their father.' I lay there—myself in pain, mind you—and the first thing I'd hear some old and valued friend would be moved into the Death Ward. I thought your father was a goner when they moved him in."

Chet's throat was suddenly dry as dust. "Pa isn't in there!"

"Ira," said Mrs. Chance, and shook her head and smiled and wiped the tears away. "Now you've got the child all worked up."

"He isn't in there now," said Mr. Chance. "By the grace of the Almighty—" he bent his head and his lips moved, "he came out again. He's a hard man to kill. Hands and feet frozen, double pneumonia, and still he came out."

"Is he all right now?" Chet said.

"Convalescing," Mr. Chance said. "Convalescing beautifully." He raised a finger under Chet's nose. "Some people are just hard to kill. But on the other hand, you take a person like that George Valet. I hesitate to say before the young what went on in that ward. Shameful, even though the man was sick." His tongue ticked against his teeth, and his eyebrows raised at Chet. "They cleaned his bed six times a day," he said, and pressed his lips together. "It makes a man wonder about God's wisdom," he said. "A man like that, his morals are as loose as his bowels."

297

"Ira!" Mrs. Chance said.

"I would offer you a wager," Mr. Chance said. "I wager that a man as loose and discombobulated as that doesn't live through this epidemic."

"I wouldn't bet on a person's life that way," she said.

"Ma," Harvey called from the next room, where he was lying down. "What's all the noise about?"

They stopped talking and listened. The church bell was ringing madly. In a minute the bell in the firehouse joined it. The heavy bellow of a shotgun, both barrels, rolled over the snowflats between their street and the main part of town. A six-shooter went off, bang-bang-bang-bang-bang-bang, and there was the sound of distant yelling.

"Fire?" Mr. Chance said, stooping to the window.

"Here comes somebody," Ed said. The figure of a boy was streaking across the flat. Mr. Chance opened the door and shouted at him. The boy ran closer, yelling something unintelligible. It was Spot Orullian.

"What?" Mr. Chance yelled.

Spot cupped his hands to his mouth, standing in the road in front of Chet's as if unwilling to waste a moment's time. "War's over!" he shouted, and wheeled and was gone up the street toward Van Dam's.

Mr. Chance closed the door slowly. Mrs. Chance looked at him, and her lips jutted and trembled, her weak eyes ran over with tears, and she fell into his arms. The three boys, not quite sure how one acted when a war ended, but knowing it called for celebration, stood around uneasily. They shot furtive grins at one another, looked with furrowed brows at Mrs. Chance's shaking back.

"Now Uncle Joe can come home," Ed said. "That's what she's bawling about."

Chet bolted out the door, raced over to his own house, pulled the loaded shotgun from the mantel, and burst out into the yard again. He blew the lid off the silence in their end of town, and followed the shooting with a wild yell. Ed and Harvey, leaning out their windows, answered him, and the heavy boom-boom of a shotgun came from the downtown district.

Carrying the gun, Chet went back to Chance's. He felt grown up, a householder. The end of the war had to be celebrated; neighbors had to get together and raise cain. He watched Mrs. Chance, still incoherent, rush to the calendar and put a circle around the date, November 11. "I don't ever want to forget what day it happened on," she said.

"Everyone in the world will remember this day," said Mr. Chance, solemnly, like a preacher. Chet looked at him, his mind clicking.

"Mr. Chance," he said, "would you like a drink, to celebrate?"

Mr. Chance looked startled. "What?"

"Pa's got some whisky. He'd throw a big party if he was home."

"I don't think we should," said Mrs. Chance dubiously. "Your father might . . ."

"Oh, Mama," Mr. Chance said, and laid his arm across her back like a log. "One bumper to honor the day. One leetle stirrup-cup to those boys of the Allies. Chester here is carrying on his father's tradition like a man." He bowed and shook Chet's hand formally. "We'd be delighted, sir," he said, and they all laughed.

Somehow, nobody knew just how, the party achieved proportions. Mr. Chance suggested, after one drink, that it would be pleasant to have a neighbor or two, snatched from the terrors of the plague, come and join in the thanksgiving; and Chet, full of hospitality, said sure, that would be a keen idea. So Mr. Chance called Jewel King, and when Jewel came he brought Chubby Klein with him, and a few minutes later three more came, knocked, looked in to see the gathering with cups in their hands, and came in with alacrity when Chet held the door wide. Within an hour there were eight men, three women, and the two Chance boys, besides Chet. Mr. Chance wouldn't let the boys have any whisky, but Chet, playing bartender, sneaked a cup into the dining room and all sipped it and smacked their lips.

"Hey, look, I'm drunk," Harvey said. He staggered, hiccoughed, caught himself, bowed low and apologized, staggered again. "Hic," he said. "I had a drop too much." The three laughed together secretly while loud voices went up in the kitchen.

"Gentlemen," Mr. Chance was saying, "I give you those heroic laddies in khaki who looked undaunted into the eyes of death and saved this ga-lorious empire from the rapacious Huns."

"Yay!" the others said, banging cups on the table. "Give her the other barrel, Dictionary."

"I crave your indulgence for a moment," Mr. Chance said. "For one leetle moment, while I imbibe a few swallows of this delectable amber fluid."

The noise went up and up. Chet went among them stiff with pride at having done all this, at being accepted here as host, at having men pat him on the back and shake his hand and tell him, "You're all right, kid, you're a chip off the old block. What's the word from the folks?" He guggled liquor out of the sloshing cask into a milk crock, and the men dipped largely and frequently. About four o'clock, two more families arrived and were welcomed with roars. People bulged the big kitchen; their laughter rattled the window frames. Occasionally Dictionary Chance rose to propose a toast to "those gems of purest ray serene, those unfailing companions on life's bitter pilgrimage, the ladies, God bless 'em!" Every so often he suggested that it might be an idea worth serious consideration that some liquid refreshments be decanted from the aperture in the receptacle.

The more liquid refreshments Chet decanted from the aperture in the receptacle, the louder and more eloquent Mr. Chance became. He dominated the kitchen like an evangelist. He swung and swayed and stamped, he led a rendition of "God Save the King," he thundered denunciations on the Beast of Berlin, he thrust a large fist into the lapels of new arrivals and demanded detailed news of the war's end. Nobody knew more than that it was over.

But Dictionary didn't forget to be grateful, either. At least five times during the afternoon he caught Chet up in a long arm and publicly blessed him. Once he rose and cleared his throat for silence. Chubby Klein and Jewel King booed and hissed, but he bore their insults with dignity. "Siddown!" they said. "Speech!" said others. Mr. Chance waved his hands abroad, begging for quiet. Finally they gave it to him, snickering.

"Ladies and gen'lemen," he said, "we have come together on this auspicious occasion . . ."

"What's suspicious about it?" Jewel King said.

" . . . on this auspicious occasion, to do honor to our boys in Flanders' fields, to celebrate the passing of the dread incubus of Spanish influenza . . ."

"Siddown!" said Chubby Klein.

" . . . and last, but not least, we are gathered here to honor our friendship with the owners of this good and hospitable house, Bo Mason and Sis, may their lives be long and strewn with flowers, and this noble scion of a noble stock, this tender youth who kept the home fires burning through shock and shell and who opened his house and his keg to us as his father would have done. Ladies and gen'lemen, the Right Honorable Chester Mason, may he live to bung many a barrel."

Embarrassed and squirming and unsure of what to do with so many faces laughing at him, so many mouths cheering him, Chet crowded into the dining room door and tried to act casual, tried to pretend he didn't feel proud and excited and a man among men. And while he stood there with the noise beating at him in raucous approbation, the back door opened and the utterly flabbergasted face of his father looked in.

There was a moment of complete silence. Voices dropped away to nothing, cups hung at lips. Then in a concerted rush they were helping Bo Mason in. He limped heavily on bandaged and slippered feet, his hands wrapped in gauze, his face drawn and hollow-eyed and noticeably thinner than it had been ten days ago. After him came Chet's mother, half-carrying Bruce, and staggering under his weight. Hands took Bruce away from her, sat him on the open oven door, and led her to a chair. All three of them, hospital-pale, rested and looked around the room. And Chet's father did not look pleased.

"What the devil is this?" he said.

From his station in the doorway Chet squeaked, "The war's over!"

"I know the war's over, but what's this?" He jerked a bandaged hand at the uncomfortable ring of people. Chet swallowed and looked at Dictionary Chance.

Dictionary's suspended talents came back to him. He strode to lay a friendly hand on his host's back; he swung and shook his hostess' hand; he twinkled at the white-faced, big-eyed Bruce on the oven door.

"This, sir," he boomed, "is a welcoming committee of your friends and neighbors, met here to rejoice over your escape from the dread sickness which has swept to untimely death so many of our good friends, God rest their souls! On the invitation of your manly young son here we have been celebrating not only that emancipation, but the emancipation of the entire world from the dread plague of war." With the cup in his hand he bent and twinkled at Bo Mason. "How's it feel to get back, old hoss?"

Bo grunted. He looked across at his wife and laughed a short, choppy laugh. The way his eyes came around and rested on Chet made Chet stop breathing. But his father's voice was hearty enough when it came "You got a snootful," he said. "Looks like you've all got a snootful."

"Sir," said Dictionary Chance, "I haven't had such a delightful snootful since the misguided government of this province suspended the God-given right of its free people to purchase and imbibe and ingest intoxicating beverages."

He drained his cup and set it on the table. "And now," he said, "it is clear that our hosts are not completely recovered in their strength. I suggest that we do whatever small jobs our ingenuity and gratitude can suggest, and silently steal away."

"Yeah," the others said. "Sure. Sure thing." They brought in the one bed from the sled and set it up, swooped together blankets and mattresses and turned them over to the women. Before the beds were made people began to leave. Dictionary Chance, voluble to the last, stopped to praise the excellent medicinal waters he had imbibed, and to say a word for Chet, before Mrs. Chance, with a quick pleading smile, led him away. The door had not even closed before Chet felt his father's cold eye on him.

"All right," his father said. "Will you please tell me why in the name of Christ you invited that God damned windbag and all the rest of those sponges over here to drink up my whisky?"

Chet stood sullenly in the door, boiling with sulky resentment. He had held the fort, milked the cow, kept the house, sold all that whisky for all it was worth, run Louis Treat and the other man out with a gun. Everybody else praised him, but you could depend on Pa to think more of that whisky the neighbors had drunk than of anything else. He wasn't going to explain or defend himself. If the old man was going to be that stingy, he could take a flying leap in the river.

"The war was over," he said. "I asked them over to celebrate."

His father's head wagged. He looked incredulous and at his wits' end. "You asked them over!" he said. "You said, 'Come right on over and drink up all the whisky my dad almost killed himself bringing in.'" He stuck his bandaged hands out. "Do you think I got these and damned near died in that hospital just to let a bunch of blotters. . . . Why, God damn you," he said. "Leave the house for ten days, tell you exactly what to do, and by Jesus everything goes wrong. How long have they been here?"

"Since about two."

"How much did they drink?"

"I don't know. Three crocks full, I guess."

His father's head weaved back and forth, he looked at his wife and then at the ceiling. "Three crocks. At least a gallon, twelve dollars' worth. Oh Jesus Christ, if you had the sense of a piss-ant . . ."

Laboriously, swearing with the pain, he hobbled to the keg. When he put his hand down to shake it, his whole body stiffened.

"It's half empty!" he said. He swung on Chet, and Chet met his furious look. Now! his mind said. Now let him say I didn't hold the fort.

"I sold some," he said, and held his father's eyes for a minute before he marched out stiff-backed into the living room, dug the wad of bills from the vase on the mantel, and came back. He laid the money in his father's hand. "I sold a hundred and twenty-four dollars' worth," he said.

The muscles in his father's jaw moved. He glanced at Chet's mother, let the breath out hard through his nose. "So you've been selling whisky," he said. "I thought I told you to leave that alone?"

"People wanted it for medicine," Chet said. "Should I've let them die with the flu? They came here wanting to buy it and I sold it. I thought that was what it was for."

The triumph that had been growing in him ever since he went for the money was hot in his blood now. He saw the uncertainty in his father's face, and he almost beat down his father's eyes.

"I suppose," his father said finally, "you sold it for a dollar a bottle, or something."

"I sold it for plenty," Chet said. "Four-fifty for bottles and four for quarts out of the keg. That's more than you were going to get, because I heard you tell Ma."

His father sat down on the chair and fingered the bills, looking at him. "You didn't have any business selling anything," he said. "And then you overcharge people."

"Yeah!" Chet said, defying him now. "If it hadn't been for me there wouldn't 'ave been any to sell. Louis Treat and another man came and tried to steal that whole keg, and I run 'em out with a shotgun."

"What?" his mother said.

"I did!" Chet said. "I made 'em put it down and get out."

Standing in the doorway still facing his father, he felt the tears hot in his eyes and was furious at himself for crying. He hoped his father would try thrashing him. He just hoped he would. He wouldn't make a sound; he'd grit his teeth and show him whether he was man enough to stand it. . . . He looked at his father's gray expressionless face and shouted, "I wish I'd let them take it! I just wish I had!"

And suddenly his father was laughing. He reared back in the chair and threw back his head and roared, his bandaged hands held tenderly before him like helpless paws. He stopped, caught his breath, looked at Chet again, and shook with a deep internal rumbling. "Okay," he said. "Okay, kid. You're a man. I wouldn't take it away from you."

305

"Well, there's no need to laugh," Chet said. "I don't see anything to laugh about."

He watched his father twist in the chair and look at his mother. "Look at him," his father said. "By God, he'd eat me if I made a pass at him."

"Well, don't laugh!" Chet said. He turned and went into the living room, where he sat on the couch and looked at his hands the way he had when Louis Treat and the other man were walking up the ditch. His hands were trembling, the same way. But there was no need to laugh, any more than there was need to get sore over a little whisky given to the neighbors.

His mother came in and sat down beside him, laid a hand on his head. "Don't be mad at Pa," she said. "He didn't understand. He's proud of you. We all are."

"Yeah?" said Chet. "Why doesn't he come and tell me that?"

His mother's smile was gentle and a little amused. "Because he's ashamed of himself for losing his temper, I suppose," she said. "He never did know how to admit he was wrong."

Chet set his jaw and looked at the shotgun above the mantel. He guessed he had looked pretty tough himself when he had the drop on Louis Treat and his thieving friend. He stiffened his shoulders under his mother's arm. "Just let him start anything," he said. "Just let him try to get hard."

His mother's smile broadened, but he glowered at her. "And there's no need to laugh!" he said.

IRWIN SHAW

Irwin Shaw was born in the Bronx, New York City, on February 27, 1913, but grew up in Brooklyn, where he went to school and to Brooklyn College. "I don't know," he writes, "whether an account of my early days as a writer would encourage young writers or tempt them to go into another line of business. I wrote five plays that I didn't think were good enough even to show to my mother, and I wrote countless short stories, only one of which was published (in my college magazine, with the result that the magazine was banned and I myself threatened with expulsion)."

At the end of his freshman year he was expelled—for failing calculus—and before he was readmitted he worked in a cosmetics factory, a department store, as a truck driver, and at a variety of other jobs. Back in school he conducted a column for the college newspaper for three years (where he first saw himself in print) and wrote seven or eight one-act plays that were produced by the college dramatic association. He also played football for four years—he was quarterback on the varsity eleven—and found time to support himself by typing manuscripts, tutoring, and working in the library.

After graduating in 1934 at the age of twenty-one, he spent two years writing for radio—dramatic serializations of various comic strips, among them "The Gumps" and

"Dick Tracy." "I still wonder," he writes, "how I survived that." Meanwhile he was working on short stories and one-act plays. In 1936 he submitted Bury the Dead, a powerful indictment against war, in a contest sponsored by the New Theater League. It was two weeks late for the contest, but it was produced in a little theater on Fourteenth Street, where it quickly attracted such attention that it was moved to the Barrymore Theater on Broadway. The night after it opened Mr. Shaw woke up to find himself famous. Since then, Bury the Dead has been played by practically every little theater group in the country.

Mr. Shaw gave up his radio writing and signed a contract with RKO in Hollywood to write movie scripts, none of them, he said, of any consequence. He kept on writing for the theater, but was unable to repeat this early success. Of his seven subsequent plays only one, The Gentle People (1939), which ran four and a half months on Broadway, had more than the briefest of runs. His last play, Patate (1958), an adaptation of a French comedy by Marcel Achard, closed shortly after it opened.

During World War II, in spite of his attitude toward war, he served in the army signal corps as a private and warrant officer, stationed in Africa, England, France, and Germany. While in the service he wrote for the army publications, Yank and Stars and Stripes, and also picked up information for a number of his outstanding short stories.

The short story has been Mr. Shaw's most successful medium. He has published close to a hundred stories in the New Yorker, Esquire, Story, Yale Review, Collier's, and other magazines, and his collected editions have indicated his craftsmanship, his ear for dialogue. "Walking Wounded" won the O. Henry Memorial Award first prize

308

in 1944, and four other stories, including "Act of Faith," have won O. Henry awards. "Act of Faith," *which appeared originally in the* New Yorker, *February 2, 1946, was also reprinted in the* Best American Short Stories of 1947, *and five more of his stories have appeared in this anthology. Among his collected stories are:* Sailor Off the Bremen (*1939*), Welcome to the City (*1942*), Act of Faith (*1946*), Mixed Company (*1950*), *and* Tip on a Dead Jockey (*1957*).

Mr. Shaw has also written a number of novels, among them The Young Lions (*1948*), Lucy Crown (*1956*), *and* Two Weeks in Another Town (*1959*).

ACT OF FAITH

"Present it to him in a pitiful light," Olson was saying as they picked their way through the almost frozen mud toward the orderly-room tent. "Three combat-scarred veterans, who fought their way from Omaha Beach to . . . What was the name of the town we fought our way to?"

"Königstein," Seeger said.

"Königstein." Olson lifted his right foot heavily out of a puddle and stared admiringly at the three pounds of mud clinging to his overshoe. "The backbone of the Army. The noncommissioned officer. We deserve better of our country. Mention our decorations, in passing."

"What decorations should I mention?" Seeger asked. "The Marksman's Medal?"

"Never quite made it," Olson said. "I had a cross-eyed scorer at the butts. Mention the Bronze Star, the Silver Star, the Croix de Guerre with palms, the Unit Citation, the Congressional Medal of Honor."

"I'll mention them all." Seeger grinned. "You don't think the C.O.'ll notice that we haven't won most of them, do you?"

"Gad, sir," Olson said with dignity, "do you think that one Southern military gentleman will dare doubt the word of another Southern military gentleman in the hour of victory?"

"I come from Ohio," Seeger said.

"Welch comes from Kansas," Olson said, coolly staring down a second lieutenant who was passing. The lieutenant made a nervous little jerk with his hand, as though he expected a salute, then kept it rigid, as a slight, superior smile of scorn twisted at the corner of Olson's mouth. The lieutenant dropped his eyes and splashed on through the mud. "You've heard of Kansas," Olson said. "Magnolia-scented Kansas."

"Of course," said Seeger, "I'm no fool."

"Do your duty by your men, Sergeant." Olson stopped to wipe the cold rain off his face and lectured him. "Highest ranking noncom present took the initiative and saved his comrades, at great personal risk, above and beyond the call of you-know-what, in the best traditions of the American Army."

"I will throw myself in the breach," Seeger said.

"Welch and I can't ask more," said Olson.

They walked heavily through the mud on the streets between the rows of tents. The camp stretched drearily over the Reims plain, with the rain beating on the sagging tents. The division had been there over three weeks, waiting to be shipped home, and all the meagre diversions of the neighborhood had been sampled and exhausted, and there was an air of watchful suspicion and impatience with the military life hanging over the camp now, and there was even reputed to be a staff sergeant in C Company who was laying odds they would not get back to America before July 4th.

"I'm redeployable," Olson sang. "It's so enjoyable." It was a jingle he had composed, to no recognizable melody, in the early days after the victory in Europe, when he had added up his points and found they came to only sixty-three, but he persisted in singing it. He was a short, round boy who had been flunked out of air cadets' school and transferred to the infantry but whose spirits had not been damaged in the process. He had a high, childish voice and a pretty, baby face. He was very good-natured, and had a girl waiting for him at the University of

California, where he intended to finish his course at government expense when he got out of the Army, and he was just the type who is killed off early and predictably and sadly in moving pictures about the war, but he had gone through four campaigns and six major battles without a scratch.

Seeger was a large, lanky boy, with a big nose, who had been wounded at St.-Lô but had come back to his outfit in the Siegfried Line quite unchanged. He was cheerful and dependable and he knew his business. He had broken in five or six second lieutenants, who had later been killed or wounded, and the C.O. had tried to get him commissioned in the field, but the war had ended while the paperwork was being fumbled over at headquarters.

They reached the door of the orderly tent and stopped. "Be brave, Sergeant," Olson said. "Welch and I are depending on you."

"O.K.," Seeger said, and went in.

The tent had the dank, Army-canvas smell that had been so much a part of Seeger's life in the past three years. The company clerk was reading an October, 1945, issue of the Buffalo *Courier-Express*, which had just reached him, and Captain Taney, the company C.O., was seated at a sawbuck table which he used as a desk, writing a letter to his wife, his lips pursed with effort. He was a small, fussy man, with sandy hair that was falling out. While the fighting had been going on, he had been lean and tense and his small voice had been cold and full of authority. But now he had relaxed, and a little pot belly was creeping up under his belt and he kept the top button of his trousers open when he could do it without too public loss of dignity. During the war, Seeger had thought of him as a natural soldier—tireless, fanatic about detail, aggressive, severely anxious to kill Germans. But in the last few months, Seeger had seen him relapsing gradually and pleasantly into the small-town hardware merchant he had beeen before the war, sedentary and a little shy, and as he had once told Seeger, worried, here in the bleak champagne fields of France, about his daughter, who had just turned twelve and had a tendency to go after the boys and had been caught by her mother kissing a fifteen-year old neighbor in the hammock after school.

"Hello, Seeger," he said, returning the salute with a mild, offhand gesture. "What's on your mind?"

"Am I disturbing you, sir?"

"Oh, no. Just writing a letter to my wife. You married, Seeger?" He peered at the tall boy standing before him.

"No, sir."

"It's very difficult." Taney sighed, pushing dissatisfiedly at the letter before him. "My wife complains I don't tell her I love her often enough. Been married fifteen years. You'd think she'd know by now." He smiled at Seeger. "I thought you were going to Paris," he said. "I signed the passes yesterday."

"That's what I came to see you about, sir."

"I suppose something's wrong with the passes." Taney spoke resignedly, like a man who has never quite got the hang of Army regulations and has had requisitions, furloughs, and requests for courts-martial returned for correction in a baffling flood.

"No, sir," Seeger said. "The passes're fine. They start tomorrow. Well, it's just—" He looked around at the company clerk, who was on the sports page.

"This confidential?" Taney asked.

"If you don't mind, sir."

"Johnny," Taney said to the clerk, "go stand in the rain someplace."

"Yes, sir," the clerk said, and slowly got up and walked out.

Taney looked shrewdly at Seeger and spoke in a secret whisper. "You pick up anything?" he asked.

Seeger grinned. "No, sir, haven't had my hands on a girl since Strasbourg."

"Ah, that's good." Taney leaned back, relieved, happy that he didn't have to cope with the disapproval of the Medical Corps.

"It's—well," said Seeger, embarrassed, "it's hard to say—but it's money."

Taney shook his head sadly. "I know."

"We haven't been paid for three months, sir, and—"

"Damn it!" Taney stood up and shouted furiously. "I would like to take every bloody, chair-warming old lady in the Finance Department and wring their necks."

The clerk stuck his head into the tent. "Anything wrong? You call for me, sir?"

"No!" Taney shouted. "Get out of here!"

The clerk ducked out.

Taney sat down again. "I suppose," he said, in a more normal voice, "they have their problems. Outfits being broken up, being moved all over the place. But it's rugged."

"It wouldn't be so bad," Seeger said, "but we're going to Paris tomorrow. Olson, Welch, and myself. And you need money in Paris."

"Don't I know it?" Taney wagged his head. "Do you know what I paid for a bottle of champagne on the Place Pigalle in September?" He paused significantly. "I won't tell you. You wouldn't have any respect for me for the rest of your life."

Seeger laughed. "Hanging is too good for the guy who thought up the rate of exchange," he said.

"I don't care if I never see another franc as long as I live." Taney waved his letter in the air, although it had been dry for a long time.

There was silence in the tent, and Seeger swallowed a little embarrassedly. "Sir," he said, "the truth is, I've come to borrow some money for Welch, Olson and myself. We'll pay it back out of the first pay we get, and that can't be too long from now. If you don't want to give it to us, just tell me and I'll understand and get the hell out of here. We don't like to ask, but you might just as well be dead as be in Paris broke."

Taney stopped waving his letter and put it down thoughtfully. He peered at it, wrinkling his brow, looking like an aged bookkeeper in the single, gloomy light that hung in the middle of the tent.

"Just say the word, Captain," Seeger said, "and I'll blow."

"Stay where you are, son," said Taney. He dug in his shirt pocket and took out a worn, sweat-stained wallet. He looked at it for a moment. "Alligator," he said, with automatic, absent pride. "My wife sent it to me when we were in England. Pounds don't fit in it. However . . ." He opened it and took out all the contents. There was a small pile of francs on the table in front of him when he finished. He counted them. "Four hundred francs," he said. "Eight bucks."

"Excuse me," Seeger said humbly. "I shouldn't 've asked."

"Delighted," Taney said vigorously. "Absolutely delighted." He started dividing the francs into two piles. "Truth is, Seeger, most of my money goes home in allotments. And the truth is, I lost eleven hundred francs in a poker game three nights ago, and I ought to be ashamed of myself. Here." He shoved one pile toward Seeger. "Two hundred francs."

Seeger looked down at the frayed, meretricious paper, which always seemed to him like stage money anyway. "No sir," he said, "I can't take it."

"Take it," Taney said. "That's a direct order."

Seeger slowly picked up the money, not looking at Taney. "Sometimes, sir," he said, "after we get out, you have to come over to my house, and you and my father and my brother and I'll go on a real drunk."

"I regard that," Taney said gravely, "as a solemn commitment."

They smiled at each other, and Seeger started out.

"Have a drink for me," said Taney, "at the Café de la Paix. A small drink." He was sitting down to tell his wife he loved her when Seeger went out of the tent.

Olson fell into step with Seeger and they walked silently through the mud between the tents.

"Well, *mon vieux?*" Olson said finally.

"Two hundred francs," said Seeger.

Olson groaned. "Two hundred francs! We won't be able to pinch a whore's behind on the Boulevard des Capucines for two hundred francs. That miserable, penny-loving Yankee!"

"He only had four hundred," Seeger said.

"I revise my opinion," said Olson.

They walked disconsolately and heavily back toward their tent.

Olson spoke only once before they got there. "These raincoats," he said, patting his. "Most ingenious invention of the war. Highest saturation point of any modern fabric. Collect more water per square inch, and hold it, than any material known to man. All hail the quartermaster!"

Welch was waiting at the entrance of their tent. He was standing there peering excitedly and shortsightedly out at the rain through his glasses, looking angry and tough, like a big-city hack driver, individual and incorruptible even in the ten-million colored uniform. Every time Seeger came upon Welch unexpectedly, he couldn't help smiling at the belligerent stance, the harsh stare through the steel-rimmed G.I. glasses, which had nothing at all to do with the way Welch really was. "It's a family inheritance," Welch had once explained. "My whole family stands as though we were getting ready to rap a drunk with a beer glass. Even my old lady." Welch had six brothers, all devout, according to Welch, and Seeger from time to time idly pictured them standing in a row, on Sunday mornings in church, seemingly on the verge of general violence, amid the hushed Latin and the Sabbath millinery.

"How much?" Welch asked loudly.

"Don't make us laugh," Olson said, pushing past him into the tent.

"What do you think I could get from the French for my combat jacket?" Seeger said. He went into the tent and lay down on his cot.

Welch followed them in and stood between the two of them. "Boys," he said, "on a man's errand."

"I can just see us now," Olson murmured, lying on his cot with his hands clasped behind his head, "painting Montmartre red. Please bring on the naked dancing girls. Four bucks' worth."

"I am not worried," Welch announced.

"Get out of here." Olson turned over on his stomach.

"I know where we can put our hands on sixty-five bucks." Welch looked triumphantly first at Olson, then at Seeger.

Olson turned over slowly and sat up. "I'll kill you," he said, "if you're kidding."

"While you guys are wasting your time fooling around with the infantry," Welch said, "I used my head. I went into Reems and used my head."

"Rance," Olson said automatically. He had had two years of French in college and he felt, now that the war was over, that he had to introduce his friends to some of his culture.

"I got to talking to a captain in the Air Force," Welch said eagerly. "A little, fat old paddle-footed captain that never got higher off the ground than the second floor of Com Z head-quarters, and he told me that what he would admire to do more than anything else is take home a nice shiny German Luger pistol with him to show to the boys back in Pacific Grove, California."

Silence fell on the tent, and Welch and Olson looked at Seeger.

"Sixty-five bucks for a Luger, these days," Olson said, "is a very good figure."

"They've been sellin' for as low as thirty-five," said Welch hesitantly. "I'll bet," he said to Seeger, "you could sell yours now and buy another one back when you got some dough, and make a clear twenty-five on the deal."

Seeger didn't say anything. He had killed the owner of the Luger, an enormous S.S. major, in Coblenz, behind some bales of paper in a warehouse, and the major had fired at Seeger three times with it, once nicking his helmet, before Seeger hit him in the face at twenty feet. Seeger had kept the Luger, a heavy well-balanced gun, lugging it with him, hiding it at the bottom of his bedroll, oiling it three times a week, avoiding all opportunities of selling it, although he had once been offered a hundred dollars for it and several times eighty and ninety, while the war was still on, before German weapons became a glut on the market.

"Well," said Welch, "there's no hurry. I told the captain I'd see him tonight around eight o'clock in front of the Lion d'Or Hotel. You got five hours to make up your mind. Plenty of time."

"Me," said Olson, after a pause, "I won't say anything."

Seeger looked reflectively at his feet, and the two other men avoided looking at him.

Welch dug in his pocket. "I forgot," he said. "I picked up a letter for you." He handed it to Seeger.

"Thanks," Seeger said. He opened it absently, thinking about the Luger.

"Me," said Olson, "I won't say a bloody word. I'm just going to lie here and think about that nice, fat Air Force captain."

Seeger grinned a little at him and went to the tent opening to read the letter in the light. The letter was from his father, and even from one glance at the handwriting, scrawly and hurried and spotted, so different from his father's usual steady, handsome, professorial script, he knew that something was wrong.

"Dear Norman," it read, "sometime in the future, you must forgive me for writing this letter. But I have been holding this in so long, and there is no one here I can talk to, and because of your brother's condition I must pretend to be cheerful and optimistic all the time at home, both with him and your mother, who has never been the same since Leonard was killed. You're the oldest now, and although I know we've never talked very seriously about anything before, you have been through a great deal by now, and I imagine you must have matured considerably, and you've seen so many different places and people. Norman, I need help. While the war was on and you were fighting, I kept this to myself. It wouldn't have been fair to burden you with this. But now the war is over, and I no longer feel I can stand up under this alone. And you will have to face it sometime when you get home, if you haven't faced it already, and perhaps we can help each other by facing it together."

"I'm redeployable. It's so enjoyable," Olson was singing softly, on his cot. He fell silent after his burst of song.

Seeger blinked his eyes in the gray, wintry, rainy light, and went on reading his father's letter, on the stiff white stationery with the university letterhead in polite engraving at the top of each page.

"I've been feeling this coming on for a long time," the letter continued, "but it wasn't until last Sunday morning that something happened to make me feel it in its full force. I don't know how much you've guessed about the reason for Jacob's discharge from the Army. It's true he was pretty badly wounded in the leg at Metz, but I've asked around and I know that men with worse wounds were returned to duty after hospitalization. Jacob got a medical discharge, but I don't think it was for the shrapnel wound in his thigh. He is suffering now from what I suppose you call combat fatigue, and he is subject to fits of depression and hallucinations. Your mother and I thought that as time went by and the war and the Army receded, he would grow better. Instead, he is growing worse. Last Sunday morning when I came down into the living room from upstairs he was crouched in his old uniform, next to the window, peering out."

"What the hell," Olson was saying. "If we don't get the sixty-five bucks we can always go to the Louvre. I understand the Mona Lisa is back."

"I asked Jacob what he was doing," the letter went on. "He didn't turn around. 'I'm observing,' he said. 'V-1s and V-2s. Buzz bombs and rockets. They're coming in by the hundreds.' I tried to reason with him and he told me to crouch and save myself from flying glass. To humor him I got down on the floor beside him and tried to tell him the war was over, that we were in Ohio,

319

4,000 miles away from the nearest spot where bombs had fallen, that America had never been touched. He wouldn't listen. 'These're the new rocket bombs,' he said, 'for the Jews.'"

"Did you ever hear of the Panthéon?" Olson asked loudly.

"No," said Welch.

"It's free."

"I'll go," said Welch.

Seeger shook his head a little and blinked his eyes before he went back to the letter.

"After that," his father went on, "Jacob seemed to forget about the bombs from time to time, but he kept saying that the mobs were coming up the street armed with bazookas and Browning automatic rifles. He mumbled incoherently a good deal of the time and kept walking back and forth saying, 'What's the situation? Do you know what the situation is?' And once he told me he wasn't worried about himself, he was a soldier and he expected to be killed, but he was worried about Mother and myself and Leonard and you. He seemed to forget that Leonard was dead. I tried to calm him and get him back to bed before your mother came down, but he refused and wanted to set out immediately to rejoin his division. It was all terribly disjointed, and at one time he took the ribbon he got for winning the Bronze Star and threw it in the fireplace, then he got down on his hands and knees and picked it out of the ashes and made me pin it on him again, and he kept repeating, 'This is when they are coming for the Jews.'"

"The next war I'm in," said Olson, "they don't get me under the rank of colonel."

It had stopped raining by now, and Seeger folded the unfinished letter and went outside. He walked slowly down to the end of the company street, and facing out across the empty, soaked French fields, scarred and neglected by various armies, he stopped and opened the letter again.

"I don't know what Jacob went through in the Army," his father wrote, "that has done this to him. He never talks to me about the war and he refuses to go to a psychoanalyst, and from time to time, he is his own bouncing, cheerful self, playing handball in the afternoons and going around with a large group of girls. But he has devoured all the concentration-camp reports, and I found him weeping when the newspapers reported that a hundred Jews were killed in Tripoli some time ago.

"The terrible thing is, Norman, that I find myself coming to believe that it is not neurotic for a Jew to behave like this today. Perhaps Jacob is the normal one, and I, going about my business, teaching economics in a quiet classroom, pretending to understand that the world is comprehensible and orderly, am really the mad one. I ask you once more to forgive me for writing you a letter like this, so different from any letter or any conversation I've ever had with you. But it is crowding me, too. I do not see rockets and bombs, but I see other things.

"Wherever you go these days—restaurants, hotels, clubs, trains—you seem to hear talk about the Jews, mean, hateful, murderous talk. Whatever page you turn to in the newspapers, you seem to find an article about Jews being killed somewhere on the face of the globe. And there are large, influential newspapers and well-known columnists who each day are growing more and more outspoken and more popular. The day that Roosevelt died I heard a drunken man yelling outside a bar. 'Finally they got the Jew out of the White House.' And some of the people who heard him merely laughed, and nobody stopped him. And on V-J Day, in celebration, hoodlums in Los Angeles savagely beat a Jewish writer. It's difficult to know what to do, whom to fight, where to look for allies.

"Three months ago, for example, I stopped my Thursday-night poker game, after playing with the same men for over ten years. John Reilly happened to say that the Jews got rich out of the war and when I demanded an apology, he refused, and when I looked around at the faces of the men who had been my friends for so long, I could see they were not with me. And when I left the house, no one said good night to me. I know the poison was spreading from Germany before the war and during it, but I had not realized it had come so close.

"And in my economics class, I find myself idiotically hedging in my lectures. I discover that I am loath to praise any liberal writer or any liberal act, and find myself somehow annoyed and frightened to see an article of criticism of existing abuses signed by a Jewish name. And I hate to see Jewish names on important committees, and hate to read of Jews fighting for the poor, the oppressed, the cheated and hungry. Somehow, even in a country where my family has lived a hundred years, the enemy has won this subtle victory over me—he has made me disfranchise myself from honest causes by calling them foreign, Communist, using Jewish names connected with them as ammunition against them.

"Most hateful of all, I found myself looking for Jewish names in the casualty lists and secretly being glad when I saw them there, to prove that there, at least, among the dead and wounded, we belonged. Three times, thanks to you and your brothers, I found our name there, and may God forgive me, at the expense of your blood and your brother's life, through my tears, I felt that same twitch of satisfaction.

"When I read the newspapers and see another story that Jews are still being killed in Poland, or Jews are requesting that they be given back their homes in France or that they be allowed to enter some country where they will not be murdered, I am annoyed with them. I feel that they are boring the rest of the world with their problems, that they are making demands upon the rest of the world by being killed, that they are disturbing everyone by being hungry and asking for the return of their property. If we could all fall in through the crust of the earth and vanish in one hour, with our heroes and poets and prophets and martyrs, perhaps we would be doing the memory of the Jewish race a service.

"This is how I feel today, son. I need some help. You've been to the war, you've fought and killed men, you've seen the people of other countries. Maybe you understand things that I don't understand. Maybe you see some hope somewhere. Help me. Your loving Father."

Seeger folded the letter slowly, not seeing what he was doing, because the tears were burning his eyes. He walked slowly and aimlessly across the dead, sodden grass of the empty field, away from the camp. He tried to wipe away his tears, because, with his eyes full and dark, he kept seeing his father and brother crouched in the old-fashioned living room in Ohio, and hearing his brother, dressed in the old, discarded uniform, saying, "These're the new rocket bombs. For the Jews."

He sighed, looking out over the bleak, wasted land. Now, he thought, now I have to think about it. He felt a slight, unreasonable twinge of anger at his father for presenting him with the necessity of thinking about it. The Army was good about serious problems. While you were fighting, you were too busy and frightened and weary to think about anything, and at other times you were relaxing, putting your brain on a shelf, postponing everything to that impossible time of clarity and beauty after the war. Well, now, here was the impossible, clear, beautiful time, and here was his father, demanding that he think. There are all sorts of Jews, he thought: there are the sort whose every waking moment is ridden by the knowledge of Jewishness; who see signs against the Jew in every smile on a streetcar, every whisper; who sees pogroms in every newspaper article, threats in every change of the weather, scorn in every handshake, death behind each closed door. He had not been like that. He was young, he was big and healthy and easygoing, and people of all kinds had liked him all his life, in the Army and out. In America, especially, what was going on in Europe had been remote, unreal, unrelated to him. The chanting, bearded old men burning in the Nazi furnaces, and the dark-eyed women screaming prayers in Polish and Russian and German as they were pushed naked into the gas chambers, had seemed as shadowy and almost as unrelated to him, as he trotted out onto the stadium field for a football game, as they must have been to the men named

O'Dwyer and Wickersham and Poole who played in the line beside him.

These tortured people had seemed more related to him in Europe. Again and again, in the towns that had been taken back from the Germans, gaunt, gray-faced men had stopped him humbly, looking searchingly at him, and had asked, peering at his long, lined grimy face under the anonymous helmet, "Are you a Jew?" Sometimes they asked it in English, sometimes French, sometimes Yiddish. He didn't know French or Yiddish, but he learned to recognize that question. He had never understood exactly why they asked the question, since they never demanded anything of him, rarely even could speak to him. Then, one day in Strasbourg, a little, bent old man, and a small, shapeless woman had stopped him and asked in English, if he was Jewish. "Yes," he'd said, smiling at them. The two old people had smiled widely, like children. "Look," the old man had said to his wife, "A young American soldier. A Jew. And so large and strong." He had touched Seeger's arm reverently with the tips of his fingers, then had touched the Garand Seeger was carrying. "And such a beautiful rifle."

And there, for a moment, although he was not particularly sensitive, Seeger had got an inkling of why he had been stopped and questioned by so many before. Here, to these bent, exhausted old people, ravaged of their families, familiar with flight and death for so many years, was a symbol of continuing life. A large young man in the uniform of the liberator, blood, as they thought, of their blood, but not in hiding, not quivering in fear and helplessness, but striding secure and victorious down the street, armed and capable of inflicting terrible destruction on his enemies.

Seeger had kissed the old lady on the cheek and she had wept, and the old man had scolded her for it while shaking Seeger's hand fervently and thankfully before saying goodbye.

Thinking back on it, he knew that it was silly to pretend that, even before his father's letter, he had been like any other

324

American soldier going through the war. When he had stood over the huge, dead S.S. major with the face blown in by his bullets in the warehouse in Coblenz, and taken the pistol from the dead hand, he had tasted a strange little extra flavor of triumph. How many Jews, he'd thought, has this man killed? How fitting it is that I've killed him. Neither Olson nor Welch, who were like his brothers, would have felt that in picking up the Luger, its barrel still hot from the last shots its owner had fired before dying. And he had resolved that he was going to make sure to take this gun back with him to America, and plug it and keep it on his desk at home, as a kind of vague, half-understood sign to himself that justice had once been done and he had been its instrument.

Maybe, he thought, maybe I'd better take it back with me, but not as a memento. Not plugged, but loaded. America by now was a strange country for him. He had been away a long time and he wasn't sure what was waiting for him when he got home. If the mobs were coming down the street toward his house, he was not going to die singing and praying.

When he had been taking basic training, he'd heard a scrawny, clerkish soldier from Boston talking at the other end of the PX bar, over the watered beer. "The boys at the office," the scratchy voice was saying, "gave me a party before I left. And they told me one thing. 'Charlie,' they said, 'hold onto your bayonet. We're going to be able to use it when you get back. On the Yids.' "

He hadn't said anything then, because he'd felt it was neither possible nor desirable to fight against every random overheard voice raised against the Jews from one end of the world to the other. But again and again, at odd moments, lying on a barracks cot, or stretched out trying to sleep on the floor of a ruined French farmhouse, he had heard that voice, harsh, satisfied, heavy with hate and ignorance, saying above the beery grumble of apprentice soldiers at the bar, "Hold onto your bayonet."

And the other stories. Jews collected stories of hatred and

injustice and inklings of doom like a special, lunatic kind of miser. The story of the Navy officer, commander of a small vessel off the Aleutians, who in the officers' wardroom had complained that he hated the Jews because it was the Jews who had demanded that the Germans be beaten first, and the forces in the Pacific had been starved in consequence. And when one of his junior officers, who had just come aboard, had objected and told the commander that he was a Jew, the commander had risen from the table and said, "Mister, the Constitution of the United States says I have to serve in the same Navy with Jews, but it doesn't say I have to eat at the same table with them." In the fogs and the cold, swelling Arctic seas off the Aleutians, in a small boat, subject to sudden, mortal attack, at any moment . . . And the million other stories. Jews, even the most normal and best adjusted, became living treasuries of them, scraps of malice and bloodthirstiness, clever and confusing and cunningly twisted so that every act by every Jew became suspect and blameworthy and hateful. Seeger had heard the stories and had made an almost conscious effort to forget them. Now, holding his father's letter in his hand, he remembered them all.

He stared unseeingly out in front of him. Maybe, he thought, maybe it would've been better to have been killed in the war, like Leonard. Simpler. Leonard would never have to face a crowd coming for his mother and father. Leonard would not have to listen and collect these hideous, fascinating little stories that made of every Jew a stranger in any town, on any field, on the face of the earth. He had come so close to being killed so many times; it would have been so easy, so neat and final. Seeger shook his head. It was ridiculous to feel like that, and he was ashamed of himself for the weak moment. At the age of twenty-one, death was not an answer.

"Seeger!" It was Olson's voice. He and Welch had sloshed silently up behind Seeger, standing in the open field. "Seeger, *mon vieux*, what're you doing—grazing?"

Seeger turned slowly to them. "I wanted to read my letter," he said.

Olson looked closely at him. They had been together so long, through so many things, that flickers and hints of expression on each other's faces were recognized and acted upon. "Anything wrong?" Olson asked.

"No," said Seeger. "Nothing much."

"Norman," Welch said, his voice young and solemn. "Norman, we've been talking, Olson and me. We decided—you're pretty attached to that Luger, and maybe, if you—well—"

"What he's trying to say," said Olson, "is we withdraw the request. If you want to sell it, O.K. If you don't, don't do it for our sake. Honest."

Seeger looked at them standing there, disreputable and tough and familiar. "I haven't made up my mind yet," he said.

"Anything you decide," Welch said oratorically, "is perfectly all right with us. Perfectly."

The three of them walked aimlessly and silently across the field, away from camp. As they walked, their shoes making a wet, sliding sound in the damp, dead grass, Seeger thought of the time Olson had covered him in the little town outside Cherbourg, when Seeger had been caught, going down the side of a street, by four Germans with a machine gun in the second story of a house on the corner and Olson had had to stand out in the middle of the street with no cover at all for more than a minute, firing continuously, so that Seeger could get away alive. And he thought of the time outside St.-Lô when he had been wounded and had lain in a minefield for three hours and Welch and Captain Taney had come looking for him in the darkness and had found him and picked him up and run for it, all of them expecting to get blown up any second. And he thought of all the drinks they'd had together, and the long marches and the cold winter together, and all the girls they'd gone out with together, and he thought of his father and brother crouching behind

327

the window in Ohio waiting for the rockets and the crowds armed with Browning automatic rifles.

"Say." He stopped and stood facing them. "Say, what do you guys think of the Jews?"

Welch and Olson looked at each other, and Olson glanced down at the letter in Seeger's hand.

"Jews?" Olson said finally. "What're they? Welch, you ever hear of the Jews?"

Welch looked thoughtfully at the gray sky. "No," he said. "But remember, I'm an uneducated fellow."

"Sorry, bud," Olson said, turning to Seeger. "We can't help you. Ask us another question. Maybe we'll do better."

Seeger peered at the faces of his friends. He would have to rely upon them, later on, out of uniform, on their native streets, more than he had ever relied on them on the bullet-swept street and in the dark minefield in France. Welch and Olson stared back at him, troubled, their faces candid and tough and dependable.

"What time," Seeger asked, "did you tell that captain you'd meet him?"

"Eight o'clock," Welch said. "But we don't have to go. If you have any feeling about that gun—"

"We'll meet him," Seeger said. "We can use that sixty-five bucks."

"Listen," Olson said, "I know how much you like that gun, and I'll feel like a heel if you sell it."

"Forget it," Seeger said, starting to walk again. "What could I use it for in America?"

VICTORIA LINCOLN

Victoria Lincoln was born in Fall River, Massachusetts, on October 23, 1904. As a child she used to listen to her father and mother reading aloud to each other. They taught her to recite long passages of poetry. At the age of three she knew by heart a good deal of Matthew Arnold's "Scholar Gypsy," loving the sound of the words without understanding anything of the meaning. At three she also learned to read and to print, and by the time she started school she could read, she said, "with adult ease."

She always took it for granted that writing was to be her business. She wrote her first "book," A Cat's Outlook, at the age of four, illustrating it herself. She finished her first novel at fourteen, Sir Carl of Heldart, *a story "about high life in Central Europe." Portions of this "novell," as she called it, appeared in* Harper's Magazine, September 1950.

By the time she was in college she could turn out a well-constructed story with ease, but not until she was almost twenty-six could she interest any publisher in what she wrote. The difficulty, she says in retrospect, was that she was "involved in a love affair with the pure techniques of prose composition," quite ignoring the fact that she ought to have "something to say." In college she was also involved in a love affair with herself. "My early stories," she writes, "were almost all fantasies variously embodying my belief that the artist (namely me) was like a star and dwelt apart; their basic tragedy was always the destruction of the dream by the fact. I have a few of them still, marked 'A.' 'Beautiful work in the twilight realm,' says the instructor's comment on one of them, an instructor who was even then a good poet and who should have known better. They would make your flesh crawl."

Upon graduation from Radcliffe in 1926 she married a classmate from Harvard; they were separated in 1932. Two years later she married Victor A. Lowe, then an assistant in philosophy at Harvard, currently professor of philosophy at the Johns Hopkins University, Baltimore, Maryland. She has three children, one from her first marriage and two from her second.

Miss Lincoln's first publication was a detective novel, The Swan Island Murders (1930). In 1934 she published February Hill. It was an immediate best seller, and she found herself, at twenty-nine, very much in the public eye. She turned the novel into a drama which was produced on Broadway (1939) under the title The Primrose Path. It was also made into a movie and a play for television. For the next ten years she devoted herself to short stories, autobiographical sketches, and occasional poems, which were collected under the title Grandmother and the Comet (1944). "Down in the Reeds by the River" was published in the New Yorker, September 28, 1946. It appeared later that year as an episode in The Wind at My Back, a collection of three short novels, and in The Best American Short Stories of 1947. Two of her other stories were subsequently selected for this annual anthology. A second collection of short stories, the Wild Honey, appeared in 1953. Among her recent novels are A Dangerous Innocence (1958) and The Islands and the Sea (1959). Her stories have been translated into French and German.

For years Miss Lincoln has kept a commonplace book.

330

She writes, she says, from six to fourteen hours a day and publishes only a small part of her output. Getting the first draft of a story is, to her, a "dull chore," but rewriting is a pleasure. She has written four articles on the art of writing fiction, which have appeared in The Writer *from 1948 to 1956.*

DOWN IN THE REEDS
BY THE RIVER

Why are we never prepared, why do all the books and all the wisdom of our friends avail us nothing in the final event? How many deathbed scenes we have read, how many stories of young love, of marital infidelity, of cherished ambition fulfilled or defeated. There is nothing that can happen to us that has not happened again and again, that we have not read over a thousand times, closely, carefully, accurately recorded; before we are fully launched on life, the story of the human heart has been opened for us again and again with all the patience and skill of the human mind. But the event, when it comes, is never anything like the description; it is strange, infinitely strange and new, and we stand helpless before it and realize that the words of another convey nothing, nothing.

And still we cannot believe that personal life is, in its essence, incommunicable. We, too, having lived the moment, are impelled to convey it, to speak the words so honest in intent, so false in the final effect. Now, after so many years, I want to tell you about Mr. deRocca, although it is a queer story—not a story at all, really, only an incident in the life of a young girl—simply to show that it was not what you would have expected. It was not

From *The Wind at My Back* by Victoria Lincoln. Copyright 1946 by Victoria Lincoln Lowe. Reprinted by permission of Holt, Rinehart and Winston, Inc. and *The New Yorker*.

like the books or the whispered, ugly confidence that you remember from your school days; it was quite, quite different. I want to tell you, although I know from the outset that I shall fail, as we all fail.

But now that I come up to it, I hesitate. It should have been evil, frightening, all wrong; of course it should. It should have been the repellent accident that can queer an emotional development for years to come. And still, when it was happening, it was not like that at all.

I was fourteen, a wiry, red-headed, unimaginative little tomboy, fond of sand-lot baseball. My parents were dead, killed in an accident a year before, and I lived with an aunt and uncle in Braeburn Heights, a suburb of a small city in Kansas. Bereft, rudely transplanted from the life I had known—a happy-go-lucky life in the brown hills of California—I was lonely beyond words. I had grown up in the careless warmth of love, and for my Aunt Elsa's genuine, if worried, kindness I could feel nothing but ingratitude. The house was strange, the neighboring children were strange, with their neat, pretty bedrooms, their queer talk of dates, and formals, and going steady. I felt dry and hard and empty inside myself, day after day. I used to take my bicycle and ride out into the country, but the country was strange, too, and ugly to my eyes, all flat and dull.

And then, one day I found White Creek Row. It was the town's Hooverville, a row of shanties between the creek and the railroad, little huts like the playhouse that I had built back in the hills with the children of our Mexican gardener—a tragic, shocking, sordid shantytown, as I see it now. But to my enchanted eyes it was romantic and delightful and, more than that, comprehensible, as my aunt's house in Braeburn Heights was not.

It was in White Creek Row that, unknown to Aunt Elsa, I made my first real friends in Kansas. The squatters in the row were shy of me at first, as I was shy of the people in Braeburn Heights. My decent clothes, my bicycle, made me alien, an object for suspicion and resentment. And still, somehow or other, I

333

managed to scrape an acquaintance with Posy Moreno, an acquaintance that grew into love.

She was a gentle creature with a mop of soft black curls piled high on her head and a womanliness, at sixteen, that made me feel, for the first time, glad that I, too, was growing near to womanhood. She lived in the last shanty in the row with her little brother Manuel, and next door was Mrs. Grimes, her self-appointed duenna. She was very proud of Mrs. Grimes' watchfulness.

"Me, I'm never chasing with the feller," she used to say, "but if I was to chase with the feller, Mrs. Grimes she's knock me down, you bet. She's not let anybody get fresh with Posy Moreno."

"I wouldn't want anyone bossing me like that," I said once. And Posy, lifting her head in the pride of her womanhood, replied, "You not need. You just a kid." But as we became better acquainted she treated me less and less like a kid.

Through our long afternoons on the creek bank, listening to her conversation, I would sit spellbound, infinitely flattered that she considered me a girl and not a child, feeling within myself a new softening, a shy preening, a tremulousness delicious and unfamiliar.

Besides Posy and Manuel, the only other child on the row was Chuck Hansen, who was twelve. I liked him, too, and I used to let him ride my bicycle while Posy and I talked. I could never hear enough about life in the row, and the people who lived in it. They had everything, I used to tell myself, everything that anybody could want, for I was too young to understand the need for security, for dignity. They had everything, and they had got it all free—even a church.

Mrs. Grimes had wanted the church, and Mr. deRocca, who had been a carpenter in Italy, had built it for her, although he was a freethinker and had accompanied every hammer blow, so Posy told me, with a lot of bad talk about religion being made up by rich people to keep poor people quiet.

How I wished I might have been there to see him, sitting

on the roof, pounding down the shingles that were made from flattened tin cans, with his delicate, hard little old hands, and shouting all the time, "Opium of the people. You getta pie in a sky when you die!" The church even had a piano, with a good many keys that still sounded, nice and loud, if not true, and Mrs. Grimes played gospel hymns on it by ear.

Mr. deRocca would not go to the prayer meetings. He lived in the best shanty in the row, and in his front yard was a beautiful American flag laid out in bits of broken brick and slate and white stones. I admired it intensely and used to stop before his house, the better to enjoy it, but Posy would shy off and draw me away, throwing up her head with a sort of wild-pony elegance. "Better we're not hanging around here," she would say. "Mr. deRocca, he's liking the girl."

I did not understand. Would anyone so old want a wife as young as Posy, I wondered. It must be that, I decided when Posy told me that Mrs. Grimes had not let Mr. deRocca help with the building of Posy's shack. I supposed they thought it would not be fair to encourage him. But I saw no reason why the caution should also apply to me. I was charmed by the little I had managed to see of Mr. deRocca. He seemed to be a very clever, very nice old man.

And now I come to my story, and it is hard to tell. It is hard to tell because I should have been so different. Perhaps there were undertones that I have forgotten. That is likely, for the memory has a curiously clear and classic air, quite unlike life as I have since found it—the nymph and the old satyr frozen in attitudes of timeless innocence under the box elders by the creek bank, the sacred grove where liquid Peneus was flowing and all dark Tempe lay. And still, still, I remember it like that. If there was fear, if there was guilt, they came later.

One afternoon, Chuck Hansen met me on the cinder track, looking wistful. "I don't guess you'll want to stay today, Connie,"

335

he said. "Mrs. Grimes and Posy, they went uptown." He rubbed the handle bars of my bicycle with his hands, hard, as if he were fondling a horse. "Guess you won't have much to stick around for," he said humbly.

How nice he was, I thought, never teasing.

"Well, listen, Chuck," I said. "I'm tired, a little. I'll go down and walk around a while and sit on the creek bank."

His grin made me feel warm and pleasant. I began to saunter along the front of the row. Mr. deRocca was sitting on a packing case by his door, eating an onion. His face, lifted to the sky, wore the blank, peaceful expression of one enjoying the quiet of a village street after a procession has passed, the look of remembering in quietness.

I came along very slowly, watching Mr. deRocca from the corners of my eyes. He wore a plaid flannel shirt, ragged, and of course, unironed, but fairly clean, and the neck was unbuttoned. I noticed how the flesh under his chin was firm, and didn't hang down in wattles, and the cords in his neck didn't stick out. He looked harder and nicer than other old men.

How old was he, really? About fifty, I should guess now, looking back; maybe a little less. But if I had known it then, it would not have changed my picture of him at all. Fifty to eighty in those days were all of a piece in my mind. Mr. deRocca was an old man. And he was nice. As I came very close, I realized with a sudden throb of excitement, that he had been watching me all along, just as I had been watching him. Watching me and waiting for the moment to speak, just as I had been with him. I turned, pretending to have seen him for the first time. I smiled at him. The white teeth gleamed in the thin, brown face; the elegant, small, brown paw that held the onion described a vast semicircle of greeting. "Hi, kid," he said. "Looka for da Posy? She's a not home."

I did not answer. I had realized, quite abruptly, that it was the sight of him sitting down there below me, fully as much as Chuck's longing hands rubbing the handle bars, that made up my mind for me up there on the embankment, and I turned shy, hoping that he would not guess it.

"I always like to look at that flag, Mr. deRocca," I said.

"Come on in a yard," he said. "Looka good. It's a pretty, hey?"

We stood together, eyeing the charming sight in a sort of shared pride. He pulled out another packing case from the corner of the house and waved me to it with the flattering charm of a courtier.

"Please to sit," he said. "Scusa." He went in the house for a second and returned, extending his hand with the same grave courtesy. "You like-a onion?"

I looked at it dubiously. Father had disliked salads, saying firmly that hay was for God-damned Frenchmen, and Aunt Elsa's were of the pineapple, cream cheese and mayonnaise school. Raw onions were new to me, and alarming. But it was so lovely, being treated like a lady, that I could not disappoint him.

I took it and bit into it gingerly. The sharp, pungent, biting juice ran over my tongue, the firm fleshy layers crunched between my teeth in a stinging, breathtaking ecstasy of delicious pain.

"Oh!" I cried in sincere delight. "It's good!" Then, with the snobbery of the young guest who does not wish his host to think him ignorant of the wines he is offered, I added, "It's one of the best onions I ever ate."

"Sure," he said proudly. "Sure, you bet it's a good, it's a fine. I grow."

I regarded him happily, rejoicing in his kingly acceptance of the compliment, so unlike the mincing, genteel, self-depreciation which, of all the mannered compulsions of the Heights, I found most unfamiliar and most dismal.

I went on with my compliments, sincerely, but also eager for the continuing pleasure of his openness. "You have a wonderful house," I said. "The church is wonderful, too. You're a fine carpenter."

His eyes glowed and he swayed his head from side to side, like someone keeping time to music. "You bet I'm a good," he

337

replied. "I'm a learn in a Old Country, worka slow, take-a-pain, think for the job, for looka pretty, not think for hurry up, getta money. I'm a good like nobody's business."

"I should think you'd get lots of jobs," I said, "and be rich."

He shrugged. "Bad a time," he said. "Everywhere bad a time. Smart a man everywhere hungry, no work. Someday come a good time." He finished the onion and wiped his thin lips on the backs of his neat little fingers. "Someday, different time, all be good, not graba, graba, be man and man together, not dog and dog. First a big fight, maybe, then all be good."

I remembered something we had studied in social science. I leaned forward, trying to look intelligent and grownup. "You mean a revolution?" I said. "Are you a Communist, Mr. deRocca?"

"Pah!" He replied. "Not!" He spat to one side, to emphasize his attitude. Then, with a flashing, all embracing smile: "Lots good in de Comunista, lots smart. I read, I like, good. Only alla time boss, boss. Boss so bad like we here, now. I'm a no like all a time boss. I am Anarchista, me."

"What's that?" I asked.

"Everyone's treat everyone else right. No push around, no boss. People no gotta lot of stuff, graba, graba. No law, no boss, everyone a same. Treata them right, they treata you right. All good."

It sounded lovely.

"What do you call that? Anarchista? I guess I'm Anarchista, too." I said.

He threw both arms wide, embracing me in the universal fellowship. "That's a fine. You smart a kid."

Master and disciple, we sat happily together in the blissful country of utopian anarchy, regarding the flag of America spread out at our feet with absent, gently admiring eyes. Gradually, the conversation took a personal turn.

"You name a Constansia?"

"Constance."

"Pretty name," he said. "Pretty name for pretty girl. Nice when a pretty girl have a pretty name."

No one had told me I was pretty since my mother died. I was grateful to him, but unbelieving. "I have awful red hair," I said.

"Pretty," he said. "Pretty hair, pretty eye, pretty shape. How old?"

"Going on fifteen."

He smiled, as if I could not possibly have been a nicer age, as if it were a peculiar grace and wisdom in me to be going on fifteen.

"Last year, da little kid," he said. "Next year, da woman, look at da fella, think for da fella. Now she not know what she think—that right?"

I was deeply struck with the truth of his words. It was what I had been feeling in my inarticulate way all the time I was sitting with Posy on the creek bank, admiring her womanly young beauty, listening to her sternly virtuous, so very sex-conscious conversation, hoping that she did not still think of me as just a little kid.

I looked earnestly at Mr. deRocca sitting on his packing case, as if I could discover in the glowing, friendly eyes the source of his remarkable understanding. He was old, but I thought suddenly that he was handsome, as handsome as my father had been. His features were so sharp and delicate, his body so fine-boned, the shoulders so narrow, compared with the Mexicans with whom I unconsciously classed him. A fleeting wonder passed through my mind if all Italians were like him, so little and handsome and wise.

He held out his hand toward me, palm up and slightly cupped, almost as if he were coaxing a tame bird with seed. "That right?" he said again, quite soft.

I was surprised at my voice when I answered. It was unfamiliar—low and a little unsteady. "That's right," I said.

He stood up, smiling more than ever. "Come on down a

creek bank," he said. "I show you where I gotta good catfish net. Other guy wait to fish, watch, work. Me, I sit and they come."

Thinking back, remembering, I wonder for the first time if he spoke in any conscious analogy. I do not believe that he did.

I followed Mr. deRocca trustfully down the creek bank, under the box-elder trees. At the water's edge, he turned and looked at me, and I saw the changed look in his eyes. It was as if the door had opened and I were looking upon a landscape that was both strange and familiar. I glanced around me, and I saw that the box elders grew thick where we stood, that we were in a place that was private, sheltered from the eyes of the world. Suddenly, I understood everything that Posy had said. I knew what she meant when she said, "He's liking the girl."

"Show me the net," I said nervously.

His eyes smiled at me, reassuring, his voice quieted me. "Pretty soon," he said. "Right down here." But he made no move toward going on. Instead, he put out a lean, brown paw and touched my head. "Pretty," he said. "Pretty hair."

His hand slipped down my back and around my waist, the fingers firm and hard against me, warm through my cotton dress. And again he paused, his eyes still smiling with that same gentle reassurance.

He was old at the game, I see now, and grown wise in method, wise and patient. If he had hurried, if he had let me see his eagerness, I should have been terribly frightened, I should have run away crying. I should have run away full of fear and hate, and the fear and hate would have lived in me a long time.

But he stood, smiling at me, until I was used to his arm, his hand, feeling it not as a sexual advance but as warm, human affection in my body that was aching for human affection, for the demonstrative love on which I had thrived through a warm, loving childhood. He was quiet until I felt my fear dissolve in gratitude for the kindness of his arm, his firm, affectionate hand.

It was easy, then, for him to turn me against him, to hold me firm and close, stroking my hair, firm and close against him,

340

waiting till his accustomed, patient hands should tell him that I was ready for more.

I knew that I must be doing something bad, and still I could not feel that it was bad yet, not yet. And his slowness made me confident that I was free to decide if it was really bad, that he would let me go quickly the minute I thought it had begun to be bad. It still did not seem bad when he kissed me, or when his kissing changed and made me feel all soft and strange inside, or when his hands began to describe all the differences that the year had made in my body, and to tell me silently that they were beauties, richness, a bounty of which to be proud.

Once he made a little motion to draw me down in the thick grass and I had the sense to be frightened, but he felt it at once and waited, and I waited, too, sure that I would know when I should run away, growing softer and stranger by the moment, forgetting everything outside me. I was wholly lost when I heard Posy's shrill voice calling my name, and heard her pushing through the branches down the creek bank.

Mr. deRocca let me go and dropped to his knees at the water's edge. "Like a this," he said. "I'm a tie right here, da fish swim right in. Some net, hey?"

He looked over his shoulder and saw Posy. She was white and out of breath. "Connie!" she cried. "I don't know where you are. I'm scaring." She snatched at my hand, too relieved, too wrought up, to look at my revealing face. "Come along outa here," she said. Then remembering her manners, "Hello, Mr. deRocca."

She yanked me back to the row. "You crazy," she scolded me. "What you think, you go down there with deRocca? I'm telling you he's liking the girl."

"You said I was just a kid. That's what you said," I repeated.

"I know," she said. "Well, I'm crazy. Just as soon Chuck he tell me you down here, I'm knowing I'm crazy. You no kid, not for looks. No more. Was a little while ago, now no more. Mother

341

of God, I'm scaring." She paused, momentarily suspicious. "What you going down in there with deRocca for?"

"He said he was going to show me his catfish net."

"Ha, I bet! You poor kid, you got no sense. What he say? He talk dirty?"

"No," I replied with perfect truth. "He talked just as nice as you and Mrs. Grimes."

"Thanks God," said Posy, over and over again. "Thanks God."

In the unpleasant shock of nearly being caught out, all the new feeling that I had learned—the lovely, soft, flowing, flowering openness—was driven back in me, and the present moment closed above it so completely that the afternoon might have been lived years before, or not at all, by anything I felt in myself. Instead, I was troubled by an unwilling anger against Posy, as if she were making a disproportionate fuss.

Something of this she must have felt, or perhaps she now decided that my unwary innocence had been scolded long enough, for she took my hand, smiling again, as if, for her, too, the incident had suddenly dropped away out of sight.

"Come now," she said. "Is early yet, you don't got to going home, come now down to the house. We don't say nothing from this to Mrs. Grimes."

"No, Posy, no, I've got to get home," I said.

All the way home, I pedalled hard, as if I were very late—so hard that there was no room in me for anything else. Even before I saw the letters lying on the hall rug, where they had fallen from the mail slit in the door, I could tell from the silence that the house was empty. I stood in the sun that poured in at the open doorway, absorbing gratefully the quality of an empty house. I had not realized at all, as I forced myself home, faster and faster, how I would need, once I had got there, to be alone. I shut my eyes and sighed heavily, feeling the silence, the aloneness all through me like a merciful, unexpected blessing.

What had happened that afternoon, what had really happened? It wasn't only that I had let Mr. deRocca kiss me and touch me like that. It was something that had happened in me. There was something in me—and in the world, too—that I had never known was there before, something powerful and lovely, something powerful and new.

I stood there alone in the quiet house, in the sunshine, with my eyes closed. "I wish," I thought slowly, "that Posy hadn't come. I wish. . . ."

Suddenly, I knew that I had begun to be bad right there in Mr. deRocca's front yard, before we had ever gone down to the creek. I knew that I had been bad all along, terribly bad. Fear and guilt rose in me like a storm, shaking my body until my teeth chattered and I had to sit on the bottom step of the stairs and lean against the wall to hold myself still.

"If Posy knew," I thought, "if she knew about me, if she knew what I did, I'd die. I should die, I'd die."

Aunt Elsa found me like that when she came in a few minutes later. "Why, Connie!" she cried. "What is it, dear? You're sick."

"I got a chill," I said. "Just right now."

"Let me hang up my coat, dear," she said, "and I'll get you right into bed. Why, you poor baby!"

I let her help me up the stairs. I clung to her motherly warmth all the way, hungry for it, like a child that has been lost and found again. "Oh, Aunt Elsa," I cried. "I'm so glad you're home." And her gentle voice soothed me again and again. "There, dear, there. You're going to be all right. There, poor little girl. Aunt Elsa'll put you to bed. Yes, she will. Of course, she will."

In the complex agony of the moment, I was broken wide open. She's real, too, I thought in slow wonder; Aunt Elsa is real, too. She was my mother's sister.

I caught at her light, smooth dress, hiding my face in it. She smelled nice, clean and fresh, with a light perfume. I let my head fall against her shoulder, and it was soft and firm, comforting, comforting.

343

"Oh, Aunt Elsa," I cried, wondering because it was true, because it had not been true before, at all, and now it was wholly true. "Aunt Elsa, I love you."

That is the story, and that is all. When I woke in the morning, the ecstasy and the shame alike were gone. I had shut my mind upon them, as I had learned earlier to shut it upon grief and loss.

Oddly enough—for the defense mechanism seldom works that way—I still liked Mr. deRocca. Apparently, his attempted seduction had been quite impersonal, for, as I used to pass his yard, walking up the row to Posy's house in the warm, dusty August afternoons, he would always wave his little paw at me and say, "Hi ya, kid," amiably, but with no attempt to detain me.

For my own part, I always felt a tingling as I passed him; not enough to be unpleasant—just a sort of shy, quickening self-consciousness. It made me avoid his face as I replied, "Hello, Mr. deRocca." My voice, as I spoke, was always a trifle breathless. I told myself that it was funny how I hardly remembered that afternoon by the creek at all. But as I passed his house, I always stood up straight and moved slowly, and tried to look grownup.

DOROTHY CANFIELD FISHER

Dorothy Canfield Fisher was born on February 17, 1879, in Lawrence, Kansas, where her father, James Hulme Canfield, was currently professor of Romance Languages at the University of Kansas. She grew up in academic circles. Her adolescent years were spent in Lincoln, Nebraska, and her college days in Columbus, Ohio, her father being successively Chancellor of the University of Nebraska and President of Ohio State University.

Looking back on her youth, Mrs. Fisher said: "I hadn't the slightest idea that I would be a writer; I was being trained to be a professor of modern languages. I spent quite a little of my younger years, both as a child and as an adolescent and as a college student in France. My mother was an artist and often spent some time in Paris, and I was taken with her. So my English training was—if this is not too paradoxical—mostly in French. The rigorous French training in construction of sentences and the construction of compositions is what I have had, rather than any training in my own language."

She graduated from Ohio State University in 1899, and received her Ph.D. at Columbia University in 1905, working as secretary of the Horace Mann School in New York (1902–05) while studying for her degree. Her first book, published in 1904, was a study of Corneille and Racine; her second was a textbook for freshman English,

345

in collaboration with Professor George R. Carpenter of Columbia University.

Then, in 1907, she married John Fisher, whom she had met at Columbia, and turned her back on the academic life to live on a farm in Arlington, Vermont. Here she immersed herself in the life of the community, brought up two children, and began her career as a writer of fiction. When she was sixteen, living in Lincoln, Nebraska, she had collaborated with Willa Cather, a classmate of her older brother at the university, on a story entitled "The Fear That Walks at Night." But this juvenile effort had been her only excursion into fiction. Now she started writing regularly—novels, short stories, juveniles.

The Squirrel Cage, *which came out in* Everybody's Magazine *in 1911, made her a popular novelist from the start.* The Bent Twig *(1915) and* The Brimming Cup *(1921) are two of her better known novels. Her short stories about the people around her found a ready market and were reprinted in bound volumes such as* Hillsboro People *(1915) and* The Real Motive *(1916). Three years in France, 1916–19, aiding the French in World War I—her husband had enlisted as an ambulance driver—led to two volumes of stories:* Home Fires in France *(1918) and* Day of Glory *(1919).*

Her short stories have found favor both with a wide audience and with discriminating critics. Three of her stories received O. Henry Memorial Awards. Five of her stories, including "The Apprentice," published originally in the Ladies Home Journal *in 1948, were reprinted in* The Best American Short Stories *of the year. Concerning "The Apprentice," Mrs. Fisher wrote: "The magazine which printed the story changed the title—quite absurdly I thought [It was published as "Once and For All"]. I had called it 'The Apprentice,' meaning that the young girl was, with her collie dog, learning something of a woman's life, was an 'apprentice' to life, which was teaching her self-discipline and responsibility."*

Mrs. Fisher's own life was crowded and active. She was the first woman on the Vermont State Board of Education. She was author-in-residence, upon occasion, at the Bread Loaf Writers' Conference at Middlebury, Vermont. She was the recipient of honorary doctorates from ten colleges and universities. For twenty-five years she served on the Committee of Selection of the Book-of-the-Month Club, resigning in 1953 at the age of seventy-four. She died on November 9, 1958.

THE APPRENTICE

The day had been one of the unbearable ones, when every sound had set her teeth on edge like chalk creaking on a blackboard, when every word her father or mother said to her or did not say to her seemed an intentional injustice. And of course it would happen, as the fitting end to such a day, that just as the sun went down back of the mountain and the long twilight began, she noticed that Rollie was not around.

Tense with exasperation at what her mother would say, she began to call him in a carefully casual tone—she would simply explode if mother got going: "Here Rollie! He-ere boy! Want to go for a walk, Rollie?" Whistling to him cheerfully, her heart full of wrath at the way the world treated her, she made the rounds of his haunts: the corner of the woodshed, where he liked to curl up on the wool of father's discarded old sweater; the hay barn, the cow barn, the sunny spot on the side porch. No Rollie.

Perhaps he had sneaked upstairs to lie on her bed, where he was not supposed to go—not that *she* would have minded! That rule was a part of mother's fussiness, part, too, of mother's bossiness. It was *her* bed, wasn't it? But was she allowed the say-so about it? Not on your life. They *said* she could have things the way she wanted in her own room, now she was in her teens, but—her heart burned at unfairness as she took the stairs stormily, two steps at a time, her pigtails flopping up and down on her back. If Rollie was there, she was just going to let him stay there, and mother could say what she wanted to.

But he was not there. The bedspread and pillow were crumpled, but that was where she had flung herself down to cry that afternoon. Every nerve in her had been twanging discordantly, but she couldn't cry. She could only lie there, her hands doubled up hard, furious that she had nothing to cry about. Not really. She was too big to cry just over father's having said to her, severely, "I told you if I let you take the chess set, you were to put it away when you got through with it. One of the pawns was on the floor of our bedroom this morning. I stepped on it. If I'd had my shoes on I'd have broken it."

Well, he *had* told her that. And he hadn't said she mustn't ever take the set again. No, the instant she thought about that, she knew she couldn't cry about it. She could be, and was, in a rage about the way father kept on talking, long after she'd got his point: "It's not that I care so much about the chess set. It's because if you don't learn how to take care of things, you yourself will suffer for it. You'll forget or neglect something that will be really important for *you*. We *have* to try to teach you to be responsible for what you've said you'll take care of. If we—" on and on.

She stood there, dry-eyed, by the bed that Rollie had not crumpled and thought, *I hope mother sees the spread and says something about Rollie—I just hope she does. . . .*

She heard her mother coming down the hall, and hastily shut her door. She had a right to shut the door to her own room, hadn't she? She had *some* rights, she supposed, even if she was only thirteen and the youngest child. If her mother opened it to say, "What are you doing in here that you don't want me to see?" she'd say—she'd just say—

But her mother did not open the door. Her feet went steadily on along the hall, and then, carefully, slowly, down the stairs.

349

She probably had an armful of winter things she was bringing down from the attic. She was probably thinking that a tall, thirteen-year-old daughter was big enough to help with a chore like that. But she wouldn't *say* anything. She would just get out that insulting look of a grownup silently putting up with a crazy unreasonable kid. She had worn that expression all day; it was too much to be endured.

Up in her bedroom behind her closed door the thirteen-year-old stamped her foot in a gust of uncontrollable rage, none the less savage and heartshaking because it was mysterious to her.

But she had not located Rollie. She would be cut into little pieces before she would let her father and mother know she had lost sight of him, forgotten about him. They would not scold her, she knew. They would do worse; they would look at her. And in their silence she would hear, droning on reproachfully, what they had said when she had been begging to keep for her own the sweet, woolly collie puppy in her arms.

How warm he had felt! Astonishing how warm and alive a puppy was compared with a doll! She had never liked her dolls much after she had held Rollie, feeling him warm against her breast, warm and wriggling, bursting with life, reaching up to lick her face. He had loved her from that first instant. As he felt her arms around him his liquid, beautiful eyes had melted in trusting sweetness. And they did now, whenever he looked at her. Her dog was the only creature in the world who *really* loved her, she thought passionately.

And back then, at the very minute when, as a darling baby dog, he was beginning to love her, her father and mother were saying, so cold, so reasonable—gosh, how she *hated* reasonableness!—"Now, Peg, remember that, living where we do, with sheep on the farms around us, it is a serious responsibility to have a collie dog. If you keep him, you've got to be the one to take

350

care of him. You'll have to be the one to train him to stay at home. We're too busy with you children to start bringing up a puppy too."

Rollie, nestling in her arms, let one hind leg drop awkwardly. It must be uncomfortable. She looked down at him tenderly, tucked his leg up under him and gave him a hug. He laughed up in her face—he really did laugh, his mouth stretched wide in a cheerful grin. Now he was snug in a warm little ball.

Her parents were saying, "If you want him, you can have him. But you must be responsible for him. If he gets to running sheep, he'll just have to be shot, you know that."

They had not said, aloud, "Like the Wilsons' collie." They never mentioned that awfulness—her racing unsuspectingly down across the fields just at the horrible moment when Mr. Wilson shot their collie, caught in the very act of killing sheep. They probably thought that if they never spoke about it, she would forget it—*forget* the crack of that rifle, and the collapse of the great beautiful dog! Forget the red red blood spurting from the hole in his head. She hadn't forgotten. She never would. She knew as well as they did how important it was to train a collie puppy about sheep. They didn't have to rub it in like that. They always rubbed everything in. She had told them, fervently, indignantly, that of *course* she would take care of him, be re· sponsible for him, teach him to stay at home. Of course. Of course. *She* understood!

And now, when he was six months old, tall, rangy, powerful, standing up far above her knee, nearly to her waist, she didn't know where he was. But of course he must be somewhere around. He always was. She composed her face to look natural and went downstairs to search the house. He was probably asleep somewhere. She looked every room over carefully. Her mother was nowhere visible. It was safe to call him again, to give the special piercing whistle which always brought him racing to her, the white-feathered plume of his tail waving in elation that she wanted him.

But he did not answer. She stood still on the front porch to think.

Could he have gone up to their special place in the edge of the field where the three young pines, their branches growing close to the ground, made a triangular, walled-in space, completely hidden from the world? Sometimes he went up there with her, and when she lay down on the dried grass to dream he, too, lay down quietly, his head on his paws, his beautiful eyes fixed adoringly on her. He entered into her every mood. If she wanted to be quiet, all right, he did too. It didn't seem as though he would have gone alone there. Still—She loped up the steep slope of the field rather fast, beginning to be anxious.

No, he was not there. She stood irresolutely in the roofless, green-walled triangular hide-out, wondering what to do next.

Then, before she knew what thought had come into her mind, its emotional impact knocked her down. At least her knees crumpled under her. The Wilsons had, last Wednesday, brought their sheep down from the far upper pasture, to the home farm! They were—she herself had seen them on her way to school, and like an idiot had not thought of Rollie—on the river meadow.

She was off like a racer at the crack of the starting pistol, her long, strong legs stretched in great leaps, her pigtails flying. She took the short cut, regardless of the brambles. Their thorn-spiked, wiry stems tore at her flesh, but she did not care. She welcomed the pain. It was something she was doing for Rollie, for her Rollie.

She was in the pine woods now, rushing down the steep, stony path, tripping over roots, half falling, catching herself just in time, not slackening her speed. She burst out on the open knoll above the river meadow, calling wildly, "Rollie, here,

352

Rollie, here, boy! Here! Here!" She tried to whistle, but she was crying too hard to pucker her lips.

There was nobody to see or hear her. Twilight was falling over the bare, grassy knoll. The sunless evening wind slid down the mountain like an invisible river, engulfing her in cold. Her teeth began to chatter. "Here, Rollie, here, boy, here!" She strained her eyes to look down into the meadow to see if the sheep were there. She could not be sure. She stopped calling him as she would a dog, and called out his name despairingly, as if he were her child, "Rollie! Oh, *Rollie*, where are you?"

The tears ran down her cheeks in streams. She sobbed loudly, terribly; she did not try to control herself, since there was no one to hear. "Hou! Hou! Hou!" she sobbed, her face contorted grotesquely. "Oh, Rollie! Rollie! Rollie!" She had wanted something to cry about. Oh, how terribly now she had something to cry about.

She saw him as clearly as if he were there beside her, his muzzle and gaping mouth all smeared with the betraying blood (like the Wilsons' collie). "But he didn't *know* it was wrong!" she screamed like a wild creature. "Nobody *told* him it was wrong. It was my fault. I should have taken better care of him. I will now. I will!"

But no matter how she screamed, she could not make herself heard. In the cold gathering darkness, she saw him stand, poor, guiltless victim of his ignorance, who should have been protected from his own nature, his beautiful soft eyes looking at her with love, his splendid plumed tail waving gently. "It was my fault. I promised I would bring him up. I should have *made* him stay at home. I was responsible for him. It was my fault."

But she could not make his executioners hear her. The shot rang out. Rollie sank down, his beautiful liquid eyes glazed, the blood spurting from the hole in his head—like the Wilsons' collie. She gave a wild shriek, long, soul-satisfying, frantic. It was the scream at sudden, unendurable tragedy of a mature, full-blooded woman. It drained dry the girl of thirteen. She came

353

to herself. She was standing on the knoll, trembling and quaking with cold, the darkness closing in on her.

Her breath had given out. For once in her life she had wept all the tears there were in her body. Her hands were so stiff with cold she could scarcely close them. How her nose was running! Simply streaming down her upper lip. And she had no handkerchief. She lifted her skirt, fumbled for her slip, stooped, blew her nose on it, wiped her eyes, drew a long quavering breath—and heard something! Far off in the distance, a faint sound, like a dog's muffled bark.

She whirled on her heels and bent her head to listen. The sound did not come from the meadow below the knoll. It came from back of her, from the Wilsons' maple grove higher up. She held her breath. Yes, it came from there. She began to run again, but now she was not sobbing. She was silent, absorbed in her effort to cover ground. If she could only live to get there, to see if it really were Rollie. She ran steadily till she came to the fence, and went over this in a great plunge. Her skirt caught on a nail. She impatiently pulled at it, not hearing or not heeding the long sibilant tear as it came loose. She was in the dusky maple woods, stumbling over the rocks as she ran. As she tore on up the slope she knew it was Rollie's bark.

She stopped short and leaned weakly against a tree, sick with the breathlessness of her straining lungs, sick in the reaction of relief, sick with anger at Rollie, who had been here having a wonderful time while she had been dying, just dying in terror about him.

For she could not only hear that it was Rollie's bark; she could hear, in the dog language she knew as well as he, what he was saying in those excited yips; that he had run a woodchuck into a hole in the tumbled stone wall, that he almost had him, that the intoxicating wild-animal smell was as close to him— almost—as if he had his jaws on his quarry. Yip! Woof! Yip! Yip!

The wild, joyful quality of the dog talk enraged the girl. She was trembling in exhaustion, in indignation. So that was where he had been, when she was killing herself trying to take care of him. Plenty near enough to hear her calling and whistling to him, if he had paid attention. Just so set on having his foolish good time, he never thought to listen for her call.

She stooped to pick up a stout stick. She would teach him! It was time he had something to make him remember to listen. She started forward.

But she stopped, stood thinking. One of the things to remember about collies—everybody knew that—was their sensitiveness. A collie who had been beaten was never "right" again. His spirit was broken. "Anything but a broken-spirited collie," the farmers often said. They were no good after that.

She threw down her stick. Anyhow, she thought, he was too young to know, really, that he had done wrong. He was still only a puppy. Like all puppies, he got perfectly crazy over wild-animal smells. Probably he really and truly hadn't heard her calling and whistling.

All the same, all the same—she stared intently into the twilight—he couldn't be let to grow up just as he wanted to. She would have to make him understand that he mustn't go off this way by himself. He must be trained to know how to do what a good dog does—not because *she* wanted him to, but for his own sake.

She walked on now, steady, purposeful, gathering her inner strength together. Olympian in her understanding of the full meaning of the event.

When he heard his own special young god approaching, he turned delightedly and ran to meet her, panting, his tongue hanging out. His eyes shone. He jumped up on her in an ecstasy of welcome and licked her face.

But she pushed him away. Her face and voice were grave. "No, Rollie, *no!*" she said severely. "You're *bad.* You know you're not to go off in the woods without me! You are—a—*bad—dog.*"

He was horrified. Stricken into misery. He stood facing her,

355

frozen, the gladness going out of his eyes, the erect waving plume of his tail slowly lowered to slinking, guilty dejection.

"I know you were all wrapped up in that woodchuck. But that's no excuse. You *could* have heard me, calling you, whistling for you, if you'd paid attention," she went on. "You've got to learn, and I've got to teach you."

With a shudder of misery he lay down, his tail stretched out limp on the ground, his head flat on his paws, his ears drooping— ears ringing with doomsday awfulness of the voice he so loved and revered. He must have been utterly wicked. He trembled, and turned his head away from her august look of blame, groveling in remorse for whatever mysterious sin he had committed.

She sat down by him, as miserable as he. "I don't *want* to scold you. But I have to! I have to bring you up right, or you'll get shot, Rollie. You *mustn't* go away from the house without me, do you hear, *never!*"

Catching, with his sharp ears yearning for her approval, a faint overtone of relenting affection in her voice, he lifted his eyes to her, humbly, soft in imploring fondness.

"Oh, Rollie!" she said, stooping low over him. "I *do* love you. I do. But I *have* to bring you up. I'm responsible for you, don't you see?"

He did not see. Hearing sternness, or something else he did not recognize, in the beloved voice, he shut his eyes tight in sorrow, and made a little whimpering lament in his throat.

She had never heard him cry before. It was too much. She sat down by him and drew his head to her, rocking him in her arms, smoothing him with inarticulate small murmurs.

He leaped in her arms and wriggled happily as he had when he was a baby; he reached up to lick her face as he had then. But he was no baby now. He was half as big as she, a great, warm, pulsing, living armful of love. She clasped him closely. Her heart was brimming full, but calmed, quiet. The blood flowed in equable gentleness all over her body. She was

356

deliciously warm. Her nose was still running a little. She sniffed and wiped it on her sleeve.

It was almost dark now. "We'll be late to supper, Rollie," she said responsibly. Pushing him gently off, she stood up. "Home, Rollie, home!"

Here was a command he could understand. At once he trotted along the path toward home. His plumed tail, held high, waved cheerfully. His short dog memory had dropped into oblivion the suffering just back of him.

Her human memory was longer. His prancing gait was as care-free as a young child's. Plodding heavily like a serious adult, she trod behind him. Her very shoulders seemed bowed by what she had lived through. She felt, she thought like an old, old woman of thirty. But it was all right now. She knew she had made an impression on him.

When they came out into the open pasture, Rollie ran back to get her to play with him. He leaped around her in circles, barking in cheerful yawps, jumping up on her, inviting her to run a race with him, to throw him a stick, to come alive.

His high spirits were ridiculous. But infectious. She gave one little leap to match his. Rollie pretended that this was a threat to him, planted his forepaws low and barked loudly at her, laughing between yips. He was so funny, she thought, when he grinned that way. She laughed back, and gave another mock-threatening leap at him. Radiant that his sky was once more clear, he sprang high on his spring-steel muscles in an explosion of happiness, and bounded in circles around her.

Following him, not noting in the dusk where she was going, she felt the grassy slope drop steeply. Oh, yes, she knew where she was. They had come to the rolling-down hill just back of the house. All the kids rolled down there, even the little ones, because it was soft grass without a stone. She had rolled down that slope a million times—years and years ago, when she was a kid herself. It was fun. She remembered well the whirling dizziness of the descent, all the world turning over and over crazily.

357

And the delicious giddy staggering when you first stood up, the earth still spinning under your feet.

"All right, Rollie, let's go," she cried, and flung herself down in the rolling position, her arms straight up over her head.

Rollie had never seen this skylarking before. It threw him into almost hysterical amusement. He capered around the rapidly rolling figure, half scared, mystified, enchanted.

His wild frolicsome barking might have come from her own throat, so accurately did it sound the way she felt—crazy, foolish, like a little kid, no more than five years old, the age she had been when she had last rolled down that hill.

At the bottom she sprang up, on muscles as steel-strong as Rollie's. She staggered a little, and laughed aloud.

The living-room windows were just before them. How yellow lighted windows looked when you were in the darkness going home. How nice and yellow. Maybe mother had waffles for supper. She was a swell cook, mother was, and she certainly gave her family all the breaks, when it came to meals.

"Home, Rollie, home!" She burst open the door to the living room. "Hi, mom, what you got for supper?"

From the kitchen her mother announced coolly, "I hate to break the news to you, but it's waffles."

"Oh, *mom!*" she shouted in ecstasy.

Her mother could not see her. She did not need to. "For goodness sakes, go and wash," she called.

In the long mirror across the room she saw herself, her hair hanging wild, her long bare legs scratched, her broadly smiling face dirt-streaked, her torn skirt dangling, her dog laughing up at her. Gosh, was it a relief to feel your own age, just exactly thirteen years old!

MARJORIE KINNAN RAWLINGS

*Marjorie Kinnan Rawlings was born August 8, 1896, in
Washington, D.C. Although she grew up in the nation's
capital, the hours she most enjoyed were those spent during
the summer on her maternal grandmother's farm in Michigan or on the farm in Maryland purchased by her father,
an attorney in the United States Patent Office, as a place of
refuge from city life.*

*She had an early interest in writing. When she was
eleven, a story of hers appeared on the children's page of
the Washington* Post. *When she was fourteen, she won
$75 in a contest sponsored by McCall's Magazine. She con-
tributed to the school publications of Western High School,
from which she graduated in 1914 at the age of seventeen.*

*That fall she enrolled in the University of Wisconsin.
Her collegiate record was brilliant; she was elected to Phi
Beta Kappa in her junior year. She continued to write—
for the literary magazine and the yearbook—and had the
distinction of being included in the anthology* Poets of the
Future.

*After graduating in June 1918, she took a job at the
national headquarters of the YWCA as editor of the* War
Work Bulletin. *In 1919 she became assistant service editor
for the magazine* Home Sector *and wrote a couple of
articles for* St. Nicholas *and* Everybody's. *That same year*

she married Charles A. Rawlings, newspaperman and free-lance writer.

Her next ten years were spent as a newspaper woman, moving about from place to place. She was a feature writer for the Louisville, Kentucky, Courier-Journal *and the Rochester, New York,* Journal. *For three years she conducted a verse column, "Songs of a Housewife," for United Feature Syndicate. Journalism, she said, was a "rough school," but one that she "wouldn't have missed. You learn a lot when you must put down what people said and how they acted in great crises in their lives. And it teaches you objectivity." During those years as a journalist she tried quite unsuccessfully to write short stories for the magazine market.*

In 1928, tired of the life she was living, she resigned her job and purchased a 72-acre orange grove at Cross Creek, Hawthorne, Florida, with money that she had inherited. She was, she said, "fitted by temperament and by inheritance for farm and country living." Her intention was to make the orange grove support her while she kept on trying to write fiction. The venture brought an end to her marriage. Her husband did not share her enthusiasm for the isolated rural life at Cross Creek. They were eventually divorced in 1933.

For two or three years she struggled with the orange grove, with the primitive living conditions. She continued to write stories, but all she collected was a stack of rejection slips. Meanwhile, she had become an integral part of the life of the community, learning to know and respect the Florida "crackers" who were her neighbors. About to give up on her writing, she decided to make one more attempt. This time she wrote a story about the people around her and submitted it in the Scribner's Magazine *Long Story Contest. "Jacob's Ladder" won the $700 prize, was published in the April 1931 issue, and she found herself being hailed as a literary "find." She was thirty-four years old.*

This was the beginning of years of success as a regional writer. The next year "Gal Young Un," published in Harper's, *won the O. Henry Memorial Award first prize. Her first novel,* South Moon Under *(1933), became a Book-of-the-Month Club selection.* The Yearling *(1938) was the novel that made her famous. It topped the best-seller lists for months and won the Pulitzer Prize for fiction in 1939.* Cross Creek *(1942), another Book-of-the-Month Club selection, told the story of her Florida experiences.*

For the next ten years she devoted herself to the short story. "Black Secret," published in the New Yorker, *September 8, 1945, was the third of her stories to receive an O. Henry award. Her final novel,* The Sojourner, *came out in 1953, shortly before her death on December 14.*

BLACK SECRET

The shutters were drawn in the parlor against the afternoon sun. June lay heavy on the street outside, but the room was dark and cool. Hummingbirds droned in the honeysuckle over the window. The fragrance filtered through the shutters. Dickie flattened his face against the rose-patterned Brussels carpet. It was pleasantly harsh and faintly dusty. He moved his cheek to the smoothness of his picture book. The page was smooth and slippery. He lay comfortably, imagining that the painted lion under him was alive and his friend. He shook his loose, tucked blouse and pretended that the lion was breathing against him. He wished that it was night, when the new gas lights would flare from their brass pipes on the wall, for their yellow flickering made the lion's eyes move and shine. He lifted his head. The double doors of the parlor were sliding open. He heard his mother speak.

"The garden party was lovely, Mrs. Tipton. But aren't you exhausted?"

Dickie thinned himself to a shadow. If he were quiet, they might let him stay while they talked. There was an excitement in his mother's talk in this room with Mrs. Tipton that he heard no other place and with no other person. The women came into the parlor and Mammy Dee closed the folding doors after them. His mother saw him. She had on her flowered organdie with the ruffled flounces. They touched his ankle as she rustled past him.

She said, "Speak to Mrs. Tipton, Dickie."

He scrambled to his feet and jerked his head and put out his hand.

Mrs. Tipton said, "Precious. And how is Master Merrill today?"

"I'm reading my book," he said.

She said, "Precious."

He flopped down hurriedly on the rug and began turning the pages of the book. He sank himself in it, hopefully.

His mother said, "Straight chairs are more comfortable when it's warm, aren't they? Take this one. . . . Oh, the party was beautiful!"

The room was an empty box waiting to be filled.

"Thank you."

His mother said, "I see you had Lulu Wilson again to help."

His heart beat rapidly. They were beginning. They would forget him.

Mrs. Tipton said, "She's marvellous help for that sort of thing. Of course, no one could have her around steadily. You know—"

"I know."

His mother's voice held the vibration of the secret.

Mrs. Tipton said, "You couldn't have Judge Wimberley knocking at your back door."

His mother said, breathlessly, "Judge Wimberley?"

"He's the latest."

Turning his head casually, Dickie saw Mrs. Tipton lean forward in the cool, straight chair.

She said, "Oh, Mrs. Merrill, it's incredible, isn't it?"

"Mrs. Tipton, not Judge Wimberley!"

"Yes."

The parlor hummed, as though the birds in the honeysuckle had flown inside. He heard the soft sound of the women's bosoms rising and falling.

His mother said, "It seems as though something could be done."

Mrs. Tipton said, "If we sent them away, there'd only be others."

He knew exactly whom she meant. She meant Creecy and Long Tom and Lulu Wilson. They were nigger women, and something about them was different, even from other nigger women. Creecy was a Geechee, short and fat and blacker than the soot in the fireplace. Long Tom was as black, but tall and thin and bony. Lulu Wilson was the color of his mother's coffee when the cream and sugar were in it. She was young and slim and pretty. They were the secret. Not quite all of it, for Judy Lane was a part of it. But Judy had moved away.

Mrs. Tipton said, "I learned enough from Lulu this time to run half the men out of town."

His mother rose from her chair and walked up and down the rug. She said, "Oh, Mrs. Tipton, somehow it doesn't seem right, knowing these things."

Her voice had the sick sound that he hated and that made him weak all over. Yet he wanted to hear.

Mrs. Tipton rose too. The two women stood in the center of the dark coolness, like birds fresh caught in a cage.

Mrs. Tipton said, "Well, I want to know. That's why I have her. Women are blind. Women are stupid. I want to know."

His mother said, "Perhaps she's lying."

Her voice sounded the way it sounded when she had a headache.

"She's not lying. I tell you, Mrs. Merrill, men are beasts."

His mother sat down again, and Mrs. Tipton sat too.

Mrs. Tipton said in a low voice, "Dickie?"

His mother said, "Oh, my dear, he's only seven."

"But little pitchers have big ears."

His mother said, "Dickie, dear, wouldn't you like to go out and play?"

He pretended not to hear her.

"Dickie, dear."

He looked up from the picture book. "Mummy, do lions have long tails?"

His mother smiled at Mrs. Tipton. "You see."

They settled back.

Mrs. Tipton said, "I don't tell all this to everyone."

"I know."

"Some women—I just couldn't. Poor things. And never knowing. Oh, men, Mrs. Merrill! Men . . ."

His mother said, "The rest of us must just thank God for ours."

"If anyone could be sure, Mrs. Merrill."

His mother's voice fluttered like a butterfly.

"You mustn't say such things, Mrs. Tipton. My Richard . . . I thank God every night. I don't know what I've done to deserve such—such devotion. I suppose any woman is fortunate to be truly loved."

Dickie wanted to run and bury his head in the lace and ribbons over her soft breast. He wanted to cry out, "I love you, too." Her breast smelled of the sweet lavender that Mammy Dee raised in the herb garden and dried and laid away in all the dresser drawers.

She said, "Mrs. Tipton—it's no excuse, I know—but do you suppose the wives could be in any way to blame?"

Mrs. Tipton said coldly, "I'm sure Judge Wimberley's wife has always done her duty."

"Oh, not duty!"

His mother's voice was a cry.

Mrs. Tipton said, "I tell you, Mrs. Merrill, men are beasts."

The sun found an opening in the shutters. Dickie turned on his side and watched the dust motes dancing across the bright bar.

His mother said, "Only God can judge. . . . Tell me, do they say the cotton has had enough rain?"

Mrs. Tipton said, "I think so. At the bank, they're making more loans."

"I feel guilty sometimes, Richard being in timber and lumber—things already there, so stable—and the people dependent on their annual crops have so much anxiety."

Mrs. Tipton said, "Your husband's uncle, Mr. Baxter Merrill— I believe he has a fine stand of cotton."

"Oh, dear Uncle Baxter. He always prospers. We were at the plantation last Sunday. Everything was beautiful. We have such a gay time when we go there. We depend on Uncle Baxter to be gay. Dickie adores him."

A chime sounded in the depths of the house.

Mrs. Merrill said, "You'll have cake and sherry with me, won't you, Mrs. Tipton?"

"Thank you, Mrs. Merrill."

"Dickie, dear."

He rose in seeming abstraction and went to her. Now he might sink into her laces and her fragrance. She stroked his hair.

"Dickie, darling, I was to take you to Robert to have your hair cut. Dearest, you're such a big boy, couldn't you go alone?"

His heart was pounding.

"Yes, Mummy."

He longed for the hot sunlight outside the parlor.

"Then have Mammy Dee give you a quarter and go to Robert. Cross the streets very carefully, won't you, lamb?"

"Yes, Mummy. Goodbye."

Mrs. Tipton murmured, "Precious."

He ran from the parlor. Mammy Dee was singing in the kitchen.

"I'm old enough to have my hair cut by myself," he said. "Mummy says you're to give me a quarter."

The vast black woman fumbled in a sugar sack on the wall. "You mind how you cross the railroad tracks."

"I'll be careful."

Dickie tightened his fingers over the coin and ran from the house. He was faint from the secret. It had something to do with black women and white men. It was remote and fascinating and more sickening than too much syrup candy. The lawn grass was green, for it was watered every evening, but beyond it the grass that bordered the town sidewalks was parched and brown. He ran west for three blocks and at the corner by Mrs. Tipton's big house he turned and ran south. He had never crossed the tracks alone before.

He was afraid for a moment that he would not find the barbershop, but the striped pole lifted ahead of him like a lighted lamp. He darted inside the open door and stood an instant, catching his breath. Black Robert rose lazily from a stool, and he was at home again.

Robert said, "I declare, Mastuh Dickie. All by yo'self."

Dickie looked about him. The barbershop lay in its summer stupor. The two chairs stood a little separated, one empty, the far one filled with the shapeless form of a man buried under a white apron. Black Perchy scraped at the face of the chair's occupant. Two other white men sat nearby. They were talking together. Now and then the man in the chair joined in with them, his voice muffled by the lather and the apron. They glanced at Dickie and went on talking.

Black Robert said, "Missy know you come alone?"

Dickie nodded and held out the quarter and Robert laid it on the shelf under the glass case where lotions and tonics glittered in the sunlight.

Robert whispered, "Yo' ma ain't changed yo' haircut, is she?"

Dickie understood that he was to be quiet, so the men talking would not be interrupted.

"She's got company," he whispered in return.

Robert nodded. Dickie climbed into the great chair. The headrest was too high and Robert lowered it for him. He leaned back, feeling mature and important. Robert drew a clean white apron around him and tied it behind his neck. He turned to the case and took out a thin comb and a pair of shining scissors. The comb ran through Dickie's hair, lifting it away from his scalp with the feeling of strong wind. The scissors snipped through his upper hair, then lay suddenly, cool and ticklish, against the back of his neck.

The man in the other chair said, "What's new since I've been here?"

One man said, "What do you think? Nothing."

The other said, "We've got a new bridge over the mill creek. Progress!"

All three laughed together.

One man said, "By God, Beck, you didn't tell him Judy Lane was back in town."

The man in the chair said under his soapsuds, "That good-looking high yellow that married the white man in Chicago?"

"That's the one. Breezed into town in one of those electric broughams, dressed in ostrich feathers long enough to cover her yellow shanks."

"I'll swear. Do you suppose the Chicago guy knows?"

"Probably not."

Robert leaned close to run the scissors around Dickie's right ear.

The man in the chair said, "Strikes me she's right bold, coming back here. Was she raised here?"

"Right here. Her mammy was blacker 'n coal'll ever be. One of our leading lights is her daddy."

"Who's that?"

"Baxter Merrill."

"The cotton man?"

"Baxter Merrill, the cotton man. Cotton's the only white crop he's ever raised."

For a moment Dickie saw the secret lie shadowy, as always, in the distance. Then it rose and swelled. It rushed at him with a great roaring, shouting "Uncle Baxter!" He could not breathe. He clawed at the apron around his neck.

Robert murmured, "I'll fix it, Mastuh Dickie."

The glass case of lotions glittered. The barber's chair heaved up and down. He felt something wet on his mouth and splashing

368

on his hands. He was a big boy and he never cried. He was crying.

Robert moved in front of him and planted his bulk between him and the rest of the barbershop. The round ebony face was furrowed and strained.

He said in a low voice, "Hol' still, Mastuh Dickie."

Dickie lifted his fists and beat them on Robert's chest. He twisted his mouth and blinked his eyelids rapidly. It was no use. A sob tore from him. It ripped flesh with it, somewhere in his chest. Two drops of sweat rolled down Robert's face and sank into the white apron.

Dickie said, "I'm sick."

Suddenly Robert gathered him from the chair and wrapped the white apron around him. The black man carried him in the apron to the door and set him on his feet on the sidewalk.

Robert said, "You go down the street a while, Mastuh Dickie." He untied the apron from around his neck. "You come back about traintime. The gemmuns'll be gone then, at traintime."

Dickie drew a deep breath against the coming cyclone.

Robert said, "You come back, now, to get finished." The sweat ran down the black face like rain. "You come back. You cain't go home to yo' ma part done. A li'l man got to go home to his ma all done."

Dickie wavered on his feet. Robert reached into a pocket under his barber's smock and pulled out a penny. He put it in Dickie's palm and closed his fingers over it.

"You go down the next block and get you a ice ball. They got ras'br'y an' cherry today. Then you come back at traintime."

Dickie began to run down the street. The cyclone was on him. He sobbed so deeply that his side ached before he had gone half a block. The tears washed down his face and over his blue dimity blouse. He clutched the penny tightly. It was wet and sticky with sweat from the black hand and from his own.

RAMONA STEWART

Ramona Stewart was born in San Francisco February 19, 1922. Her father, a mining promoter, was restless, and so she grew up, she said, "propelled about the country"— Los Angeles, San Diego, Salt Lake City, Pensacola (Florida), Saratoga (New York), New York City—in a convent one semester, in a tent outside an oil well near Ogden, Utah, the next. For two years she studied at the Professional Children's School in New York City.

She started to write stories as soon as she learned to write whole sentences. She had always wanted to be a writer, and being an only child, she had time to herself, and opportunity, she said, "to make up private worlds and describe them on paper." She wrote a novelette at the age of twelve, her first novel at the age of fifteen, a second at the age of seventeen.

Winning a scholarship to the University of Southern California, she majored first in French and then in International Relations, with the thought of becoming a foreign correspondent. Meanwhile, she kept on writing. It was, she said, "as natural to me as dreaming at night." She was twenty-one when she wrote her first published novel, Desert Town, which came out initially in serial form in Collier's under the title Bitter Harvest. The motion picture Desert Fury was adapted from it.

In school and college there were no literary influences on her in the sense of people that she "actually knew," but there were "many influences from the library. When I didn't

370

know how to bridge from one episode to another in a book I was trying to write, I would run to the library and stay there till I found how Cather did it, how Colette did it, how Selma Lagerlöf did it. You will notice these are all women writers. I think I must have had a feeling that it might be easier for a girl to learn from women than it would be to learn from men. I certainly had great loves among the men writers—Dostoevsky, particularly, and James Stephens—but I never could write the slightest bit like either of them. You can be sure I tried when I was in my teens and twenties."

She was working as a secretary for Universal Studios, Hollywood, when Desert Town was published in 1945. She has also worked as secretary for the Desert Patrol Unit of the California Highway Patrol, the Department of Philosophy at UCLA, for an industrial hospital in San Francisco, and for an agricultural chemical company in New York. After the release of the motion picture based on her first novel, she lived for five years in the mining and cattle country of central Nevada, where she gathered material for her novel The Stars Abide, published in August 1961.

"The Promise" appeared originally in the American Mercury, June 1949, and was reprinted in The Best American Short Stories of 1950. Most of her other short stories appeared in Collier's.

In speaking of her writing habits, Miss Stewart says: "I recall reading that Chekhov once said that women writers, unlike men, write the way they embroider—they write a bit, then cut and pull it all tight, write and cut, write and cut. I do this, I know; I can't tell about the others."

Miss Stewart is presently living in New York City, where she is working on another novel.

THE PROMISE

Louise put her glass down on the coffee table and the clink broke the dreaming silence of the California afternoon.

"Ann, honey," she said. "I'm afraid we're going to have to tell your father after all."

Ann looked up at her quickly. "Oh, mother," she said.

Louise's soft pretty face grew troubled. "I'm no good at hiding things, baby."

"You're not hiding anything," Ann said.

She was a thin, pale girl of thirteen who still looked young and unfinished, like a bud that might open to any color. She watched her mother, her dark eyes quick and cautious.

"I don't see the harm in just telling him about it," Louise pressed gently.

"You can't. You promised," Ann said. "He'll argue and shout and you'll change your mind."

"I give you my word," Louise began.

"He'll talk you out of it. He always does."

"Now, darling, please don't get excited," Louise said. "Try to see my side of it. There are some things you just don't understand yet. Mac is your father and he's got a right to know."

"Why should he?" Ann said. "A lot he cared about me or his rights when he wanted to marry somebody else."

As soon as the words were out she realized she'd made a

Reprinted from *American Mercury* by permission of *American Mercury* and Ramona Stewart.

mistake. Louise frowned thoughtfully and lit another cigarette. Her large blue eyes were hazy with reflection and she ran long white fingers through her loosely waved black hair. She was really beautiful, Ann thought; she was glad there had been a divorce because with Mac gone Louise came to depend on her more.

"Annie, dear," Louise said. "I don't know how to explain about the divorce—there were so many things that went wrong between Mac and me. It wasn't your father's fault particularly. We just weren't suited to each other."

"It was her fault," Ann said doggedly.

"That was later, honey. We were all through long before he met Paula. We just stayed married because of you and Little Mac. And we kept quarreling so all the time."

"He kept quarreling."

"No," Louise said, and picked up her drink. "I quarreled too, baby."

"I don't care if you did. You had to be around him." Ann astonished herself by breaking into tears. "I don't want to talk about him," she said violently. "I don't ever want to talk about him." She sank down on the sofa and put her face in Louise's lap.

"Oh my God," Louise said softly.

She began to stroke Ann's hair back out of her face, gathering it together at the nape of her neck. In spite of herself, Ann felt calmness flowing into her at Louise's touch, lazy, cool, a little distracted, and after a bit she was soothed and let herself be pushed away. She watched peacefully as Louise got up, walked across the cream-colored string rug, past the bowl of cabbage roses on the grand piano, to the cabinet bar.

The room was like Louise, full of gay, unrelated pieces. The impressionistic French water color on the wall over the piano didn't fit with the Copenhagen china cat sitting on the rug beneath it. The sofa and three of the chairs had originally been lemon-yellow modern but like most of Louise's ideas, they hadn't worked out too well and now they were covered with red and green chintz slipcovers. The fireplace didn't heat but they burned colored powder in it at night and it was very pretty.

Louise made herself a scotch and then turned back to Ann resolutely. "Darling, your father will be simply furious if we don't tell him. I'm going to call him right now and get it settled."

She walked to the bookshelves and picked up the French phone before Ann could argue, and gave the operator Mac's number in Santa Monica. While it was ringing, she looked up and nodded at the square crystal ashtray on the coffee table. Ann brought it over to her and then stood kicking at the edge of the rug with the heels of her saddle shoes, staring out the long windows at the ocean beyond the garden and the cliff.

"Hello, Paula," Louise said cheerfully. "How are you?"

Ann's face was impassive. Paula was young and thin and diffident, with none of Louise's lazy warmth. She reminded Ann of a librarian. She was painful when she tried to be friends. The few visits Ann and Little Mac had made to her house were filled with agonizing silences, when they had all three sat and stared and waited hopefully for Mac to say something amusing or start a row, anything to create a diversion.

"Paula, dear, is Mac around?" Louise asked. "I'm going to upset him, I'm afraid." A pause. "Ann doesn't want to go back to Miss Taylor's and I just can't force her to against her will. But Mac was so set on it—"

Ann frowned. "You don't have to tell her," she said.

Louise raised her fine black eyebrows slightly and shook her head. Ann looked away.

"Hello, Mac," Louise said. "Did Paula tell you? . . . Well, I don't know. If Ann doesn't want to. . . . It's all very well for you to say that, but I have to live with her. . . . I think you're being too harsh." Louise's voice deepened with irritation. "But I promised her."

Mac's voice got suddenly loud. Ann heard it bumbling

through the phone like an angry bee trapped in a bottle. Louise took the instrument away from her ear, drank half her scotch and then went on listening until Mac finished.

"All right," she said quietly. "If you feel you have to. In half an hour."

She set the phone back in its cradle, strolled across the room and stood at the window, her forehead pressed against the pane.

"He's coming up," Ann said. "Isn't he?"

Louise nodded without bothering to turn around. "Why don't you take Little Mac and go down to the matinée?" she asked.

"I'll stay," Ann said.

Louise sighed. She finished the scotch.

For a moment, Ann tried to think of a way to make Louise stop drinking, so she'd keep cool and in control of herself until it was over. But there was nothing she could say that didn't sound nagging and while she was still trying words, Little Mac came running down the back hall. He stopped at the living-room arch, looked in, and then came strolling to them. He was eleven, but he was tall for his age. He was wearing jeans and a T-shirt and he had his bathing trunks and a wet towel slung over his shoulder.

"What's up?" he asked.

"Dearfather is coming over," Ann said, running the words together.

"Ann—" Louise began.

"Dad?" Pleasure spread over Little Mac's tan face and brightened the blue eyes that were so much like Louise's. "I guess I better go change clothes."

He ran out of the room and they heard him bounding up the stairs two at a time.

"You see," Louise said. "He loves Mac."

"He doesn't love Mac. He just likes the idea of having a father," Ann said. "And anyway, he's awfully young."

"Sometimes—" Louise began, and then stopped, baffled. "Aren't you going to change your dress?"

"What for?" Ann asked. "He isn't going to like the way I look anyhow."

It was quiet and serene, just the three of them sitting around the sunlit living room. Little Mac had put on a blue sport shirt and white pants, and his dark blond hair was wet and slicked back. Louise was half lying on the sofa in her long yellow hostess gown, one leg drawn under her, her eyes dazed with thought. Ann still had on her blouse, sweater, and baggy skirt. She was reading a novel and twisting a strand of hair between her fingers, nibbling occasionally at the frayed ends.

Then they heard Mac's car in the driveway and the peace was shattered. They heard the door-chimes ring and the maid letting him in, and they all looked up.

His impatient footsteps sounded in the hall and then he was standing in the living-room entrance-way.

He was a tall man with black curly hair and spaniel's eyes. He was overweight but his skin had the smooth tan of a man who has plenty of time to lie in the sun. Like Little Mac, he had obviously just changed clothes, but he was already sweating through his sport shirt.

As he came into the room, he smiled. It made him look hot, confused, irritated and pleading, all at the same time. Like a fat girl at a dancing party, Ann thought, angry and ashamed, standing alone against a wall; and suddenly she was humiliated that he should be her father and allow himself to look like that.

"Hello, Dad," Little Mac said, jumping up and offering his hand. "It's good to see you. Won't you have a seat, sir?"

Mac went on smiling but they all saw the twitch of exasperation that caught his face. He clapped Little Mac's shoulder to avoid the handshake and sat down on Little Mac's chair.

"Hello, Louise," he said. "What are you drinking?"

"Scotch. It's in the cabinet. Help yourself."

"I don't suppose you have any decent beer."

"I think so. Little Mac, run out and ask Molly for some beer."

"Yes, Mother," Little Mac said brightly.

As he left the room, Mac took a deep breath. "Can't you tone him down a little?"

"He's all right, really," Louise said. "He's not like that around his friends. It's just his way of making you like him."

"I keep expecting him to kiss my hand."

Louise removed her gaze from him and directed it into space. She sat smoking until Little Mac returned with a tall glass of beer and a coaster which he put down on the table beside Mac's chair. He handed Mac the beer and went to sit on the piano bench in the corner of the room.

"What are you reading, Ann?" Mac asked.

Ann pushed the strand of hair behind her ear and looked up from her novel. "Oh, nothing," she said.

They looked at each other. Mac's mouth went on smiling stubbornly, but at last he turned to Louise, and when he spoke his voice was low and reasonable.

"What's this all about?" he asked. "Let's talk it out sensibly without a scene."

"It's a very simple matter, actually," Louise said. "Ann doesn't like Miss Taylor's. She's gone there a year, so she's given it a fair chance and she's still unhappy."

"I see," Mac said. "And exactly how does she propose to get an education?"

"There's a public school in the village, Mac. Little Mac's been going to it and it seems to be quite good."

"It's great, Dad, really keen," Little Mac said from the piano bench. "I've learned a lot."

"Mm," Mac said. "Well, Ann?"

For a moment, she almost didn't bother answering. Mac already had it figured out his way and he wasn't going to listen. Still, she couldn't give up without trying.

"I just don't want to go back," she said slowly. "I want to stay home. I can study here as well as I can at Miss Taylor's."

"What I am trying to discover," he said with heavily good-humored patience, "is what you have against Miss Taylor's."

"Everything."

"Nothing in particular." He smiled. "Just everything."

She flushed. "All right. If you want a list. I don't like the other girls or the teachers or Miss Taylor herself or the dancing lessons or deportment lectures. And it isn't that I just don't like it—I hate it. I'd rather be in jail."

"It's one way of being decently prepared for an Eastern college," Mac said.

"And I don't want to go to college either," she said rashly.

"That I insist on."

"You don't have anything to say about it."

For a moment it seemed as if the storm would crash around them, and Ann made her face a blank to endure it. But Mac checked himself and there was merely an increased tension in the room.

"Louise," he said, "let's face facts. Ann has a stronger will than yours. At Miss Taylor's, she's subjected to some discipline. She rides horseback and swims and she's forced to mingle with girls her own age. If she goes to public school, she'll live at home and twist you around her finger. No exercise, lying on the bed in her room reading trash all day, mooning over phonograph records, living on movies and the radio. She has no friends. She never goes out without you. My God, look at her stoop. Look at her pasty complexion after a summer half a mile from the beach. Three months at home with you, and look at her."

"At that age—" Louise began weakly.

"What will she be like at twenty? A bookish neurotic, hiding behind her mother's skirts, afraid of the world. Do you think she'll ever marry? I ask you truthfully, do you think any man would be idiot enough to want to marry her?"

Ann closed her book and got up. "I don't think I shall want to marry," she said coldly. "There are too many chances of getting stuck."

"Ann!" Louise warned, but it was too late.

"You're going back to Miss Taylor's and that's final," Mac said, angrily. "We'll have no more discussion."

"I'm not," Ann said. "Mother promised."

She glanced quickly at Louise's beautiful face, a little stunned by scotch, and then she flung herself down beside Louise and took hold of her. "Tell him I'm not going back," she said. "He has nothing to say about me any more. Tell him to go away."

"Hush, honey," Louise said. "Now listen here, Mac. It's one thing to advise and talk calmly and another to come over and throw the children into fits."

"If a little common sense throws them into fits, you've done a pretty bad job as a mother."

"I've done the best I can," Louise said. "It isn't easy to bring up two high-strung kids by yourself. Once in a while I may have made mistakes—"

"You'd make fewer of them if you tried staying sober."

There was a silence. Ann felt her mother begin to tremble and drew away from her. Louise's round blue eyes were focusing at last as she gathered the diffused bits of her strength, and suddenly Ann was excited and a little sick at her stomach.

"Ann," Louise said. "You and Little Mac run down to the matinée in the village."

"Mother—"

"Take the money out of my purse," Louise said evenly. "It's lying on my bed."

Ann hesitated, but she knew she was going to obey. Even Little Mac was afraid. His face was held in a keen and pleasant expression, as if so long as he pretended not to have heard the words, they hadn't really been said. But his smile was getting tighter and more drawn each moment, and his eyes were straining against tears.

I can't stand it if he cries, Ann thought, and all at once she was on her feet, shepherding him out of the room before her.

They walked down the hill in silence, past the big white houses with rust-colored clay roofs. Eucalyptus trees shaded the winding street and the lawns on either side of them were covered with orange, avocado and lemon trees, hibiscus and camellia bushes. The warm sunny air was scented with ocean and roses. Half way to the village, they passed the school grounds. In the street stood a metal cut-out of a little girl holding a slate which read: PROTECT OUR CHILDREN. Here they had to stop while a children's party from the riding academy went by, led by an elderly man on a brown horse.

He bowed to Ann and Little Mac, and touched his tweed cap. The boys waved to Little Mac and shouted, and he waved back.

"We ought to go up to the stables some time," he said to Ann. "We must have fifty dollars' worth of lessons left."

"You go if you like," she said.

They were both silent, remembering the riding lessons had been Mac's Christmas present to them last year.

"I don't see that it would hurt you," Little Mac said.

Ann looked at him impatiently. He had recovered his air of cheerfulness, and in his anxiety for harmony she knew he was already making excuses for the outrageous thing Mac had said to Louise.

"He is a lot of fun sometimes," he said, interpreting her glance. "And he's awfully smart. Remember the time you were in trouble at school, and he went to see the principal and got him so rattled?"

"Why do you always stand up for him? He doesn't care so much for you."

She was sorry as soon as she said it. Little Mac's broad face mottled under his tan, and she wished he would lash back at her. Instead he jammed his fists into his trouser pockets and said doggedly: "Just because he likes you better is no reason I have to say everything he does is wrong. He's got a bad temper, but Mother isn't perfect either."

"I don't know what you're talking about."

She walked faster, keeping a little ahead of him so that he wouldn't have to answer. But he had been wounded deeper than she thought. He caught up with her, and before he had a chance to be afraid he threw the words directly at her.

"She does get drunk and you know it."

It was out. For the second time that day the unpardonable thing had been said, and not by herself who was brave, but by Little Mac who was a coward.

"You're horrible," she said. "You're really horrible."

For an instant, she considered walking off and leaving him. And then she saw the terror in his eyes. The boy who had spoken was as much a stranger to him as he had been to her. Now he was just Little Mac, with apology in his face, begging her to pretend that nothing unpleasant had been said.

"We'd better hurry," she said.

They stood close together in the back of the theatre, waiting to get used to the darkness. Ann kept her eyes from the figures on the screen and stared hard at the blackest places, but Little Mac was the first to become adjusted.

He put his hand on her arm and whispered: "Okay. Follow me." And together they marched quickly down the aisle.

Generally, they quarreled about the seats. Little Mac liked it best somewhere in the first three rows and Ann insisted on sitting farther back. Today he stopped half-way down the aisle and whispered: "All right?"

"Somebody has an orange in there," Ann said. "I can smell it."

He led her three more rows and stopped on the other side of the aisle. "You can have the outside seat if you want."

She almost refused it. Their most furious arguments were about who got the aisle seat, and it seemed mean to take advantage of his remorse. Still, he shouldn't have said that about Louise. She sat down on the aisle and compromised by asking him if he was sure he could see.

"Great," he said, straining tall in his seat. "I'm fine."

She gave him a package of chocolate nuts she had bought at the glass and chrome Candy Bar in the lobby and then looked at the screen.

The feature was already on, and at first she had trouble paying attention. She kept wondering about Mac and Louise, about what was going on in the house on the hill, and at the thought of Miss Taylor's she felt as if she were going down fast in an elevator. Mac was wrong; he didn't know. She might be pale and stooped and bookish, but Miss Taylor's wasn't going to fix anything. She made no more friends there than she did anyplace else, and at Miss Taylor's the stark fact of her difference from the rest was always with her, a dragging shame she was never let to escape. Always there were the interviews with the school psychologist, the sense of being a problem, the misery of the cooperative games. In the dark of the theatre, her face felt hot and she moved restlessly in her seat.

"What's the matter?" Little Mac asked.

"Keep still," she said. "Watch the picture."

A cold fog was crawling in from the ocean when they followed the crowd into the street. The village stores were gray and blurred, and drops of water stood out like goose-flesh on the cars parked at the curb.

"Will you be warm enough?" Little Mac asked.

Ann nodded. "If we walk fast."

She took his arm and they went up the hill, clinging together and pushing each other forward. The dampness had brought out the sharp, medicinal scent of the eucalyptus trees, and below them the choppy sea looked raw and lonely.

"Maybe we're going to have a storm," Little Mac said. "Do you think?"

"Keep still and *walk*."

"Okay." He gave a little skip to match his stride to hers. "Ann, I didn't mean what I said about mother."

"Forget it."

"Hokay."

This was the way he always apologized, as if it didn't matter at all and he had thought of it by purest chance. It was irritating but it didn't do any good to snap at him. It was an indelible part of him, like the automatic way he smiled when he was afraid.

"Look," she said sharply. "He's still here." They had come up over the hill where they could see the house and Mac's cream convertible parked in the driveway. They stood uncertainly, still locking arms, and after a moment Little Mac said, "What do we do now?"

"Go in. After all, it isn't his house."

"I suppose." He loosened his arm and followed her up the path.

The front door was open, and as they walked slowly down the hall toward the living room, Ann heard Mac talking. She couldn't make out the words but his voice was rumbling and full of assurance. He was pleased with himself and she knew what that meant. She felt a sudden sense of helplessness and betrayal. She walked into the living room and Mac looked up.

"Hello," His voice was hearty. "You back already?"

Louise was standing at the grand piano. She swung around unsteadily and balanced herself with one hand on the mahogany top. In the other she held an empty glass.

"Hello, darlings," she said. "Did you have a good time?"

"Yes, Mother," Little Mac said politely.

Ann could not speak. She tried to catch her mother's eyes,

but Louise was looking at Mac, pleading with him not to say anything, to keep the peace.

"Well," he said. "I'll be off."

He got up and took Little Mac's shoulder, prodding him ahead of him into the hall. Louise put her arm about Ann's waist and they all walked to the front door.

"How's the riding, son?" Mac asked. "Jumping yet?"

"Uh—no sir," Little Mac admitted. "I haven't got that far."

Ann could see Mac wasn't listening, didn't really care. He smiled around at them, then opened the front door and went out.

Ann stood and watched him go. Behind her she heard Louise and Little Mac walk off down the hall, but she stood at the door until Mac drove away. Finally, she shut the door and went back to the living room.

Little Mac was picking out a melody on the piano with one finger. Louise was at the cabinet bar. She took an ice cube from the thermojar and it skidded across the floor. She went over to it with a show of leisurely control, picked it up with the tongs and dropped it into the bowl of cabbage roses.

Ann stood straight and tall for a moment, seeing them all together again: Mac who always knew best, who had to know best; Little Mac afraid of anybody's anger; Louise who took any thumbprint, like plasticine. Suddenly she hated them all but most of all she hated Louise, for being soft.

"Mother," she said. "You promised."

Louise turned to her: "Please, honey. Let's not argue. Mac's right. It's best for you. And you'll like it better this time. Honestly you will."

Ann saw herself back at Miss Taylor's, an awkward girl with hair like string, rude and bad-tempered, with not even Louise's guilty pity standing between her and the world.

She knew what she had to do. Her shoulders ached with weariness already, and she was sick at the thought, but she had no choice.

"No," she said.

"Baby, it's all settled."

Fear came down around Ann like fog. She ran over and buried her face against Louise's breast. "No," she said. "It isn't settled. I won't let it be settled. You'll have to call him up again and tell him I won't go."

"Oh, darling, please," Louise said weakly. "Please go back to Miss Taylor's. For me."

She felt Louise's soft white hand stroking her hair, and faintly, mingled with the scent of scotch, she smelled Louise's familiar sweet perfume. She wanted to cry again, but she wouldn't.

"No, Mother. You've been drinking. You don't understand. I can't go back. I won't. I've got to stay with you. I love you. Mac doesn't love you, but I do. I love you terribly."

She hid her face and clung tightly. Louise need never know how she hated her or how she hated herself.

GRAHAM GREENE

Graham Greene was born in Hertfordshire, England, on October 2, 1904, the son of Charles Henry Greene, head-master of Berkhampstead School, which he attended from 1915 to 1921. From his early years, he says, come a number of sharply distinct memories, for one, his discovery that he could read, "not just the sentences in a reading book with the syllables coupled like railway carriages, but a real book." It opened up a new world of excitement and revelation. Another distinct memory was his initial dedication to writing. He was fourteen years old, and had just read Marjorie Bowen's The Viper of Milan. "From that moment," he said, "I began to write. All the other possible futures slid away. . . . Imitation after imitation of Miss Bowen's magnificent novel went into exercise books. . . ." Reading her made him feel that "to write was to live and to enjoy."

He did not like school, where he remembers being vastly bored and where he was bullied by two boys. Years later, however, he met one of them (the other was dead) and wondered if he would ever have written a book if it had not been for them, "if those years of humiliation had not given me an excessive desire to prove that I was good at something." At Balliol College, Oxford, where he went when he was seventeen, he wrote fantasy and poetry. His first book, Babbling April (1925), was a volume of verse.

He became a convert to Roman Catholicism the following February, when he was twenty-two.

After college he worked for the Nottingham Journal *for a brief period, without pay, merely for the experience. Experience gained, he embarked on a professional career in journalism which continued until World War II. His first job was with the London* Times *(1926–30), starting as a subeditor in the letters department. From 1935–39 he was film critic for the* Spectator, *and from 1940–41, literary editor. From 1941–44, he was with the Foreign Office on special duty in West Africa.*

During his early days on the Times, *Mr. Greene worked steadily at his self-appointed task of learning how to write prose fiction. He finished two novels, which he never published, and was halfway through a third when he broke off to write* The Man Within *(1929), his first published novel. In the same year, he began to write short stories. "The Basement Room," perhaps his most famous story, was written on his return from West Africa on board a cargo ship, a trip, he said, that had been a fixation from childhood, ever since he read* King Solomon's Mines. *It became the title story of his first collection of short stories, published in 1936. Later, it was filmed under the title* The Fallen Idol, *a title which, Greene said, did not make sense. Other story collections are* Nineteen Stories *(1949) and* Twenty-one Stories *(1954).*

Mr. Greene's novels fall into two categories: spy-chase thrillers, which he calls "entertainments," and works of serious moral and religious reflection. The two categories reflect the influence of two writers upon him, an influence he acknowledges as considerable: John Buchan (Lord Tweedsmuir), Scottish novelist and author of some first-

387

rate mystery stories, and François Mauriac, Catholic novelist. *Many of his entertainments have been made into movies, such as* Stamboul Train (*1932*) (*published as* Orient Express *in America*), A Gun for Sale (*1936*) (*America, This Gun for Hire*), The Third Man (*1950*), *and* Our Man in Havana (*1958*). *Among his serious works of fiction are* Brighton Rock (*1938*), The Power and the Glory (*1940*), The Heart of the Matter (*1948*), The End of the Affair (*1951*), *and his most recent,* A Burnt Out Case (*1961*). *He has also written a number of juveniles, such as* The Little Horse Bus (*1952*), *and several plays. Since 1958 he has been director of Bodley Head, publishers.*

In a letter to Elizabeth Bowen, Mr. Greene wrote that one of the duties of a novelist was "to tell the truth as he sees it." He went on to say, "By truth I mean accuracy—it is largely a matter of style. It is my duty to society not to write: 'I stood above a bottomless gulf' or 'going downstairs, I got into a taxi,' because these statements are untrue. My characters must not go white in the face or tremble like leaves, not because these phrases are clichés but because they are untrue. . . . Every time a phrase like one of these passes into the mind uncriticised, it muddies the stream of thought."

In 1952, Mr. Greene came to the United States to receive the Catholic Literary Award.

THE BASEMENT ROOM

I

When the front door had shut them out and the butler Baines
had turned back into the dark heavy hall, Philip began to live.
He stood in front of the nursery door, listening until he heard
the engine of the taxi die out along the street. His parents
were gone for a fortnight's holiday; he was "between nurses,"
one dismissed and the other not arrived; he was alone in the
great Belgravia house with Baines and Mrs. Baines.

He could go anywhere, even through the green baize door
to the pantry or down the stairs to the basement living-room. He
felt a stranger in his home because he could go into any room
and all the rooms were empty.

You could only guess who had once occupied them: the
rack of pipes in the smoking-room beside the elephant tusks,
the carved wood tobacco jar; in the bedroom the pink hangings
and pale perfumes and the three-quarter finished jars of cream
which Mrs. Baines had not yet cleared away; the high glaze on
the never-opened piano in the drawing-room, the china clock,
the silly little tables and the silver: but here Mrs. Baines was
already busy, pulling down the curtains, covering the chairs in
dust-sheets.

"Be off out of here, Master Philip," and she looked at him

From *Nineteen Stories* by Graham Greene. Copyright 1947, 1949 by
Graham Greene. Reprinted by permission of The Viking Press, Inc.

with her hateful peevish eyes, while she moved round, getting everything in order, meticulous and loveless and doing her duty.

Philip Lane went downstairs and pushed at the baize door; he looked into the pantry, but Baines was not there, then he set foot for the first time on the stairs to the basement. Again he had the sense: this is life. All his seven nursery years vibrated with the strange, the new experience. His crowded busy brain was like a city which feels the earth tremble at a distant earthquake shock. He was apprehensive, but he was happier than he had ever been. Everything was more important than before.

Baines was reading a newspaper in his shirtsleeves. He said: "Come in, Phil, and make yourself at home. Wait a moment and I'll do the honors," and going to a white cleaned cupboard he brought out a bottle of ginger beer and half a Dundee cake. "Half-past eleven in the morning," Baines said. "It's opening time, my boy," and he cut the cake and poured out the ginger beer. He was more genial than Philip had ever known him, more at his ease, a man in his own home.

"Shall I call Mrs. Baines?" Philip asked, and he was glad when Baines said no. She was busy. She liked to be busy, so why interfere with her pleasure?

"A spot of drink at half-past eleven," Baines said, pouring himself out a glass of ginger beer, "gives an appetite for chop and does no man any harm."

"A chop?" Philip asked.

"Old Coasters," Baines said, "call all food chop."

"But it's not a chop?"

"Well, it might be, you know, cooked with palm oil. And then some paw-paw to follow."

Philip looked out of the basement window at the dry stone yard, the ash can and the legs going up and down beyond the railings.

"Was it hot there?"

"Ah, you never felt such heat. Not a nice heat, mind, like you get in the park on a day like this. Wet," Baines said "corruption." He cut himself a slice of cake. "Smelling of rot," Baines said, rolling his eyes round the small basement room, from clean cupboard to clean cupboard, the sense of bareness, of nowhere to hide a man's secrets. With an air of regret for something lost he took a long draught of ginger beer.

"Why did father live out there?"

"It was his job," Baines said, "same as this is mine now. And it was mine then too. It was a man's job. You wouldn't believe it now, but I've had forty niggers under me, doing what I told them to."

"Why did you leave?"

"I married Mrs. Baines."

Philip took the slice of Dundee cake in his hand and munched it round the room. He felt very old, independent and judicial; he was aware that Baines was talking to him as man to man. He never called him Master Philip as Mrs. Baines did, who was servile when she was not authoritative.

Baines had seen the world; he had seen beyond the railings, beyond the tired legs of typists, the Pimlico parade to and from Victoria. He sat there over his ginger pop with the resigned dignity of an exile; Baines didn't complain; he had chosen his fate; and if his fate was Mrs. Baines he had only himself to blame.

But today, because the house was almost empty and Mrs. Baines was upstairs and there was nothing to do, he allowed himself a little acidity.

"I'd go back tomorrow if I had the chance."

"Did you ever shoot a nigger?"

"I never had any call to shoot," Baines said. "Of course I carried a gun. But you didn't need to treat them bad. That just made them stupid. Why," Baines said, bowing his thin gray hair with embarrassment over the ginger pop, "I loved some of those damned niggers. I couldn't help loving them. There they'd be, laughing, holding hands; they liked to touch each other; it made them feel fine to know the other fellow was round.

"It didn't mean anything we could understand; two of them

391

would go about all day without loosing hold, grown men; but it wasn't love; it didn't mean anything we could understand."

"Eating between meals," Mrs. Baines said. "What would your mother say, Master Philip?"

She came down the steep stairs to the basement, her hands full of pots of cream and salve, tubes of grease and paste. "You oughtn't to encourage him, Baines," she said, sitting down in a wicker armchair and screwing up her small ill-humored eyes at the Coty lipstick, Pond's cream, the Leichner rouge and Cyclax powder and Elizabeth Arden astringent.

She threw them one by one into the wastepaper basket. She saved only the cold cream. "Telling the boy stories," she said. "Go along to the nursery, Master Philip, while I get lunch."

Philip climbed the stairs to the baize door. He heard Mrs. Baines's voice like the voice in a nightmare when the small Price light has guttered in the saucer and the curtains move; it was sharp and shrill and full of malice, louder than people ought to speak, exposed.

"Sick to death of your ways, Baines, spoiling the boy. Time you did some work about the house," but he couldn't hear what Baines said in reply. He pushed open the baize door, came up like a small earth animal in his grey flannel shorts into a wash of sunlight on a parquet floor, the gleam of mirrors dusted and polished and beautified by Mrs. Baines.

Something broke downstairs, and Philip sadly mounted the stairs to the nursery. He pitied Baines; it occurred to him how happily they could live together in the empty house if Mrs. Baines were called away. He didn't want to play with his Meccano sets; he wouldn't take out his train or his soldiers; he sat at the table with his chin on his hands: this is life; and suddenly he felt responsible for Baines, as if he were the master of the house and Baines an aging servant who deserved to be cared for. There was not much one could do; he decided at least to be good.

He was not surprised when Mrs. Baines was agreeable at lunch; he was used to her changes. Now it was "another helping of meat, Master Philip," or "Master Philip, a little more of this nice pudding." It was a pudding he liked, Queen's pudding with a perfect meringue, but he wouldn't eat a second helping lest she might count that a victory. She was the kind of woman who thought that any injustice could be counterbalanced by something good to eat.

She was sour, but she liked making sweet things; one never had to complain of a lack of jam or plums; she ate well herself and added soft sugar to the meringue and the strawberry jam. The half light through the basement window set the motes moving above her pale hair like dust as she sifted the sugar, and Baines crouched over his plate saying nothing.

Again Philip felt responsibility. Baines had looked forward to this, and Baines was disappointed: everything was being spoilt. The sensation of disappointment was one which Philip could share; knowing nothing of love or jealousy or passion, he could understand better than anyone this grief, something hoped for not happening, something promised not fulfilled, something exciting turning dull. "Baines," he said, "will you take me for a walk this afternoon?"

"No," Mrs. Baines said, "no. That he won't. Not with all the silver to clean."

"There's a fortnight to do it in," Baines said.

"Work first, pleasure afterwards." Mrs. Baines helped herself to some more meringue.

Baines suddenly put down his spoon and fork and pushed his plate away. "Blast," he said.

"Temper," Mrs. Baines said softly, "temper. Don't you go breaking any more things, Baines, and I won't have you swearing in front of the boy. Master Philip, if you've finished you can get down." She skinned the rest of the meringue off the pudding.

"I want to go for a walk," Philip said.

"You'll go and have a rest."

"I will go for a walk."

"Master Philip," Mrs. Baines said. She got up from the table,

393

leaving her meringue unfinished, and came towards him, thin, menacing, dusty in the basement room. "Master Philip, you do as you're told." She took him by the arm and squeezed it gently; she watched him with a joyless passionate glitter and above her head the feet of the typists trudged back to the Victoria offices after the lunch interval.

"Why shouldn't I go for a walk?" But he weakened; he was scared and ashamed of being scared. This was life; a strange passion he couldn't understand moving in the basement room. He saw a small pile of broken glass swept into a corner by the wastepaper basket. He looked to Baines for help and only intercepted hate; the sad hopeless hate of something behind bars.

"Why shouldn't I?" he repeated.

"Master Philip," Mrs. Baines said, "you've got to do as you're told. You mustn't think just because your father's away there's nobody here to—"

"You wouldn't dare," Philip cried, and was startled by Baines's low interjection, "There's nothing she wouldn't dare."

"I hate you," Philip said to Mrs. Baines. He pulled away from her and ran to the door, but she was there before him; she was old, but she was quick.

"Master Philip," she said, "you'll say you're sorry." She stood in front of the door quivering with excitement. "What would your father do if he heard you say that?"

She put a hand out to seize him, dry and white with constant soda, the nails cut to the quick, but he backed away and put the table between them, and suddenly to his surprise she smiled; she became again as servile as she had been arrogant. "Get along with you, Master Philip," she said with glee. "I see I'm going to have my hands full till your father and mother come back."

She left the door unguarded and when he passed her she slapped him playfully. "I've got too much to do today to trouble about you. I haven't covered half the chairs," and suddenly even the upper part of the house became unbearable to him as he

394

thought of Mrs. Baines moving round shrouding the sofas, laying out the dustsheets.

So he wouldn't go upstairs to get his cap but walked straight out across the shining hall into the street, and again, as he looked this way and looked that way, it was life he was in the middle of.

II

It was the pink sugar cakes in the window on a paper doily, the ham, the slab of mauve sausage, the wasps driving like small torpedoes across the pane that caught Philip's attention. His feet were tired by pavements; he had been afraid to cross the road, had simply walked first in one direction, then in the other. He was nearly home now; the square was at the end of the street; this was a shabby outpost of Pimlico, and he smudged the pane with his nose, looking for sweets, and saw between the cakes and ham a different Baines. He hardly recognized the bulbous eyes, the bald forehead. It was a happy, bold and buccaneering Baines, even though it was, when you looked closer, a desperate Baines.

Philip had never seen the girl. He remembered Baines had a niece and he thought that this might be her. She was thin and drawn, and she wore a white mackintosh; she meant nothing to Philip; she belonged to a world about which he knew nothing at all. He couldn't make up stories about her, as he could make them up about withered Sir Hubert Reed, the Permanent Secretary, about Mrs. Wince-Dudley, who came up once a year from Penstanley in Suffolk with a green umbrella and an enormous black handbag, as he could make them up about the upper servants in all the houses where he went to tea and games. She just didn't belong; he thought of mermaids and Undine; but she didn't belong there either, nor to the adventures of Emil, nor to the Bastables. She sat there looking at an iced pink cake in the detachment and mystery of the completely disinherited, looking at the half-used pots of powder which Baines had set out on the marble-topped table between them.

Baines was urging, hoping, entreating, commanding, and the girl looked at the tea and the china pots and cried. Baines passed his handkerchief across the table, but she wouldn't wipe her eyes; she screwed it in her palm and let the tears run down, wouldn't do anything, wouldn't speak, would only put up a silent despairing resistance to what she dreaded and wanted and refused to listen to at any price. The two brains battled over the teacups loving each other, and there came to Philip outside, beyond the ham and wasps and dusty Pimlico pane, a confused indication of the struggle.

He was inquisitive and he didn't understand and he wanted to know. He went and stood in the doorway to see better, he was less sheltered than he had ever been; other people's lives for the first time touched and pressed and molded. He would never escape that scene. In a week he had forgotten it, but it conditioned his career, the long austerity of his life; when he was dying he said, "Who is she?"

Baines had won; he was cocky and the girl was happy. She wiped her face, she opened a pot of powder, and their fingers touched across the table. It occurred to Philip that it would be amusing to imitate Mrs. Baines's voice and call "Baines" to him from the door.

It shrivelled them; you couldn't describe it in any other way; it made them smaller, they weren't happy any more and they weren't bold. Baines was the first to recover and trace the voice, but that didn't make things as they were. The sawdust was spilled out of the afternoon; nothing you did could mend it, and Philip was scared. "I didn't mean . . ." He wanted to say that he loved Baines, that he had only wanted to laugh at Mrs. Baines. But he had discovered that you couldn't laugh at Mrs. Baines. She wasn't Sir Hubert Reed, who used steel nibs and carried a pen-wiper in his pocket; she wasn't Mrs. Wince-Dudley; she was darkness when the night-light went out in a draught;

she was the frozen blocks of earth he had seen one winter in a graveyard when someone said, "They need an electric drill"; she was the flowers gone bad and smelling in the little closet room at Penstanley. There was nothing to laugh about. You had to endure her when she was there and forget about her quickly when she was away, suppress the thought of her, ram it down deep.

Baines said, "It's only Phil," beckoned him in and gave him the pink iced cake the girl hadn't eaten, but the afternoon was broken, the cake was like dry bread in the throat. The girl left them at once; she even forgot to take the powder; like a small blunt icicle in her white mackintosh she stood in the doorway with her back to them, then melted into the afternoon.

"Who is she?" Philip asked. "Is she your niece?"

"Oh, yes," Baines said, "that's who she is; she's my niece," and poured the last drops of water on to the coarse black leaves in the teapot.

"May as well have another cup," Baines said.

"The cup that cheers," he said hopelessly, watching the bitter black fluid drain out of the spout.

"Have a glass of ginger pop, Phil?"

"I'm sorry. I'm sorry, Baines."

"It's not your fault, Phil. Why, I could believe it wasn't you at all, but her. She creeps in everywhere." He fished two leaves out of his cup and laid them on the back of his hand, a thin soft flake and a hard stalk. He beat them with his hand: "Today," and the stalk detached itself, "tomorrow, Wednesday, Thursday, Friday, Saturday, Sunday," but the flake wouldn't come, stayed where it was, drying under his blows, with a resistance you wouldn't believe it to possess. "The tough one wins," Baines said.

He got up and paid the bill and out they went into the street. Baines said, "I don't ask you to say what isn't true. But you needn't mention to Mrs. Baines you met us here."

"Of course not," Philip said, and catching something of Sir Hubert Reed's manner, "I understand, Baines." But he didn't understand a thing; he was caught up in other people's darkness.

"It was stupid," Baines said. "So near home, but I hadn't time to think, you see. I'd got to see her."

"Of course, Baines."

"I haven't time to spare," Baines said. "I'm not young. I've got to see that she's all right."

"Of course you have, Baines."

"Mrs. Baines will get it out of you if she can."

"You can trust me, Baines," Philip said in a dry important Reed voice; and then, "Look out. She's at the window watching." And there indeed she was, looking up at them, between the lace curtains, from the basement room, speculating. "Need we go in, Baines?" Philip asked, cold lying heavy on his stomach like too much pudding; he clutched Baines's arm.

"Careful," Baines said softly, "careful."

"But need we go in, Baines? It's early. Take me for a walk in the park."

"Better not."

"But I'm frightened, Baines."

"You haven't any cause," Baines said. "Nothing's going to hurt you. You just run along upstairs to the nursery. I'll go down by the area and talk to Mrs. Baines." But even he stood hesitating at the top of the stone steps, pretending not to see her where she watched between the curtains. "In at the front door, Phil, and up the stairs."

Philip didn't linger in the hall; he ran, slithering on the parquet Mrs. Baines had polished, to the stairs. Through the drawing-room doorway on the first floor he saw the draped chairs; even the china clock on the mantel was covered like a canary's cage; as he passed it, it chimed the hour, muffled and secret under the duster. On the nursery table he found his supper laid out: a glass of milk and a piece of bread and butter, a sweet biscuit and a little cold Queen's pudding without the meringue. He had no appetite; he strained his ears for Mrs. Baines's coming, for the sound of voices, but the basement held its secrets; the green baize door shut off that world. He drank the milk and ate the biscuit, but he didn't touch the rest, and presently he could hear the soft precise footfalls of Mrs. Baines on the stairs: she was a good servant, she walked softly; she was a determined woman, she walked precisely.

But she wasn't angry when she came in; she was ingratiating as she opened the night nursery door—"Did you have a good walk, Master Philip?"—pulled down the blinds, laid out his pajamas, came back to clear his supper. "I'm glad Baines found you. Your mother wouldn't have liked your being out alone." She examined the tray. "Not much appetite, have you, Master Philip? Why don't you try a little of this nice pudding? I'll bring you up some more jam for it."

"No, no, thank you, Mrs. Baines," Philip said.

"You ought to eat more," Mrs. Baines said. She sniffed round the room like a dog. "You didn't take any pots out of the waste-paper basket in the kitchen, did you, Master Philip?"

"No," Philip said.

"Of course you wouldn't. I just wanted to make sure." She patted his shoulder and her fingers flashed to his lapel; she picked off a tiny crumb of pink sugar. "Oh, Master Philip," she said, "that's why you haven't any appetite. You've been buying sweet cakes. That's not what your pocket money's for."

"But I didn't," Philip said. "I didn't."

She tasted the sugar with the tip of her tongue.

"Don't tell lies to me, Master Philip. I won't stand for it any more than your father would."

"I didn't, I didn't," Philip said. "They gave it me. I mean Baines," but she had pounced on the word "they." She had got what she wanted; there was no doubt about that, even when you didn't know what it was she wanted. Philip was angry and miserable and disappointed because he hadn't kept Baines's secret. Baines oughtn't to have trusted him; grown-up people should keep their own secrets, and yet here was Mrs. Baines immediately entrusting him with another.

399

"Let me tickle your palm and see if you can keep a secret."
But he put his hand behind him; he wouldn't be touched. "It's
a secret between us, Master Philip, that I know all about them.
I suppose she was having tea with him," she speculated.

"Why shouldn't she?" he said, the responsibility for Baines
weighing on his spirit, the idea that he had got to keep her
secret when he hadn't kept Baines's making him miserable with
the unfairness of life. "She was nice."

"She was nice, was she?" Mrs. Baines said in a bitter voice
he wasn't used to.

"And she's his niece."

"So that's what he said," Mrs. Baines struck softly back at
him like the clock under the duster. She tried to be jocular. "The
old scoundrel. Don't you tell him I know, Master Philip." She
stood very still between the table and the door, thinking very
hard, planning something. "Promise you won't tell. I'll give you
that Meccano set, Master Philip. . . ."

He turned his back on her; he wouldn't promise, but he
wouldn't tell. He would have nothing to do with their secrets,
the responsibilities they were determined to lay on him. He was
only anxious to forget. He had received already a larger dose of
life than he had bargained for, and he was scared. "A 2A Meccano set, Master Philip." He never opened his Meccano set again,
never built anything, never created anything, died, the old
dilettante, sixty years later, with nothing to show rather than
preserve the memory of Mrs. Baines's malicious voice saying
good night, her soft determined footfalls on the stairs to the
basement, going down, going down.

III

The sun poured in between the curtains and Baines was beating
a tattoo on the watercan. "Glory, glory," Baines said. He sat down
on the end of the bed and said, "I beg to announce that Mrs.

Baines has been called away. Her mother's dying. She won't be back till tomorrow."

"Why did you wake me up so early?" Philip said. He watched Baines with uneasiness; he wasn't going to be drawn in; he'd learnt his lesson. It wasn't right for a man of Baines's age to be so merry. It made a grown person human in the same way that you were human. For if a grown-up could behave so childishly, you were liable too to find yourself in their world. It was enough that it came at you in dreams: the witch at the corner, the man with a knife. So "It's very early," he complained, even though he loved Baines, even though he couldn't help being glad that Baines was happy. He was divided by the fear and the attraction of life.

"I want to make this a long day," Baines said. "This is the best time." He pulled the curtains back. "It's a bit misty. The cat's been out all night. There she is, sniffing round the area. They haven't taken in any milk at 59. Emma's shaking out the mats at 63." He said, "This was what I used to think about on the Coast: somebody shaking mats and the cat coming home. I can see it today," Baines said, "just as if I was still in Africa. Most days you don't notice what you've got. It's a good life if you don't weaken." He put a penny on the washstand. "When you've dressed, Phil, run and get a *Mail* from the barrow at the corner. I'll be cooking the sausages."

"Sausages?"

"Sausages," Baines said. "We're going to celebrate today. A fair bust." He celebrated at breakfast, reckless, cracking jokes, unaccountably merry and nervous. It was going to be a long, long day, he kept on coming back to that: for years he had waited for a long day, he had sweated in the damp Coast heat, changed shirts, gone down with fever, lain between the blankets and sweated, all in the hope of this long day, that cat sniffing round the area, a bit of mist, the mats beaten at 63. He propped the *Mail* in front of the coffee-pot and read pieces aloud. He said, "Cora Down's been married for the fourth time." He was

401

amused, but it wasn't his idea of a long day. His long day was the Park, watching the riders in the Row, seeing Sir Arthur Stillwater pass beyond the rails ("He dined with us once in Bo; up from Freetown; he was governor there"), lunch at the Corner House for Philip's sake (he'd have preferred himself a glass of stout and some oysters at the York bar), the Zoo, the long bus ride home in the last summer light: the leaves in the Green Park were beginning to turn and the motors nuzzled out of Berkeley Street with the low sun gently glowing on their wind-screens. Baines envied no one, not Cora Down, or Sir Arthur Stillwater, or Lord Sandale, who came out on to the steps of the Army and Navy and then went back again because he hadn't got anything to do and might as well look at another paper. "I said don't let me see you touch that black again." Baines had led a man's life; everyone on top of the bus pricked their ears when he told Philip all about it.

"Would you have shot him?" Philip asked, and Baines put his head back and tilted his dark respectable man-servant's hat to a better angle as the bus swerved round the artillery memorial.

"I wouldn't have thought twice about it. I'd have shot to kill," he boasted, and the bowed figure went by, the steel helmet, the heavy cloak, the down-turned rifle and the folded hands.

"Have you got the revolver?"

"Of course I've got it," Baines said. "Don't I need it with all the burglaries there've been?" This was the Baines whom Philip loved: not Baines singing and carefree, but Baines responsible, Baines behind barriers, living his man's life.

All the buses streamed out from Victoria like a convoy of airplanes to bring Baines home with honor. "Forty blacks under me," and there waiting near the area steps was the proper conventional reward, love at lighting-up time.

"It's your niece," Philip said, recognizing the white mackintosh, but not the happy sleepy face. She frightened him like an unlucky number; he nearly told Baines what Mrs. Baines had said; but he didn't want to bother, he wanted to leave things alone.

"Why, so it is," Baines said. "I shouldn't wonder if she was going to have a bite of supper with us." But he said they'd play a game, pretend they didn't know her, slip down the area steps, "and here," Baines said, "we are," lay the table, put out the cold sausages, a bottle of beer, a bottle of ginger pop, a flagon of harvest burgundy. "Everyone his own drink," Baines said. "Run upstairs, Phil, and see if there's been a post."

Philip didn't like the empty house at dusk before the lights went on. He hurried. He wanted to be back with Baines. The hall lay there in quiet and shadow prepared to show him something he didn't want to see. Some letters rustled down, and someone knocked. "Open in the name of the Republic." The tumbrils rolled, the head bobbed in the bloody basket. Knock, knock, and the postman's footsteps going away. Philip gathered the letters. The slit in the door was like the grating in a jeweller's window. He remembered the policeman he had seen peer through. He had said to his nurse, "What's he doing?" and when she said, "He's seeing if everything's all right," his brain immediately filled with images of all that might be wrong. He ran to the baize door and the stairs. The girl was already there and Baines was kissing her. She leant breathless against the dresser.

"This is Emmy, Phil."

"There's a letter for you, Baines."

"Emmy," Baines said, "it's from her." But he wouldn't open it. "You bet she's coming back."

"We'll have supper, anyway," Emmy said. "She can't harm that."

"You don't know her," Baines said. "Nothing's safe. Damn it," he said, "I was a man once," and he opened the letter.

"Can I start?" Philip asked, but Baines didn't hear; he presented in his stillness and attention an example of the importance grown-up people attached to the written word: you had to write your thanks, not wait and speak them, as if letters couldn't lie. But Philip knew better than that, sprawling his thanks across a page to Aunt Alice who had given him a doll he was too old for. Letters could lie all right, but they made the lie permanent: they lay as evidence against you; they made you meaner than the spoken word.

"She's not coming back till tomorrow night," Baines said. He opened the bottles, he pulled up the chairs, he kissed Emmy again against the dresser.

"You oughtn't to," Emmy said, "with the boy here."

"He's got to learn," Baines said, "like the rest of us," and he helped Philip to three sausages. He only took one himself; he said he wasn't hungry; but when Emmy said she wasn't hungry either he stood over her and made her eat. He was timid and rough with her; he made her drink the harvest burgundy because he said she needed building up; he wouldn't take no for an answer, but when he touched her his hands were light and clumsy too, as if he were afraid to damage something delicate and didn't know how to handle anything so light.

"This is better than milk and biscuits, eh?"

"Yes," Philip said, but he was scared, scared for Baines as much as for himself. He couldn't help wondering at every bite, at every draught of the ginger pop, what Mrs. Baines would say if she ever learnt of this meal; he couldn't imagine it, there was a depth of bitterness and rage in Mrs. Baines you couldn't sound. He said, "She won't be coming back tonight?" but you could tell by the way they immediately understood him that she wasn't really away at all; she was there in the basement with them, driving them to longer drinks and louder talk, biding her time for the right cutting word. Baines wasn't really happy; he was only watching happiness from close to instead of from far away.

"No," he said, "she'll not be back till late tomorrow." He couldn't keep his eyes off happiness; he'd played around as much as other men, he kept on reverting to the Coast as if to excuse himself for his innocence; he wouldn't have been so innocent if he'd lived his life in London, so innocent when it came to tenderness. "If it was you, Emmy," he said, looking at the white dresser, the scrubbed chairs, "this'd be like a home." Already the room was not quite so harsh; there was a little dust in corners, the silver needed a final polish, the morning's paper lay untidily on a chair. "You'd better go to bed, Phil; it's been a long day."

They didn't leave him to find his own way up through the dark shrouded house; they went with him, turning on lights, touching each other's fingers on the switches; floor after floor they drove the night back; they spoke softly among the covered chairs; they watched him undress, they didn't make him wash or clean his teeth, they saw him into bed and lit his nightlight and left his door ajar. He could hear their voices on the stairs, friendly, like the guests he heard at dinner-parties when they moved down to the hall, saying good night. They belonged; wherever they were they made a home. He heard a door open and a clock strike, he heard their voices for a long while, so that he felt they were not far away and he was safe. The voices didn't dwindle, they simply went out, and he could be sure that they were still somewhere not far from him, silent together in one of the many empty rooms, growing sleepy together as he grew sleepy after the long day.

He just had time to sigh faintly with satisfaction, because this too perhaps had been life, before he slept and the inevitable terrors of sleep came round him: a man with a tricolor hat beat at the door on His Majesty's service, a bleeding head lay on the kitchen table in a basket, and the Siberian wolves crept closer. He was bound hand and foot and couldn't move; they leapt round him breathing heavily; he opened his eyes and Mrs. Baines was there, her gray untidy hair in threads over his face, her black hat askew. A loose hairpin fell on the pillow and one musty thread brushed his mouth. "Where are they?" she whispered. "Where are they?"

IV

Philip watched her in terror. Mrs. Baines was out of breath as if she had been searching all the empty rooms, looking under loose covers.

With her untidy gray hair and her black dress buttoned to her throat, her gloves of black cotton, she was so like the witches of his dreams that he didn't dare to speak. There was a stale smell in her breath.

"She's here," Mrs. Baines said; "you can't deny she's here." Her face was simultaneously marked with cruelty and misery; she wanted to "do things" to people, but she suffered all the time. It would have done her good to scream, but she daren't do that: it would warn them. She came ingratiatingly back to the bed where Philip lay rigid on his back and whispered, "I haven't forgotten the Meccano set. You shall have it tomorrow, Master Philip. We've got secrets together, haven't we? Just tell me where they are."

He couldn't speak. Fear held him as firmly as any nightmare. She said, "Tell Mrs. Baines, Master Philip. You love your Mrs. Baines, don't you?" That was too much; he couldn't speak, but he could move his mouth in terrified denial, wince away from her dusty image.

She whispered, coming closer to him, "Such deceit. I'll tell your father. I'll settle with you myself when I've found them. You'll smart; I'll see you smart." Then immediately she was still, listening. A board had creaked on the floor below, and a moment later, while she stooped listening above his bed, there came the whispers of two people who were happy and sleepy together after a long day. The nightlight stood beside the mirror and Mrs. Baines could see bitterly there her own reflection, misery and cruelty wavering in the glass, age and dust and nothing to hope for. She sobbed without tears, a dry, breathless sound; but her cruelty was a kind of pride which kept her going; it was her best quality, she would have been merely pitiable without it. She went out of the door on tiptoe, feeling her way across the landing, going so softly down the stairs that no one behind a shut door could hear her. Then there was complete silence again; Philip could move; he raised his knees; he sat up in bed; he wanted to die. It wasn't fair, the walls were down again between his world and theirs; but this time it was something worse than merriment that the grown people made him share; a passion moved in the house he recognized but could not understand.

It wasn't fair, but he owed Baines everything: the Zoo, the ginger pop, the bus ride home. Even the supper called on his loyalty. But he was frightened; he was touching something he touched in dreams: the bleeding head, the wolves, the knock, knock, knock. Life fell on him with savagery: you couldn't blame him if he never faced it again in sixty years. He got out of bed, carefully from habit put on his bedroom slippers, and tiptoed to the door: it wasn't quite dark on the landing below because the curtains had been taken down for the cleaners and the light from the street came in through the tall windows. Mrs. Baines had her hand on the glass doorknob; she was very carefully turning it; he screamed, "Baines, Baines."

Mrs. Baines turned and saw him cowering in his pajamas by the banisters; he was helpless, more helpless even than Baines, and cruelty grew at the sight of him and drove her up the stairs. The nightmare was on him again and he couldn't move; he hadn't any more courage left for ever; he'd spent it all, had been allowed no time to let it grow, no years of gradual hardening; he couldn't even scream.

But the first cry had brought Baines out of the best spare bedroom and he moved quicker than Mrs. Baines. She hadn't reached the top of the stairs before he'd caught her round the waist. She drove her black cotton gloves at his face and he bit her hand. He hadn't time to think, he fought her savagely like a stranger, but she fought back with knowledgeable hate. She was going to teach them all and it didn't really matter whom she began with; they had all deceived her; but the old image in the glass was by her side, telling her she must be dignified, she wasn't young enough to yield her dignity; she could beat his face, but she mustn't bite; she could push, but she mustn't kick.

Age and dust and nothing to hope for were her handicaps. She went over the banisters in a flurry of black clothes and fell into the hall; she lay before the front door like a sack of coals which should have gone down the area into the basement. Philip saw; Emmy saw; she sat down suddenly in the doorway of the best spare bedroom with her eyes open as if she were too tired to stand any longer. Baines went slowly down into the hall.

It wasn't hard for Philip to escape; they'd forgotten him completely; he went down the back, the servants' stairs because Mrs. Baines was in the hall; he didn't understand what she was doing lying there; like the startling pictures in a book no one had read to him, the things he didn't understand terrified him. The whole house had been turned over to the grown-up world; he wasn't safe in the night nursery; their passions had flooded it. The only thing he could do was to get away, by the back stair, and up through the area, and never come back. You didn't think of the cold, of the need of food and sleep; for an hour it would seem quite possible to escape from people for ever.

He was wearing pajamas and bedroom slippers when he came up into the square, but there was no one to see him. It was that hour of the evening in a residential district when everyone is at the theater or at home. He climbed over the iron railings into the little garden: the plane-trees spread their large pale palms between him and the sky. It might have been an illimitable forest into which he had escaped. He crouched behind a trunk and the wolves retreated; it seemed to him between the little iron seat and the tree-trunk that no one would ever find him again. A kind of embittered happiness and self-pity made him cry; he was lost; there wouldn't be any more secrets to keep; he surrendered responsibility once and for all. Let grown-up people keep to their world and he would keep to his, safe in the small garden between the plane-trees. "In the lost childhood of Judas Christ was betrayed"; you could almost see the small unformed face hardening into the deep dilettante selfishness of age.

Presently the door of 48 opened and Baines looked this way and that; then he signalled with his hand and Emmy came; it was as if they were only just in time for a train, they hadn't

408

a chance of saying goodby; she went quickly by, like a face at a window swept past the platform, pale and unhappy and not wanting to go. Baines went in again and shut the door; the light was lit in the basement, and a policeman walked round the square, looking into the areas. You could tell how many families were at home by the lights behind the first-floor curtains.

Philip explored the garden: it didn't take long: a twenty-yard square of bushes and plane-trees, two iron seats and a gravel path, a padlocked gate at either end, a scuffle of old leaves. But he couldn't stay: something stirred in the bushes and two illuminated eyes peered out at him like a Siberian wolf, and he thought how terrible it would be if Mrs. Baines found him there. He'd have no time to climb the railings; she'd seize him from behind.

He left the square at the unfashionable end and was immediately among the fish-and-chip shops, the little stationers selling Bagatelle, among the accommodation addresses and the dingy hotels with open doors. There were few people about because the pubs were open, but a blowzy woman carrying a parcel called out to him across the street and the commissionaire outside a cinema would have stopped him if he hadn't crossed the road. He went deeper: you could go farther and lose yourself more completely here than among the plane-trees. On the fringe of the square he was in danger of being stopped and taken back: it was obvious where he belonged: but as he went deeper he lost the marks of his origin. It was a warm night: any child in those free-living parts might be expected to play truant from bed. He found a kind of camaraderie even among grown-up people; he might have been a neighbor's child as he went quickly by, but they weren't going to tell on him, they'd been young once themselves. He picked up a protective coating of dust from the pavements, of smuts from the trains which passed along the backs in a spray of fire. Once he was caught in a knot of children running away from something or somebody, laughing as they ran; he was whirled with them round a turning and abandoned, with a sticky fruit-drop in his hand.

He couldn't have been more lost; but he hadn't the stamina to keep on. At first he feared that someone would stop him; after an hour he hoped that someone would. He couldn't find his way back, and in any case he was afraid of arriving home alone; he was afraid of Mrs. Baines, more afraid than he had ever been. Baines was his friend, but something had happened which gave Mrs. Baines all the power. He began to loiter on purpose to be noticed, but no one noticed him. Families were having a last breather on the doorsteps, the refuse bins had been put out and bits of cabbage stalks soiled his slippers. The air was full of voices, but he was cut off; these people were strangers and would always now be strangers; they were marked by Mrs. Baines and he shied away from them into a deep class-consciousness. He had been afraid of policemen, but now he wanted one to take him home; even Mrs. Baines could do nothing against a policeman. He sidled past a constable who was directing traffic, but he was too busy to pay him any attention. Philip sat down against a wall and cried.

It hadn't occurred to him that that was the easiest way, that all you had to do was to surrender, to show you were beaten and accept kindness. . . . It was lavished on him at once by two women and a pawnbroker. Another policeman appeared, a young man with a sharp incredulous face. He looked as if he noted everything he saw in pocketbooks and drew conclusions. A woman offered to see Philip home, but he didn't trust her: she wasn't a match for Mrs. Baines immobile in the hall. He wouldn't give his address; he said he was afraid to go home. He had his way; he got his protection. "I'll take him to the station," the policeman said, and holding him awkwardly by the hand (he wasn't married; he had his career to make) he led him round the corner, up the stone stairs into the little bare overheated room where Justice waited.

V

Justice waited behind a wooden counter on a high stool; it wore a heavy moustache; it was kindly and had six children ("three of them nippers like yourself"); it wasn't really interested in Philip, but it pretended to be, it wrote the address down and sent a constable to fetch a glass of milk. But the young constable was interested; he had a nose for things.

"Your home's on the telephone, I suppose," Justice said. "We'll ring them up and say you are safe. They'll fetch you very soon. What's your name, sonny?"

"Philip."

"Your other name."

"I haven't got another name." He didn't want to be fetched; he wanted to be taken home by someone who would impress even Mrs. Baines. The constable watched him, watched the way he drank the milk, watched him when he winced away from questions.

"What made you run away? Playing truant, eh?"

"I don't know."

"You oughtn't to do it, young fellow. Think how anxious your father and mother will be."

"They are away."

"Well, your nurse."

"I haven't got one."

"Who looks after you, then?" That question went home. Philip saw Mrs. Baines coming up the stairs at him, the heap of black cotton in the hall. He began to cry.

"Now, now, now," the sergeant said. He didn't know what to do; he wished his wife were with him; even a policewoman might have been useful.

"Don't you think it's funny," the constable said, "that there hasn't been an inquiry?"

"They think he's tucked up in bed."

411

"You are scared, aren't you?" the constable said. "What scared you?"

"I don't know."

"Somebody hurt you?"

"No."

"He's had bad dreams," the sergeant said. "Thought the house was on fire, I expect. I've brought up six of them. Rose is due back. She'll take him home."

"I want to go home with you," Philip said; he tried to smile at the constable, but the deceit was immature and unsuccessful.

"I'd better go," the constable said. "There may be something wrong."

"Nonsense," the sergeant said. "It's a woman's job. Tact is what you need. Here's Rose. Pull up your stockings, Rose. You're a disgrace to the Force. I've got a job of work for you." Rose shambled in: black cotton stockings drooping over her boots, a gawky Girl Guide manner, a hoarse hostile voice. "More tarts, I suppose."

"No, you've got to see this young man home." She looked at him owlishly.

"I won't go with her," Philip said. He began to cry again. "I don't like her."

"More of that womanly charm, Rose," the sergeant said. The telephone rang on his desk. He lifted the receiver. "What? What's that?" he said. "Number 48? You've got a doctor?" He put his hand over the telephone mouth. "No wonder this nipper wasn't reported," he said. "They've been too busy. An accident. Woman slipped on the stairs."

"Serious?" the constable asked. The sergeant mouthed at him; you didn't mention the word death before a child (didn't he know? he had six of them), you made noises in the throat, you grimaced, a complicated shorthand for a word of only five letters anyway.

"You'd better go, after all," he said, "and make a report. The doctor's there."

Rose shambled from the stove; pink apply-dapply cheeks, loose stockings. She stuck her hands behind her. Her large morgue-like mouth was full of blackened teeth. "You told me to take him and now just because something interesting . . . I don't expect justice from a man . . ."

"Who's at the house?" the constable asked.

"The butler."

"You don't think," the constable said, "he saw . . ."

"Trust me," the sergeant said. "I've brought up six. I know 'em through and through. You can't teach me anything about children."

"He seemed scared about something."

"Dreams," the sergeant said.

"What name?"

"Baines."

"This Mr. Baines," the constable said to Philip, "you like him, eh? He's good to you?" They were trying to get something out of him; he was suspicious of the whole roomful of them; he said "yes" without conviction because he was afraid at any moment of more responsibilities, more secrets.

"And Mrs. Baines?"

"Yes."

They consulted together by the desk: Rose was hoarsely aggrieved; she was like a female impersonator, she bore her womanhood with an unnatural emphasis even while she scorned it in her creased stockings and her weather-exposed face. The charcoal shifted in the stove; the room was overheated in the mild late summer evening. A notice on the wall described a body found in the Thames, or rather the body's clothes: wool vest, wool pants, wool shirt with blue stripes, size ten boots, blue serge suit worn at the elbows, fifteen and a half celluloid collar. They couldn't find anything to say about the body, except its measurements, it was just an ordinary body.

"Come along," the constable said. He was interested, he was glad to be going, but he couldn't help being embarrassed by

413

his company, a small boy in pajamas. His nose smelt something, he didn't know what, but he smarted at the sight of the amusement they caused: the pubs had closed and the streets were full again of men making as long a day of it as they could. He hurried through the less frequented streets, chose the darker pavements, wouldn't loiter, and Philip wanted more and more to loiter, pulling at his hand, dragging with his feet. He dreaded the sight of Mrs. Baines waiting in the hall: he knew now that she was dead. The sergeant's mouthings had conveyed that; but she wasn't buried, she wasn't out of sight; he was going to see a dead person in the hall when the door opened.

The light was on in the basement, and to his relief the constable made for the area steps. Perhaps he wouldn't have to see Mrs. Baines at all. The constable knocked on the door because it was too dark to see the bell, and Baines answered. He stood there in the doorway of the neat bright basement room and you could see the sad complacent plausible sentence he had prepared wither at the sight of Philip; he hadn't expected Philip to return like that in the policeman's company. He had to begin thinking all over again; he wasn't a deceptive man; if it hadn't been for Emmy he would have been quite ready to let the truth lead him where it would.

"Mr. Baines?" the constable asked.

He nodded; he hadn't found the right words; he was daunted by the shrewd knowing face, the sudden appearance of Philip there.

"This little boy from here?"

"Yes," Baines said. Philip could tell that there was a message he was trying to convey, but he shut his mind to it. He loved Baines, but Baines had involved him in secrets, in fears he didn't understand. The glowing morning thought, "This is life," had become under Baines's tuition the repugnant memory, "That was life": the musty hair across the mouth, the breathless cruel tortured inquiry, "Where are they?" the heap of black cotton tipped into the hall. That was what happened when you loved: you got

414

involved; and Philip extricated himself from life, from love, from Baines, with a merciless egotism.

There had been things between them, but he laid them low, as a retreating army cuts the wires, destroys the bridges. In the abandoned country you may leave much that is dear—a morning in the Park, an ice at a corner house, sausages for supper—but more is concerned in the retreat than temporary losses. There are old people who, as the tractors wheel away, implore to be taken, but you can't risk the rearguard for their sake: a whole prolonged retreat from life, from care, from human relationships is involved.

"The doctor's here," Baines said. He nodded at the door, moistened his mouth, kept his eyes on Philip, begging for something like a dog you can't understand. "There's nothing to be done. She slipped on these stone basement stairs. I was in here. I heard her fall." He wouldn't look at the notebook, at the constable's tiny spidery writing which got a terrible lot on one page.

"Did the boy see anything?"

"He can't have done. I thought he was in bed. Hadn't he better go up? It's a shocking thing. Oh," Baines said, losing control, "it's a shocking thing for a child."

"She's through there?" the constable asked.

"I haven't moved her an inch," Baines said.

"He'd better then—"

"Go up the area and through the hall," Baines said and again he begged dumbly like a dog: one more secret, keep this secret, do this for old Baines, he won't ask another.

"Come along," the constable said. "I'll see you up to bed. You're a gentleman; you must come in the proper way through the front door like the master should. Or will you go along with him, Mr. Baines, while I see the doctor?"

"Yes," Baines said, "I'll go." He came across the room to Philip, begging, begging, all the way with his soft old stupid expression: this is Baines, the old Coaster; what about a palmoil chop, eh?; a man's life; forty niggers; never used a gun; I

415

tell you I couldn't help loving them: it wasn't what we call love, nothing we could understand. The messages flickered out from the last posts at the border, imploring, beseeching, reminding: this is your old friend Baines; what about an eleven's; a glass of ginger pop won't do you any harm; sausages; a long day. But the wires were cut, the messages just faded out into the enormous vacancy of the neat scrubbed room in which there had never been a place where a man could hide his secrets.

"Come along, Phil, it's bedtime. We'll just go up the steps . . ." Tap, tap, tap, at the telegraph; you may get through, you can't tell, somebody may mend the right wire. "And in at the front door."

"No," Philip said, "no. I won't go. You can't make me go. I'll fight. I won't see her."

The constable turned on them quickly. "What's that? Why won't you go?"

"She's in the hall," Philip said. "I know she's in the hall. And she's dead. I won't see her."

"You moved her then?" the constable said to Baines. "All the way down here? You've been lying, eh? That means you had to tidy up. . . . Were you alone?"

"Emmy," Philip said, "Emmy." He wasn't going to keep any more secrets: he was going to finish once and for all with everything, with Baines and Mrs. Baines and the grown-up life beyond him; it wasn't his business and never, never again, he decided, would he share their confidences and companionship. "It was all Emmy's fault," he protested with a quaver which reminded Baines that after all he was only a child; it had been hopeless to expect help there; he was a child; he didn't understand what it all meant; he couldn't read this shorthand of terror; he'd had a long day and he was tired out. You could see him dropping asleep where he stood against the dresser, dropping back into the comfortable nursery peace. You couldn't blame him. When he woke in the morning, he'd hardly remember a thing.

"Out with it," the constable said, addressing Baines with professional ferocity, "who is she?" just as the old man sixty years later startled his secretary, his only watcher, asking, "Who is she? Who is she?" dropping lower and lower into death, passing on the way perhaps the image of Baines: Baines hopeless, Baines letting his head drop, Baines "coming clean."

TRUMAN CAPOTE

Truman Capote was born in New Orleans on September 30, 1924, and spent his early childhood in the deep South. When he was four years old, his parents were divorced, and for the next seven years he lived with one or another of his aunts, most of the time in a little Alabama town near Mobile. It was not a happy childhood. "I had the most insecure childhood I know of," Mr. Capote once said. "I felt isolated from other people. I had few friends my own age."

His interest in writing dates from his earliest years. As a boy he submitted a serial story to a newspaper in Mobile in a contest for schoolchildren. The story was published, and when it appeared on the newsstand it caused a minor sensation. He had taken his characters from people in his home town, and so accurate was his portrayal of them that everyone recognized the originals.

He was sent to Trinity School and St. John's Academy, New York City. Then, his mother having married again, he lived with her and his stepfather in Millbrook, Connecticut, and attended Greenwich High School. He was not a good student. With one exception, he recalls, he was "a nuisance and a bother" to his teachers. That one exception was his English teacher in high school, who gave him special assignments and encouraged him to write poems and stories for the school paper, the Green Witch.

When he graduated from high school in 1942, at the age of seventeen, he had no desire to go to college; all he wanted to do was write fiction. He rented an apartment in New Orleans, where he read, wrote short stories, worked on a novel. The novel was never finished, and the short stories never found a publisher, at least not at the time. "My Side of the Matter," one of the stories he wrote that winter, appeared in 1945 in Story. The summer of 1943 found him in New York City working as an errand boy in the art department of the New Yorker. After a year he quit and once more returned to the South to write, this time on a farm in Alabama.

Then, at the age of nineteen, he began to find a market for his stories. "The Walls Are Cold" came out in the Fourth Quarter issue of Decade, 1944. In June 1945, "Miriam" appeared in Mademoiselle. It caused an immediate stir. Eight New York publishers approached Mr. Capote, bidding for his future work. The offer he accepted was a $1,500 advance on a forthcoming novel, to be paid at $100 a month. Before the year was out two more of his stories appeared: "Tree of Night," in Harper's Bazaar (October) and "Jug of Silver," in Mademoiselle (December). "Miriam" received an O. Henry Memorial Award. "Shut a Final Door," published in the Atlantic Monthly, August 1947, won the O. Henry first prize the following year.

With the publication of his first novel, Other Voices, Other Rooms (1948), Mr. Capote found himself, at twenty-four, a literary celebrity. A Tree of Night and Other Stories (1949) increased his reputation. Now that he was able to do so, Mr. Capote followed his natural inclination to travel. Since 1948 he has lived for varying periods in Haiti, Paris, Tangiers, Venice, and Sicily. Local Color

(1950) is a collection of sketches about the various places he has visited. He turned The Grass Harp *(1951), his second novel, into a drama that was a success on Broadway in 1952. In 1954 he wrote the book for the musical comedy* House of Flowers. Breakfast at Tiffany's, *his latest novel, was published in 1958. In 1959 he received a creative writing award from the National Institute of Arts and Letters.*

A TREE OF NIGHT

It was winter. A string of naked light bulbs, from which it seemed all warmth had been drained, illuminated the little depot's cold, windy platform. Earlier in the evening it had rained, and now icicles hung along the station-house eaves like some crystal monster's vicious teeth. Except for a girl, young and rather tall, the platform was deserted. The girl wore a gray flannel suit, a raincoat, and a plaid scarf. Her hair, parted in the middle and rolled up neatly on the sides, was rich blondish-brown; and, while her face tended to be too thin and narrow, she was, though not extraordinarily so, attractive. In addition to an assortment of magazines and a gray suede purse on which elaborate brass letters spelled Kay, she carried conspicuously a green Western guitar.

When the train, spouting steam and glaring with light, came out of the darkness and rumbled to a halt, Kay assembled her paraphernalia and climbed up into the last coach.

The coach was a relic with a decaying interior of ancient red-plush seats, bald in spots, and peeling iodine-colored wood-work. An old-time copper lamp, attached to the ceiling, looked romantic and out of place. Gloomy dead smoke sailed the air; and the car's heated closeness accentuated the stale odor of discarded sandwiches, apple cores, and orange hulls: this garbage, including Lily cups, soda-pop bottles, and mangled newspapers, littered the long aisle. From a water cooler, embedded in the wall, a steady stream trickled to the floor. The passengers, who glanced up wearily when Kay entered, were not, it seemed, at all conscious of any discomfort.

Kay resisted a temptation to hold her nose and threaded her way carefully down the aisle, tripping once, without disaster, over a dozing fat man's protruding leg. Two nondescript men turned an interested eye as she passed; and a kid stood up in his seat squalling, "Hey, Mama, look at de banjo! Hey, lady, lemme play ya banjo!" till a slap from Mama quelled him.

There was only one empty place. She found it at the end of the car in an isolated alcove occupied already by a man and woman who were sitting with their feet settled lazily on the vacant seat opposite. Kay hesitated a second then said, "Would you mind if I sat here?"

The woman's head snapped up as if she had not been asked a simple question, but stabbed with a needle, too. Nevertheless, she managed a smile. "Can't say as I see what's to stop you, honey," she said, taking her feet down and also, with a curious impersonality, removing the feet of the man who was staring out the window, paying no attention whatsoever.

Thanking the woman, Kay took off her coat, sat down, and arranged herself with purse and guitar at her side, magazines in her lap: comfortable enough, though she wished she had a pillow for her back.

The train lurched; a ghost of steam hissed against the window; slowly the dingy lights of the lonesome depot faded past.

"Boy, what a jerkwater dump," said the woman. "No town, no nothin'."

Kay said, "The town's a few miles away."

"That so? Live there?"

No. Kay explained she had been at the funeral of an uncle. An uncle who, though she did not of course mention it, had left her nothing in his will but the green guitar. Where was she going? Oh, back to college.

After mulling this over, the woman concluded, "What'll you ever learn in a place like that? Let me tell you, honey, I'm plenty educated and I never saw the inside of no college."

"You didn't?" murmured Kay politely and dismissed the matter by opening one of her magazines. The light was dim for reading and none of the stories looked in the least compelling. However, not wanting to become involved in a conversational marathon, she continued gazing at it stupidly till she felt a furtive tap on her knee.

"Don't read," said the woman. "I need somebody to talk to. Naturally, it's no fun talking to *him*." She jerked a thumb toward the silent man. "He's afflicted: deaf and dumb, know what I mean?"

Kay closed the magazine and looked at her more or less for the first time. She was short; her feet barely scraped the floor. And like many undersized people she had a freak of structure, in her case an enormous, really huge head. Rouge so brightened her sagging, flesh-featured face it was difficult even to guess at her age: perhaps fifty, fifty-five. Her big sheep eyes squinted, as if distrustful of what they saw. Her hair was an obviously dyed red, and twisted into parched, fat corkscrew curls. A once-elegant lavender hat of impressive size flopped crazily on the side of her head, and she was kept busy brushing back a drooping cluster of celluloid cherries sewed to the brim. She wore a plain, somewhat shabby blue dress. Her breath had a vividly sweetish gin smell.

"You do wanna talk to me, don't you honey?"

"Sure," said Kay, moderately amused.

"Course you do. You bet you do. That's what I like about a train. Bus people are a close-mouthed buncha dopes. But a train's the place for putting your cards on the table, that's what I always say." Her voice was cheerful and booming, husky as a

423

man's. "But on accounta *him*, I always try to get us this here seat; it's more private, like a swell compartment, see?"

"It's very pleasant," Kay agreed. "Thanks for letting me join you."

"Only too glad to. We don't have much company; it makes some folks nervous to be around him."

As if to deny it, the man made a queer, furry sound deep in his throat and plucked the woman's sleeve. "Leave me alone, dear-heart," she said, as if she were talking to an inattentive child. "I'm O.K. We're just having us a nice little ol' talk. Now behave yourself or this pretty girl will go away. She's very rich; she goes to college." And winking, she added, "He thinks I'm drunk."

The man slumped in the seat, swung his head sideways, and studied Kay intently from the corners of his eyes. These eyes, like a pair of clouded milky-blue marbles, were thickly lashed and oddly beautiful. Now, except for a certain remoteness, his wide, hairless face had no real expression. It was as if he were incapable of experiencing or reflecting the slightest emotion. His gray hair was clipped close and combed forward into uneven bangs. He looked like a child aged abruptly by some uncanny method. He wore a frayed blue serge suit, and he had anointed himself with a cheap, vile perfume. Around his wrist was strapped a Mickey Mouse watch.

"He thinks I'm drunk," the woman repeated. "And the real funny part is, I am. Oh, shoot—you gotta do something, ain't that right?" She bent closer. "Say, ain't it?"

Kay was still gawking at the man; the way he was looking at her made her squeamish, but she could not take her eyes off him. "I guess so," she said.

"Then let's us have us a drink," suggested the woman. She plunged her hand into an oilcloth satchel and pulled out a partially filled gin bottle. She began to unscrew the cap, but, seeming to think better of this, handed the bottle to Kay. "Gee,

424

I forgot about you being company," she said. "I'll go get us some nice paper cups."

So, before Kay could protest that she did not want a drink, the woman had risen and started none too steadily down the aisle toward the water cooler.

Kay yawned and rested her forehead against the window-pane, her fingers idly strumming the guitar: the strings sang a hollow, lulling tune, as monotonously soothing as the Southern landscape, smudged in darkness, flowing past the window. An icy winter moon rolled above the train across the night sky like a thin white wheel.

And then, without warning, a strange thing happened: the man reached out and gently stroked Kay's cheek. Despite the breathtaking delicacy of this movement, it was such a bold gesture Kay was at first too startled to know what to make of it: her thoughts shot in three or four fantastic directions. He leaned forward till his queer eyes were very near her own; the reek of his perfume was sickening. The guitar was silent while they exchanged a searching gaze. Suddenly, from some spring of compassion, she felt for him a keen sense of pity; but also, and this she could not suppress, an overpowering disgust, an absolute loathing: something about him, an elusive quality she could not quite put a finger on, reminded her of—of what?

After a little, he lowered his hand solemnly and sank back in the seat, an asinine grin transfiguring his face, as if he had performed a clever stunt for which he wished applause.

"Giddyup! Giddyup! my little bucker-ROOS . . ." shouted the woman. And she sat down, loudly proclaiming to be, "Dizzy as a witch! Dog tired! Whew!" From a handful of Lily cups she separated two and casually thrust the rest down her blouse. "Keep 'em safe and dry, ha ha ha. . . ." A coughing spasm seized her, but when it was over she appeared calmer. "Has my boy friend been entertaining?" she asked, patting her bosom rever-ently. "Ah, he's so sweet." She looked as if she might pass out. Kay rather wished she would.

425

"I don't want a drink," Kay said, returning the bottle. "I never drink: I hate the taste."

"Mustn't be a kill-joy," said the woman firmly. "Here now, hold your cup like a good girl."

"No please . . ."

"Formercysake, hold it still. Imagine, nerves at your age! Me, I can shake like a leaf, I've got reasons. Oh, Lordy, have I got 'em."

"But . . ."

A dangerous smile tipped the woman's face hideously awry. "What's the matter? Don't you think I'm good enough to drink with?"

"Please, don't misunderstand," said Kay, a tremor in her voice. "It's just that I don't like being forced to do something I don't want to. So look, couldn't I give this to the gentleman?"

"Him? No sirree: he needs what little sense he's got. Come on, honey, down the hatch."

Kay, seeing it was useless, decided to succumb and avoid a possible scene. She sipped and shuddered. It was terrible gin. It burned her throat till her eyes watered. Quickly, when the woman was not watching, she emptied the cup out into the sound hole of the guitar. It happened, however, that the man saw; and Kay, realizing it, recklessly signaled to him with her eyes a plea not to give her away. But she could not tell from his clear-blank expression how much he understood.

"Where you from, kid?" resumed the woman presently.

For a bewildered moment, Kay was unable to provide an answer. The names of several cities came to her all at once. Finally, from this confusion, she extracted: "New Orleans. My home is in New Orleans."

The woman beamed. "N.O.'s where I wanna go when I kick off. One time, oh, say 1923, I ran me a sweet little fortune-teller parlor there. Let's see, that was on St. Peter Street." Pausing, she stooped and set the empty gin bottle on the floor. It rolled into the aisle and rocked back and forth with a drowsy

;ound. "I was raised in Texas—on a big ranch—my papa was rich. Us kids always had the best; even Paris, France, clothes. I'll bet you've got a big swell house, too. Do you have a garden? Do you grow flowers?"

"Just lilacs."

A conductor entered the coach, preceded by a cold gust of wind that rattled the trash in the aisle and briefly livened the dull air. He lumbered along, stopping now and then to punch a ticket or talk with a passenger. It was after midnight. Someone was expertly playing a harmonica. Someone else was arguing the merits of a certain politician. A child cried out in his sleep.

"Maybe you wouldn't be so snotty if you knew who we was," said the woman, bobbing her tremendous head. "We ain't nobodies, not by a long shot."

Embarrassed, Kay nervously opened a pack of cigarettes and lighted one. She wondered if there might not be a seat in a car up ahead. She could not bear the woman, or, for that matter, the man, another minute. But she had never before been in a remotely comparable situation. "If you'll excuse me now," she said, "I have to be leaving. It's been very pleasant, but I promised to meet a friend on the train. . . ."

With almost invisible swiftness the woman grasped the girl's wrist. "Didn't your mama ever tell you it was sinful to lie?" she stage-whispered. The lavender hat tumbled off her head but she made no effort to retrieve it. Her tongue flicked out and wetted her lips. And, as Kay stood up, she increased the pressure of her grip. "Sit down, dear . . . there ain't any friend . . . Why, we're your only friends and we wouldn't have you leave us for the world."

"Honestly, I wouldn't lie."

"Sit down, dear."

Kay dropped her cigarette and the man picked it up. He slouched in the corner and became absorbed in blowing a chain

427

of lush smoke rings that mounted upward like hollow eyes and expanded into nothing.

"Why, you wouldn't want to hurt his feelings by leaving us, now, would you, dear?" crooned the woman softly. "Sit down—down—now, that's a good girl. My, what a pretty guitar. What a pretty, pretty guitar . . ." Her voice faded before the sudden whooshing, static noise of a second train. And for an instant the lights in the coach went off; in the darkness the passing train's golden windows winked black-yellow-black-yellow-black-yellow. The man's cigarette pulsed like the glow of a firefly, and his smoke rings continued rising tranquilly. Outside, a bell pealed wildly.

When the lights came on again, Kay was massaging her wrist where the woman's strong fingers had left a painful bracelet mark. She was more puzzled than angry. She determined to ask the conductor if he would find her a different seat. But when he arrived to take her ticket, the request stuttered on her lips incoherently.

"Yes, miss?"

"Nothing," she said.

And he was gone.

The trio in the alcove regarded one another in mysterious silence till the woman said, "I've got something here I wanna show you, honey." She rummaged once more in the oilcloth satchel. "You won't be so snotty after you get a gander at this."

What she passed to Kay was a handbill, published on such yellowed, antique paper it looked as if it must be centuries old. In fragile, overly fancy lettering, it read:

LAZARUS

THE MAN WHO IS BURIED ALIVE
A MIRACLE
SEE FOR YOURSELF

Adults, 25¢—Children, 10¢

428

"I always sing a hymn and read a sermon," said the woman. "It's awful sad: some folks cry, especially the old ones. And I've got me a perfectly elegant costume: a black veil and a black dress, oh, very becoming. *He* wears a gorgeous made-to-order bridegroom suit and a turban and lotsa talcum on his face. See, we try to make it as much like a bonafide funeral as we can. But shoot, nowadays you're likely to get just a buncha smart alecks come for laughs—so sometimes I'm real glad he's afflicted like he is on accounta otherwise his feelings would be hurt, maybe."

Kay said, "You mean you're with a circus or a side-show or something like that?"

"Nope, us alone," said the woman as she reclaimed the fallen hat. "We've been doing it for years and years—played every tank town in the South: Singasong, Mississippi—Spunky, Louisiana—Eureka, Alabama . . ." these and other names rolled off her tongue musically, running together like rain. "After the hymn, after the sermon, we bury him."

"In a coffin?"

"Sort of. It's gorgeous, it's got silver stars painted all over the lid."

"I should think he would suffocate," said Kay, amazed. "How long does he stay buried?"

"All told it takes maybe an hour—course that's not counting the lure."

"The lure?"

"Uh huh. It's what we do the night before the show. See, we hunt up a store, any ol' store with a big glass window'll do, and get the owner to let *him* sit inside this window, and, well, hypnotize himself. Stays there all night stiff as a poker and people come and look: scares the livin' hell out of 'em. . . ." While she talked she jiggled a finger in her ear, withdrawing it occasionally to examine her find. "And one time this ol' bindle-stiff Mississippi sheriff tried to . . ."

The tale that followed was baffling and pointless: Kay did

not bother to listen. Nevertheless, what she had heard already inspired a reverie, a vague recapitulation of her uncle's funeral; an event which, to tell the truth, had not much affected her since she had scarcely known him. And so, while gazing abstractedly at the man, an image of her uncle's face, white next the pale silk casket pillow, appeared in her mind's eye. Observing their faces simultaneously, both the man's and uncle's, as it were, she thought she recognized an odd parallel: there was about the man's face the same kind of shocking, embalmed, secret stillness, as though, in a sense, he were truly an exhibit in a glass cage, complacent to be seen, uninterested in seeing.

"I'm sorry, what did you say?"

"I said: I sure wish they'd lend us the use of a regular cemetery. Like it is now we have to put on the show wherever we can . . . mostly in empty lots that are nine times outa ten smack up against some smelly fillin' station which ain't exactly a big help. But like I say, we got us a swell act, the best. You oughta come see it if you get a chance."

"Oh, I should love to," Kay said, absently.

"Oh, I should love to," mimicked the woman. "Well, who asked you? Anybody ask you?" She hoisted up her skirt and enthusiastically blew her nose on the ragged hem of a petticoat. "Bu-leeve me, it's a hard way to turn a dollar. Know what our take was last month? Fifty-three bucks! Honey, you try living on that sometime." She sniffed and rearranged her skirt with considerable primness. "Well, one of these days my sweet boy's sure enough going to die down there; and even then somebody'll say it was a gyp."

At this point the man took from his pocket what seemed to be a finely shellacked peach seed and balanced it on the palm of his hand. He looked across at Kay and, certain of her attention, opened his eyelids wide and began to squeeze and caress the seed in an undefinably obscene manner.

Kay frowned. "What does he want?"

"He wants you to buy it."

"But what is it?"

"A charm," said the woman. "A love charm."

Whoever was playing the harmonica stopped. Other sounds, less unique, became at once prominent: someone snoring, the gin bottle seesaw rolling, voices in sleepy argument, the train wheels' distant hum.

"Where could you get love cheaper, honey?"

"It's nice. I mean it's cute. . . ." Kay said, stalling for time. The man rubbed and polished the seed on his trouser leg. His head was lowered at a supplicating, mournful angle, and presently he stuck the seed between his teeth and bit it, as if it were a suspicious piece of silver. "Charms always bring me bad luck. And besides . . . please, can't you make him stop acting that way?"

"Don't look so scared," said the woman, more flat-voiced than ever. "He ain't gonna hurt you."

"Make him stop, damn it!"

"What can I do?" asked the woman, shrugging her shoulders. "You're the one that's got money. You're rich. All he wants is a dollar, one dollar."

Kay tucked her purse under her arm. "I have just enough to get back to school," she lied, quickly rising and stepping out into the aisle. She stood there a moment, expecting trouble. But nothing happened.

The woman, with rather deliberate indifference, heaved a sigh and closed her eyes; gradually the man subsided and stuck the charm back in his pocket. Then his hand crawled across the seat to join the woman's in a lax embrace.

Kay shut the door and moved to the front of the observation platform. It was bitterly cold in the open air, and she had left her raincoat in the alcove. She loosened her scarf and draped it over her head.

Although she had never made this trip before, the train was traveling through an area strangely familiar: tall trees, misty, painted pale by malicious moonshine, towered steep on either side without a break or clearing. Above, the sky was a stark, un-explorable blue thronged with stars that faded here and there. She could see streamers of smoke trailing from the train's engine like long clouds of ectoplasm. In one corner of the platform a red kerosene lantern cast a colorful shadow.

She found a cigarette and tried to light it: the wind snuffed match after match till only one was left. She walked to the corner where the lantern burned and cupped her hands to protect the last match: the flame caught, sputtered, died. Angrily she tossed away the cigarette and empty folder; all the tension in her tight-ened to an exasperating pitch and she slammed the wall with her fist and began to whimper softly, like an irritable child.

The intense cold made her head ache, and she longed to go back inside the warm coach and fall asleep. But she couldn't, at least not yet; and there was no sense in wondering why, for she knew the answer very well. Aloud, partly to keep her teeth from chattering and partly because she needed the reassurance of her own voice, she said: "We're in Alabama now, I think, and to-morrow we'll be in Atlanta and I'm nineteen and I'll be twenty in August and I'm a sophomore. . . ." She glanced around at the darkness, hoping to see a sign of dawn, and finding the same end-less wall of trees, the same frosty moon. "I hate him, he's horrible and I hate him. . . ." She stopped, ashamed of her foolishness and too tired to evade the truth: she was afraid.

Suddenly she felt an eerie compulsion to kneel down and touch the lantern. Its graceful glass funnel was warm, and the red glow seeped through her hands, making them luminous. The heat thawed her fingers and tingled along her arms.

She was so preoccupied she did not hear the door open. The train wheels roaring clickety-clack-clackety-click hushed the sound of the man's footsteps.

It was a subtle zero sensation that warned her finally; but some seconds passed before she dared look behind.

He was standing there with mute detachment, his head tilted, his arms dangling at his sides. Staring up into his harmless, vapid

432

face, flushed brilliant by the lantern light, Kay knew of what she was afraid: it was a memory, a childish memory of terrors that once, long ago, had hovered above her like haunted limbs on a tree of night. Aunts, cooks, strangers—each eager to spin a tale or teach a rhyme of spooks and death, omens, spirits, demons. And always there had been the unfailing threat of the wizard man: stay close to the house, child, else a wizard man'll snatch you and eat you alive! He lived everywhere, the wizard man, and everywhere was danger. At night, in bed, hear him tapping at the window? Listen!

Holding onto the railing, she inched upward till she was standing erect. The man nodded and waved his hand toward the door. Kay took a deep breath and stepped forward. Together they went inside.

The air in the coach was numb with sleep: a solitary light now illuminated the car, creating a kind of artificial dusk. There was no motion but the train's sluggish sway, and the stealthy rattle of discarded newspapers.

The woman alone was wide awake. You could see she was greatly excited: she fidgeted with her curls and celluloid cherries, and her plump little legs, crossed at the ankles, swung agitatedly back and forth. She paid no attention when Kay sat down. The man settled in the seat with one leg tucked beneath him and his arms folded across his chest.

In an effort to be casual, Kay picked up a magazine. She realized the man was watching her, not removing his gaze an instant; she knew this though she was afraid to confirm it, and she wanted to cry out and waken everyone in the coach. But suppose they did not hear? What if they were not really *asleep?* Tears started in her eyes, magnifying and distorting the print on a page till it became a hazy blur. She shut the magazine with fierce abruptness and looked at the woman.

"I'll buy it," she said. "The charm, I mean. I'll buy it, if that's all—just all you want."

The woman made no response. She smiled apathetically as she turned toward the man.

As Kay watched, the man's face seemed to change form and recede before her like a moon-shaped rock sliding downward under a surface of water. A warm laziness relaxed her. She was dimly conscious of it when the woman took away her purse, and when she gently pulled the raincoat like a shroud above her head.